9 Feel
19 Disease
29 Bright Lights
41 Unwell
51 Cold
60 All I Need
69 Hand Me Down
88 Could I Be You
100 Downfall
111 Soul
120 You're So Real
130 The Difference
139 So Sad So Lonely
151 Guitar Notation Legend

Music transcriptions by Steve Gorenberg, Jeff Jacobson, David Stocher, and Jeff Story

7777 W. Bluemound Rd. P.O. Box 13819 Milwaukee, WI 53213

Visit Hal Leonard Online at
www.halleonard.com

MELISMA ARTISTS AGAINST management: michael lippman/ LIPPMAN ENTERTAINMENT produced by matt serletic for melisma productions

W YO
CITY

www.matchboxtwenty.com

Feel

Words and Music by Rob Thomas, Paul Doucette and Kyle Cook

E5
G
A5
Csus2
Dadd9/F♯
G5
G6/B
Dsus4
D
11
21 34
11
2 34
T 13
2 34
2 3
134
132

Intro
Slow Rock ♩ = 84
Gtr. 2 (dist.)
*A5
C5
D/F♯
G5
f
1/4
Gtr. 1 (dist.)
f
1/4

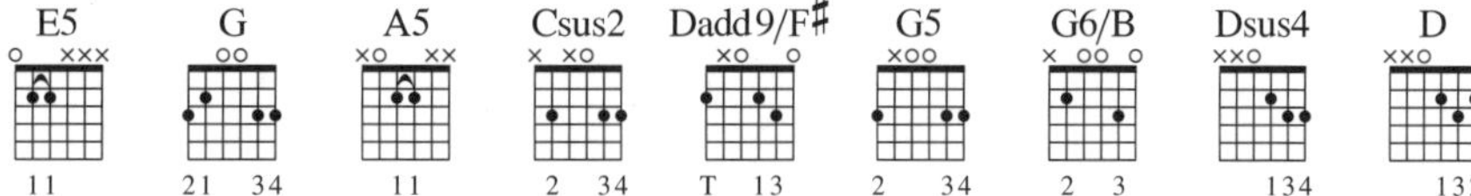

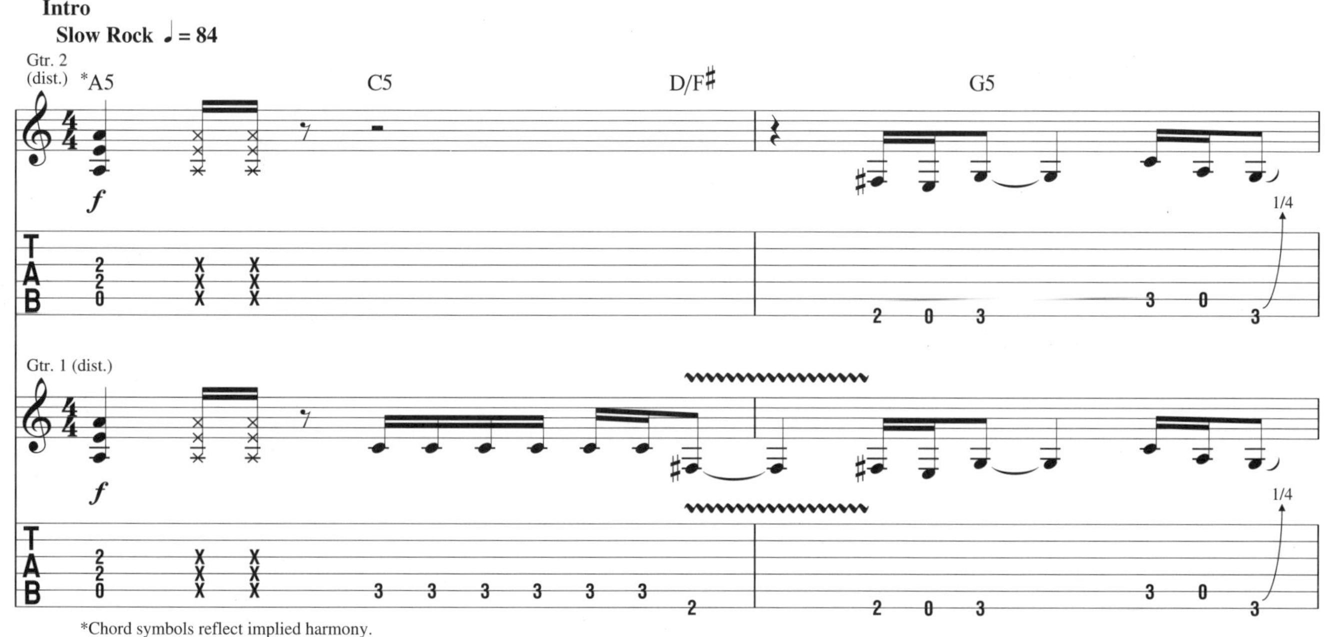

*Chord symbols reflect implied harmony.

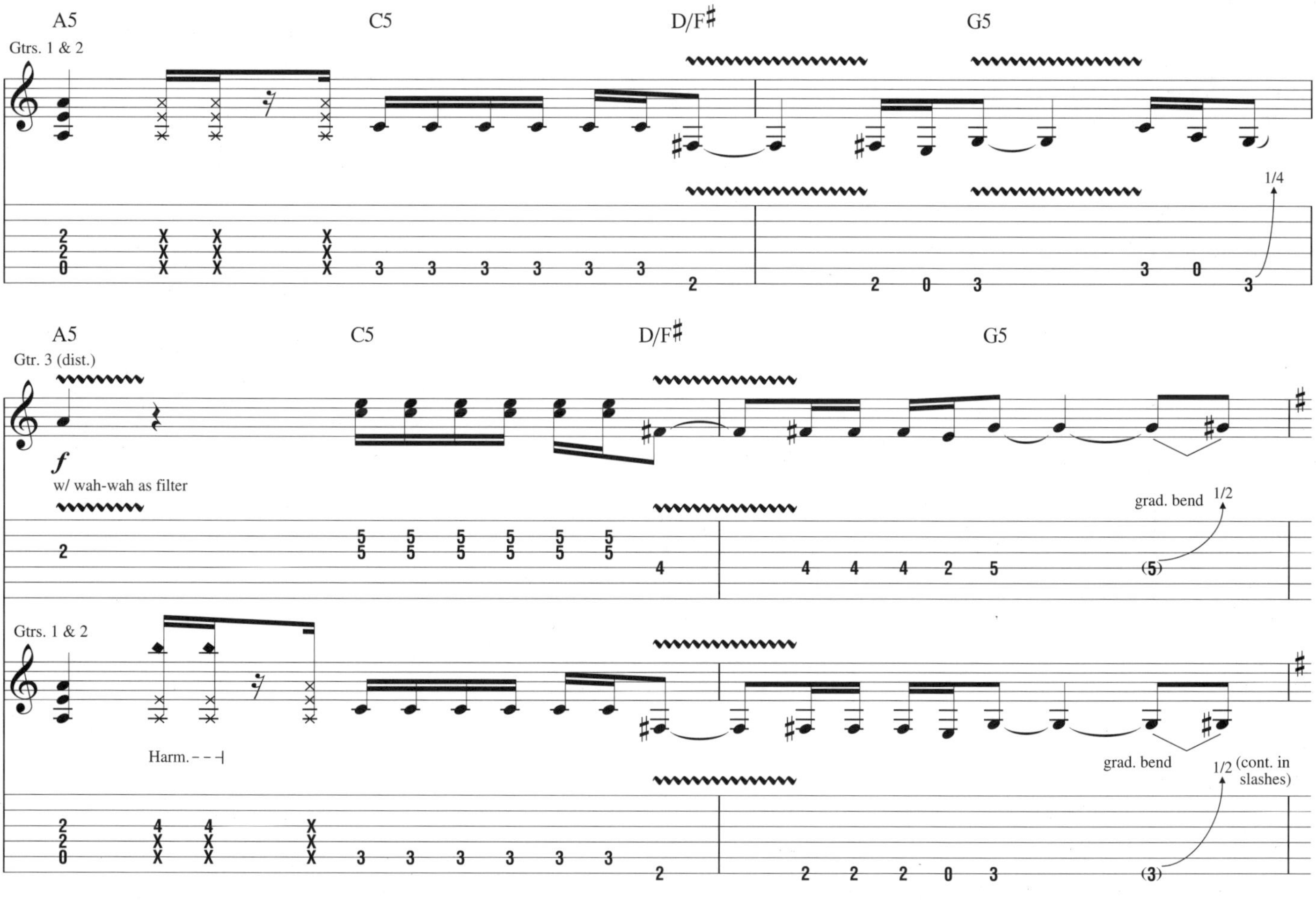

A5
C5
D/F♯
G5
Gtrs. 1 & 2
1/4
A5
C5
D/F♯
G5
Gtr. 3 (dist.)
f
w/ wah-wah as filter
grad. bend
1/2
Gtrs. 1 & 2
Harm.
grad. bend
1/2 (cont. in slashes)

Gtr. 3 tacet
E5
Verse
E5
Gtrs. 1 & 2
mp
1. What you want, what you got, live your life in a crawl space.
Gtr. 4 (dist.)
Riff A
End Riff A
f
Harm.
Gtr. 4 tacet
G
Gtr. 4: w/ Riff A
E5
I help you out but you don't want a chance at a bet - ter life.
Gtr. 5 (dist.)
f
G
E5
You said you nev - er took a ride and now you wan - na play.
Gtr. 5
Riff B
End Riff B
Gtr. 4

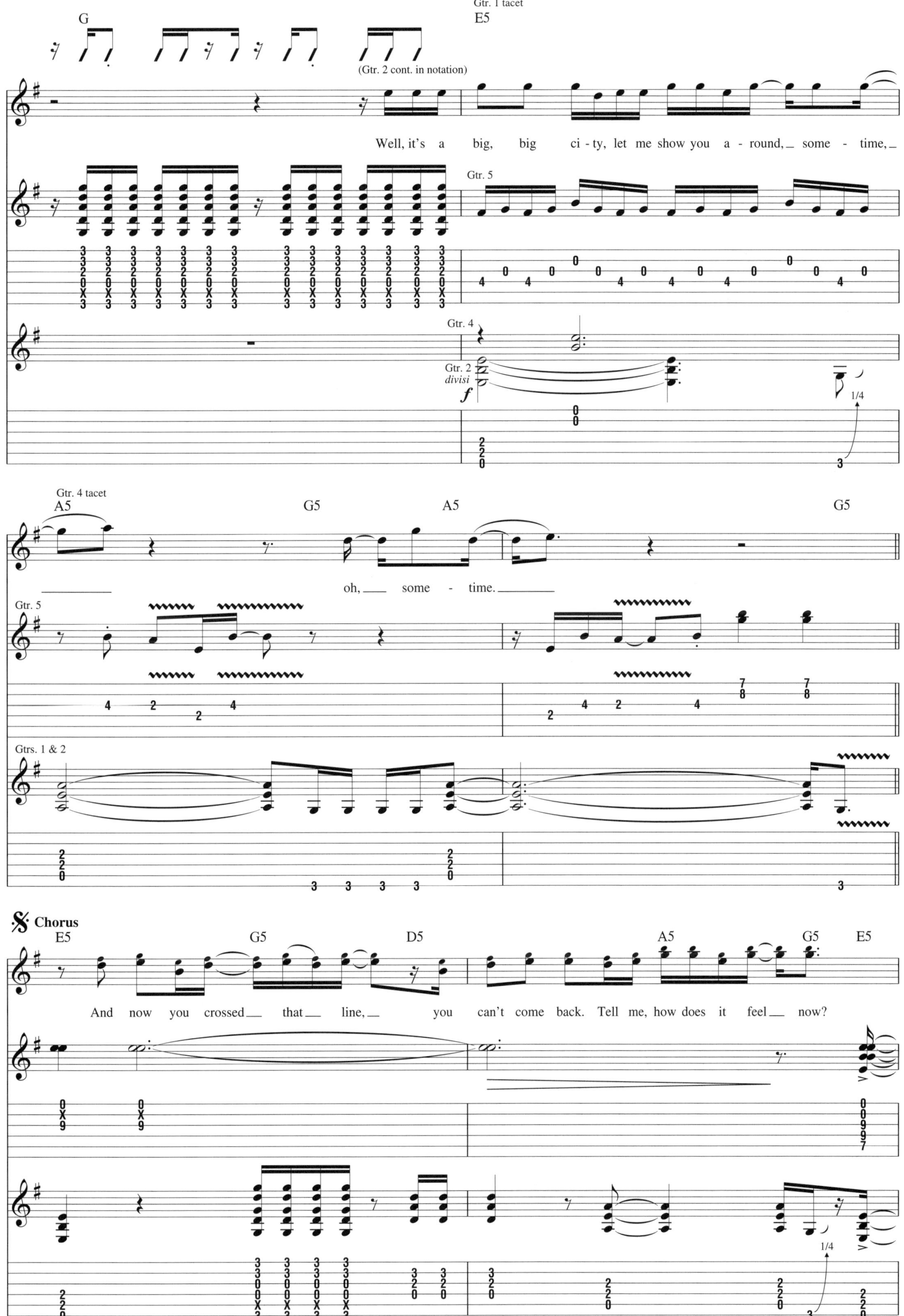

G
Gtr. 1 tacet
E5
(Gtr. 2 cont. in notation)
Well, it's a big, big ci - ty, let me show you a - round, some - time,
Gtr. 5
Gtr. 4
Gtr. 2
divisi
1/4
Gtr. 4 tacet
A5
G5
A5
G5
oh, some - time.
Gtr. 5
Gtrs. 1 & 2
Chorus
E5
G5
D5
A5
G5
E5
And now you crossed that line, you can't come back. Tell me, how does it feel now?
1/4

G5
D5
A5
G5
E5
It's too late, too much to for-get a-bout. Can't stop now, how does it feel now?
1/4
To Coda
G5
D5
A5
G5
I'm on-ly ask-ing be-cause I wan-na know
E5
G5
D5
N.C.
how you wan-na feel.
Gtr. 3
Gtr. 5
divisi
1/4
1/4

Interlude
Gtr. 5 tacet
A5
C5
D/F#
G5
N.C.
Gtr. 3
Gtrs. 1 & 2
Harm.
Verse
Gtr. 3 tacet
*Gtr. 4: w/ Riff A
E5
Gtrs. 1 & 2
2. I'm a wreck, I'm a mess, I'm a spot on the pave - ment.
(Ah.)
grad. bend
(cont. in slashes)
*Played p till D.S.
G
(cont. in notation)
I'm a
Riff C
End Riff C
Gtr. 5
grad. bend

Gtr. 4: w/ Riff A
Gtr. 5 tacet
E5
Gtr. 5: w/ Riff C
G
num - ber on the wall, I'll make you soul - tir - ed.
Yeah, and
Gtrs. 1 & 2

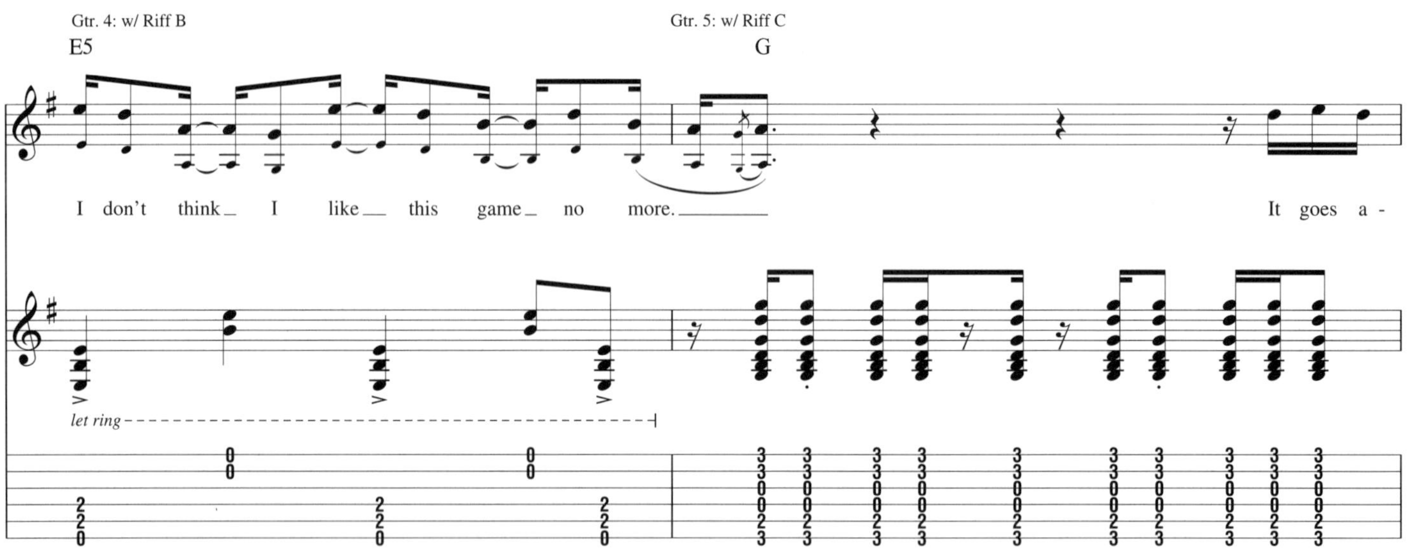
Gtr. 4: w/ Riff B
E5
Gtr. 5: w/ Riff C
G
I don't think I like this game no more.
It goes a -
let ring

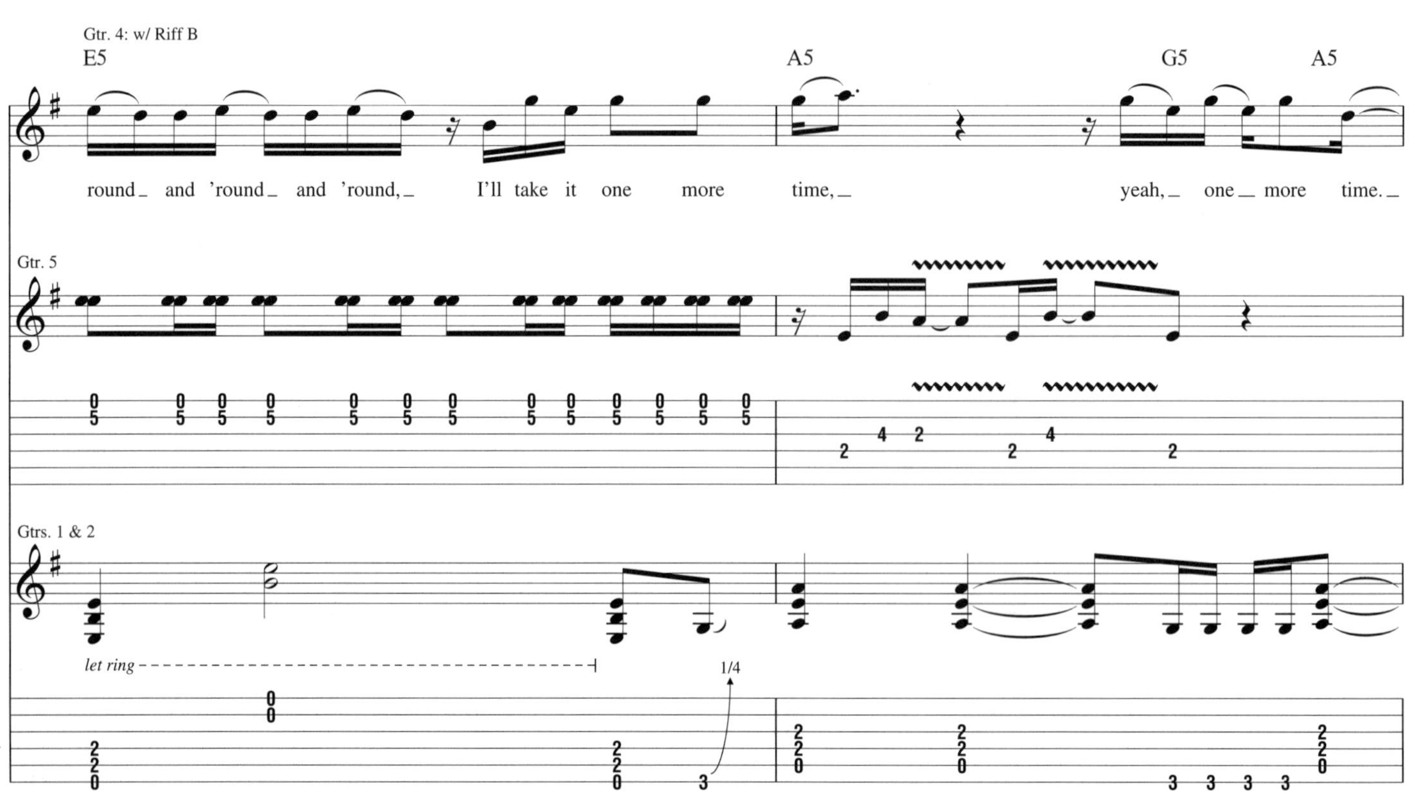
Gtr. 4: w/ Riff B
E5
A5
G5
A5
round and 'round and 'round, I'll take it one more time,
yeah, one more time.
Gtr. 5
Gtrs. 1 & 2
let ring
1/4

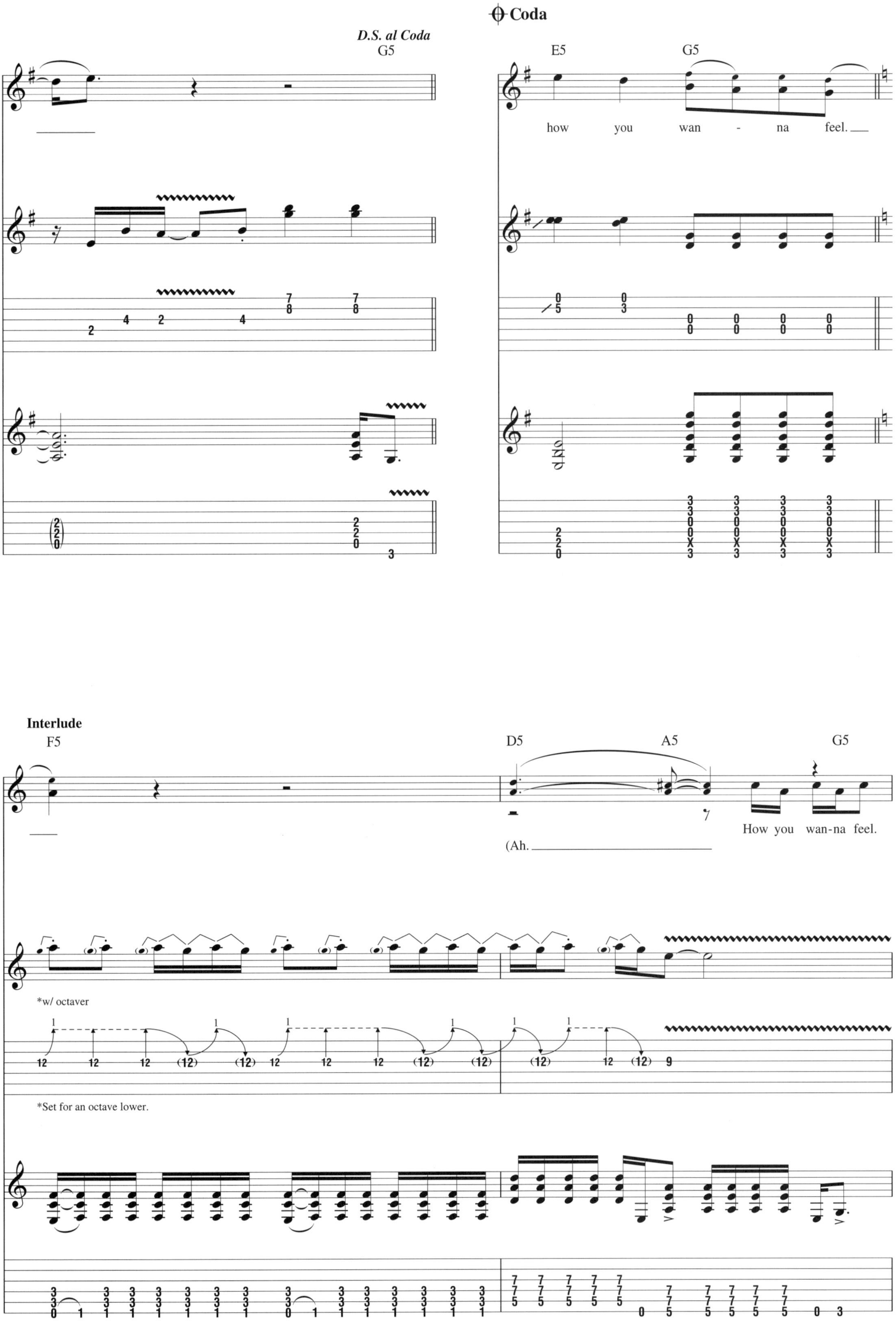

Interlude

F5

D5 A5 G5

How you wan-na feel.

(Ah.

*w/ octaver

*Set for an octave lower.

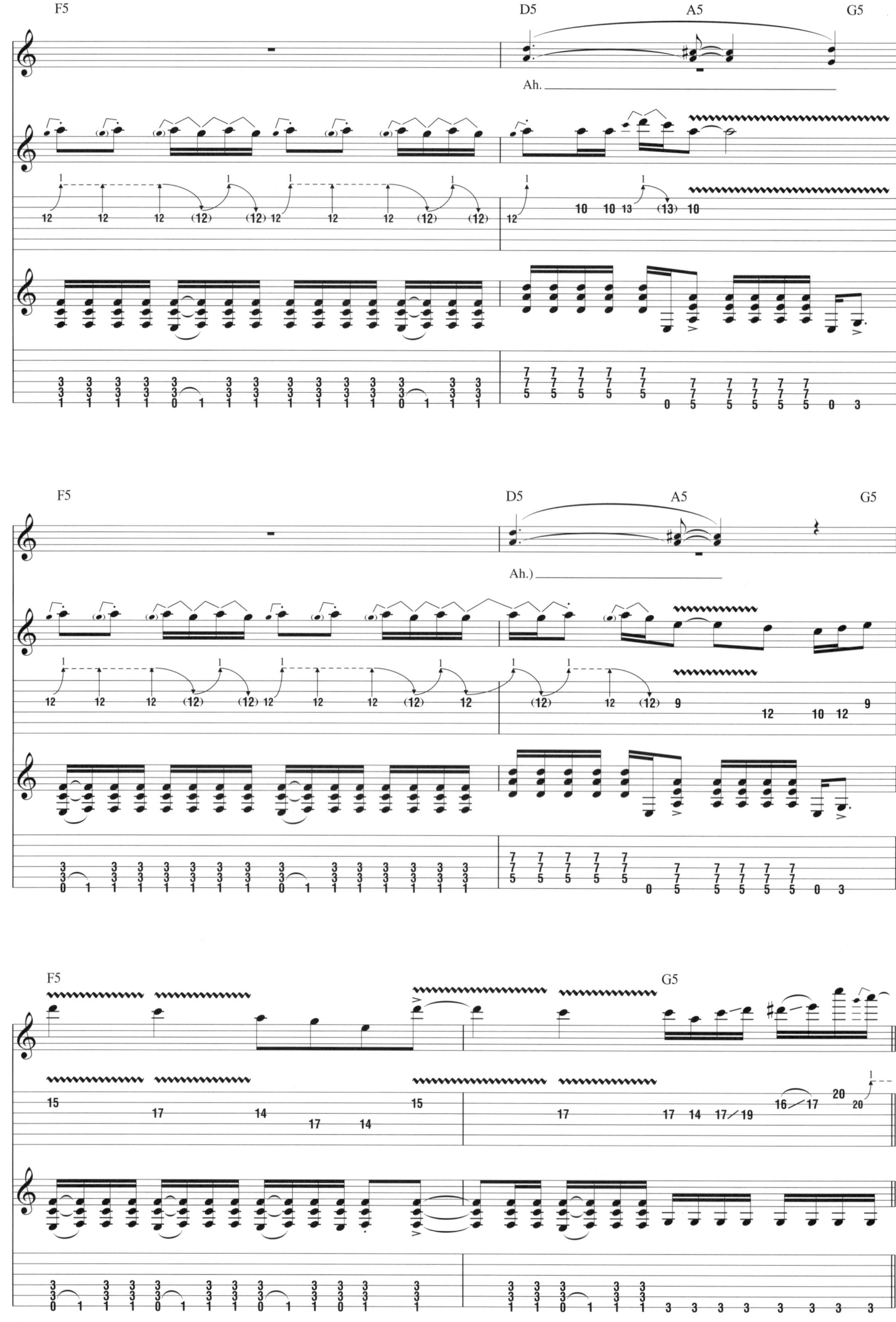

F5
D5
A5
G5
Ah.
F5
D5
A5
G5
Ah.)
F5
G5

Chorus
A5
Csus2
Dadd9/F♯
G5
A5
Gtr. 6
(dist.)
f
And now you crossed that line, you can't come back. Tell me, how does it feel now?
octaver off
Gtr. 5 tacet
Csus2
Dadd9/F♯
G5
A5
It's too late, too much to for-get a-bout. Can't stop now, how does it feel now?
Gtrs. 1 & 2
Csus2
Dadd9/F♯
G5
(cont. in notation)
Well, I'm on-ly ask-ing be-cause I wan-na know

A5
G5
Dadd9/F♯
Dsus2
how___ you wan - na feel,___
*Gtrs. 1, 2 & 6
** T
T
T
*Composite arrangement
** T = Thumb on 6th string

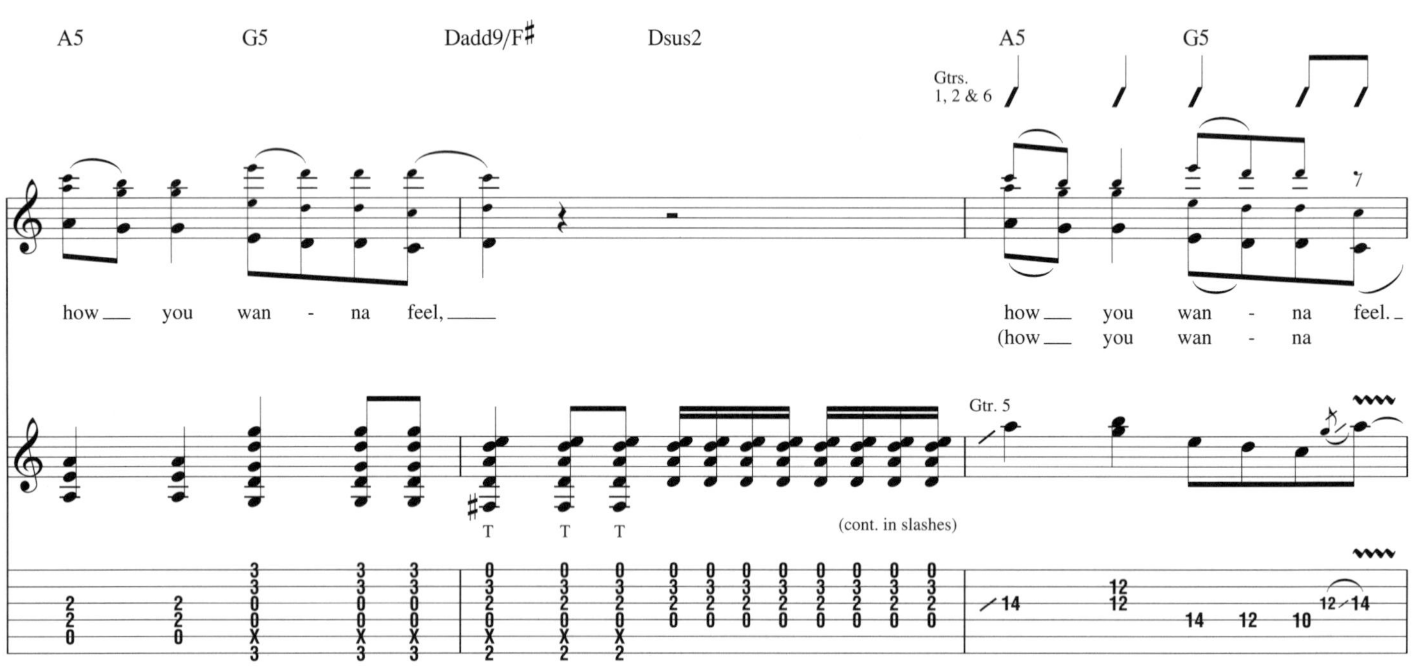
A5
G5
Dadd9/F♯
Dsus2
A5
G5
Gtrs. 1, 2 & 6
how___ you wan - na feel,___
how___ you wan - na feel.___
(how___ you wan - na
Gtr. 5
T
T
T
(cont. in slashes)

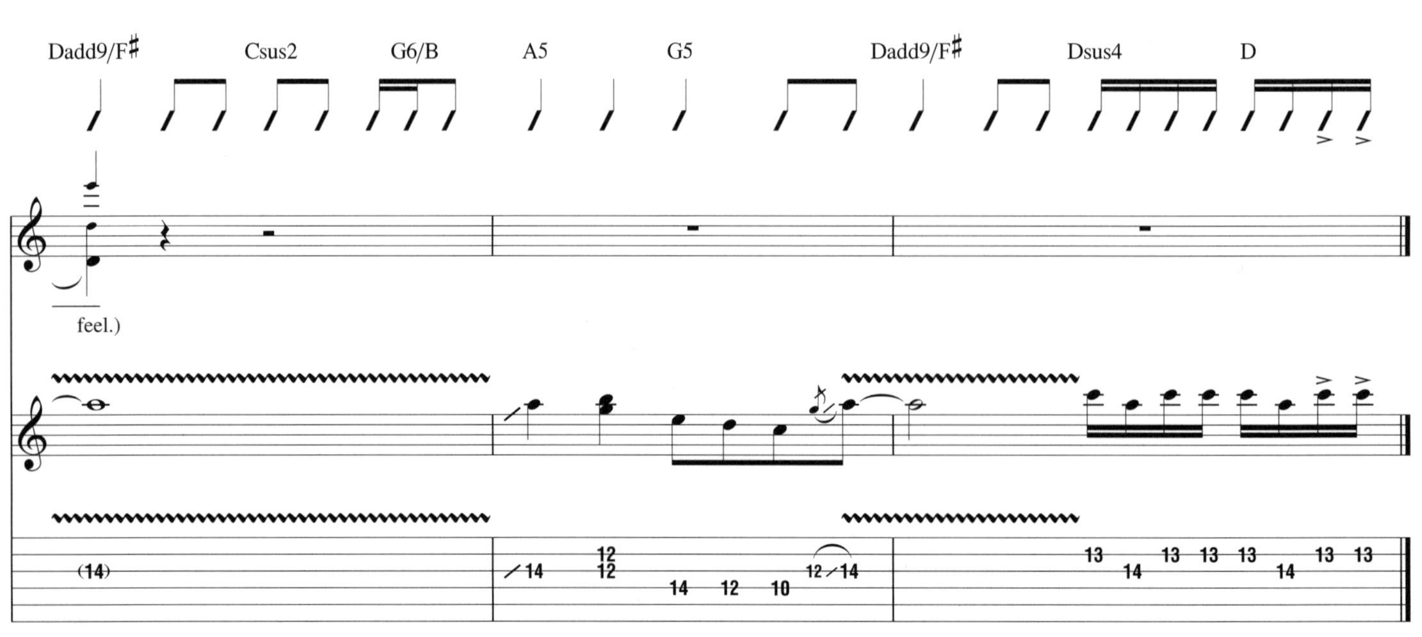
Dadd9/F♯
Csus2
G6/B
A5
G5
Dadd9/F♯
Dsus4
D
feel.)

Disease

Words and Music by Rob Thomas and Mick Jagger

Verse
Gtrs. 2, 3 & 4 tacet
Gtr. 1 tacet
Am Gsus4/A Am
Am Gsus4/A Am
you made some - bod - y's heart break.
Gtr. 1
Gtr. 6 (elec.)
mf
w/ dist.
P.M.
Gtr. 5 (acous.)
mf
Dm C/D Dm
But now I have to let you go,
I have to let you
Gtr. 7 (elec.)
**w/ dist., panning delay, harmonizer & volume pedal
w/ bar
Gtr. 6
P.M.
Gtr. 5
*Vol. off
**Panning delay set for dotted eighth note regeneration w/ multiple repeats, panning in quarter note rhythm. Harmonizer set for one and two octaves above. Volume pedal is last effect in chain.
***Vol. swell
†Vol. off

Am Gsus4/A Am
Gtrs. 5 & 6 tacet
Gtr. 7 tacet
A5 G5/A A5 G5/A E/B
go.
You left a stain
*Gtrs. 8 & 9
(elec.) Rhy. Fig. 2
w/ dist.
Harm.
*Composite arrangement
P.M.
F/C E/B F/C E/B
on ev - 'ry one of my good days.
But I am strong - er than you
Gtrs. 8 & 9
Dm **A5/D Dm A5/D D5
A5 G5/A A5 G5/A E/B
know,
I have to let you go.
**Bass plays D.

Pre-Chorus
2nd time, Gtr. 10 tacet
Gtr. 9 tacet
F5
G5
Gtr. 8
mf
No one's ev - er turned you o - ver, no one's tried to
thing you do is trag - ic, all my life
End Rhy. Fig. 2
Gtr. 6
(Gtr. 8 cont. in slashes)
1st time, Gtr. 8 tacet
2nd time, Gtr. 8: w/ Rhy. Fill 1
A5
D5/A
F/C
ev - er let you down. Beau - ti - ful girl, bless your
be - fore was mag - ic. Beau - ti - ful girl, I can't
Chorus
1st time, Gtr. 4: w/ Rhy. Fig. 1 (2 times)
2nd time, Gtr. 4: w/ Rhy. Fig. 1 (3 1/2 times)
3rd time, Gtr. 4: w/ Rhy. Fig. 1 (4 1/2 times)
3rd time, Gtr. 11: w/ Riff A (3 3/4 times)
Gtr. 6 tacet
E/B
A5 type2
D5
Rhy. Fig. 3A
Gtrs. 8 & 9
f
heart.
breathe.
I got a dis - ease deep in - side me, makes me feel un - eas - y, ba - by.
Gtr. 1
mp
Gtrs. 2 & 3
Rhy. Fig. 3
let ring
Rhy. Fill 1
Gtr. 8
Riff A
Gtr. 11

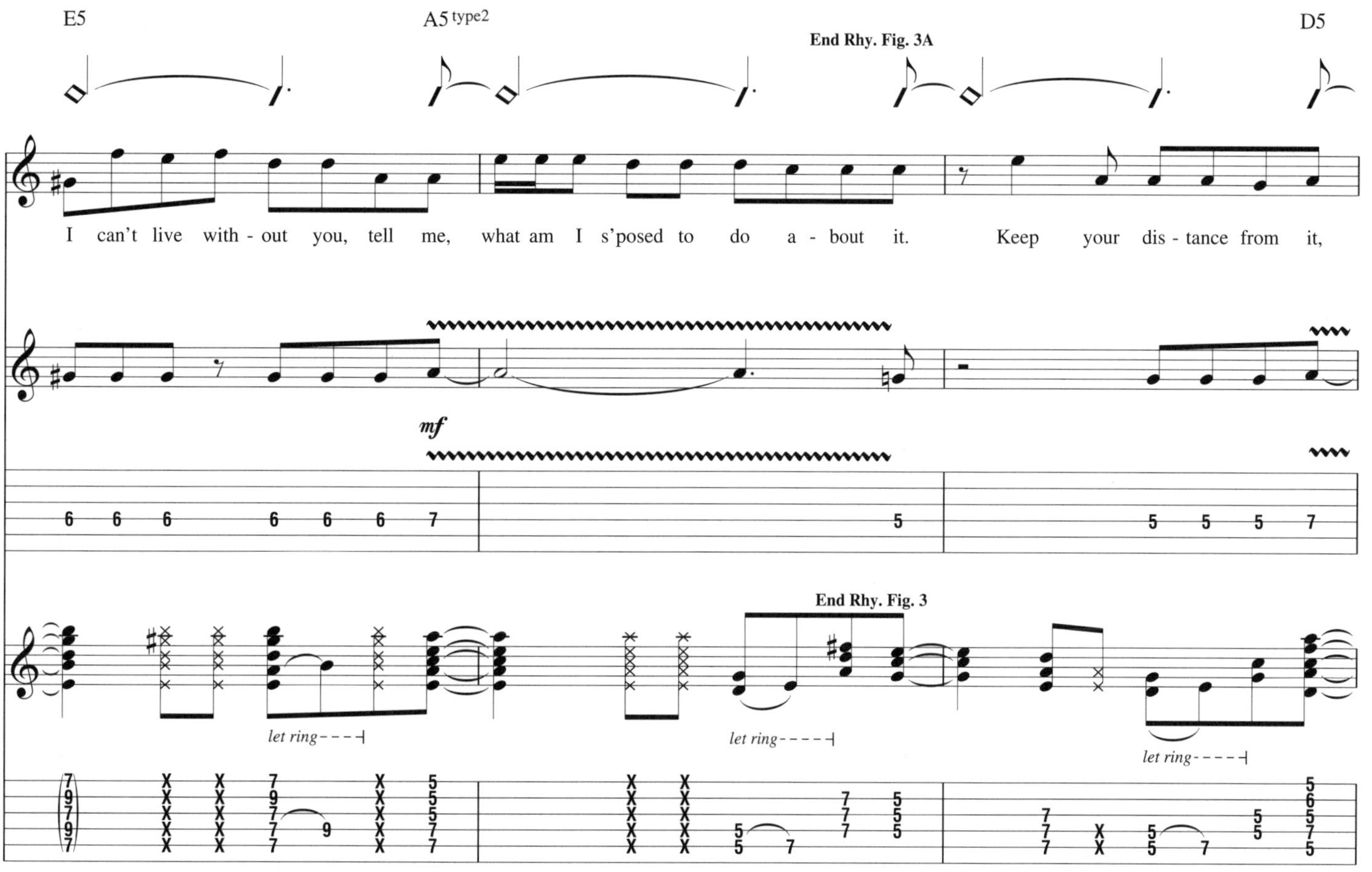

To Coda 1

To Coda 2

E5

A5 type2

Am V

don't pay no at - ten - tion to me, I got a dis - ease.

Gtr. 10 (elec.)

f

w/ dist.

Gtr. 1

divisi

Verse
Gtrs. 1, 2, 3, 8 & 9 tacet
N.C.
Gtrs. 8 & 9: w/ Rhy. Fig. 2
A5 G5/A A5
G5/A
E/B
2. Feels like you're mak - ing a mess,
you're hell on wheels in a black
Gtr. 10
F/C E/B F/C
E/B
Dm A5/D Dm
A5/D
D5
dress.
You drove me to the fi - re
w/ phaser
D.S. al Coda 1
A5 G5/A A5
G5/A
E/B
and left me there to burn.
Ev - 'ry lit - tle
Coda 1
Gtrs. 2 & 3: w/ Rhy. Fig. 3 (last meas.)
Gtrs. 8 & 9: w/ Rhy. Fig. 3A (last meas.)
Gtrs. 2 & 3: w/ Rhy. Fig. 3 (1 1/2 times)
Gtrs. 8 & 9: w/ Rhy. Fig. 3A (1 1/2 times)
Dm
Yeah, well, I think that I'm sick,
but leave me be while my world
Gtr. 1
f
1/4

E
Am
is com - ing down on me.
You taste like hon - ey, hon - ey, tell me can I be your hon - ey -
Dm
- bee. Be strong, keep tell - ing my - self that it won't take long till
1/4
E5
Gtrs. 8 & 9
Bridge
Gtr. 4 tacet
Dm
I'm free of my dis - ease, yeah, I'm free of my
Gtr. 1
Gtr. 11 (elec.)
w/ dist.
Gtr. 1 divisi
*Gtr. 11 plays tab numbers on top 2 strings, next 8 meas.
Gtrs. 2 & 3
Rhy. Fill 2
End Rhy. Fill 2
Gtr. 4
Rhy. Fill 2A
End Rhy. Fill 2A

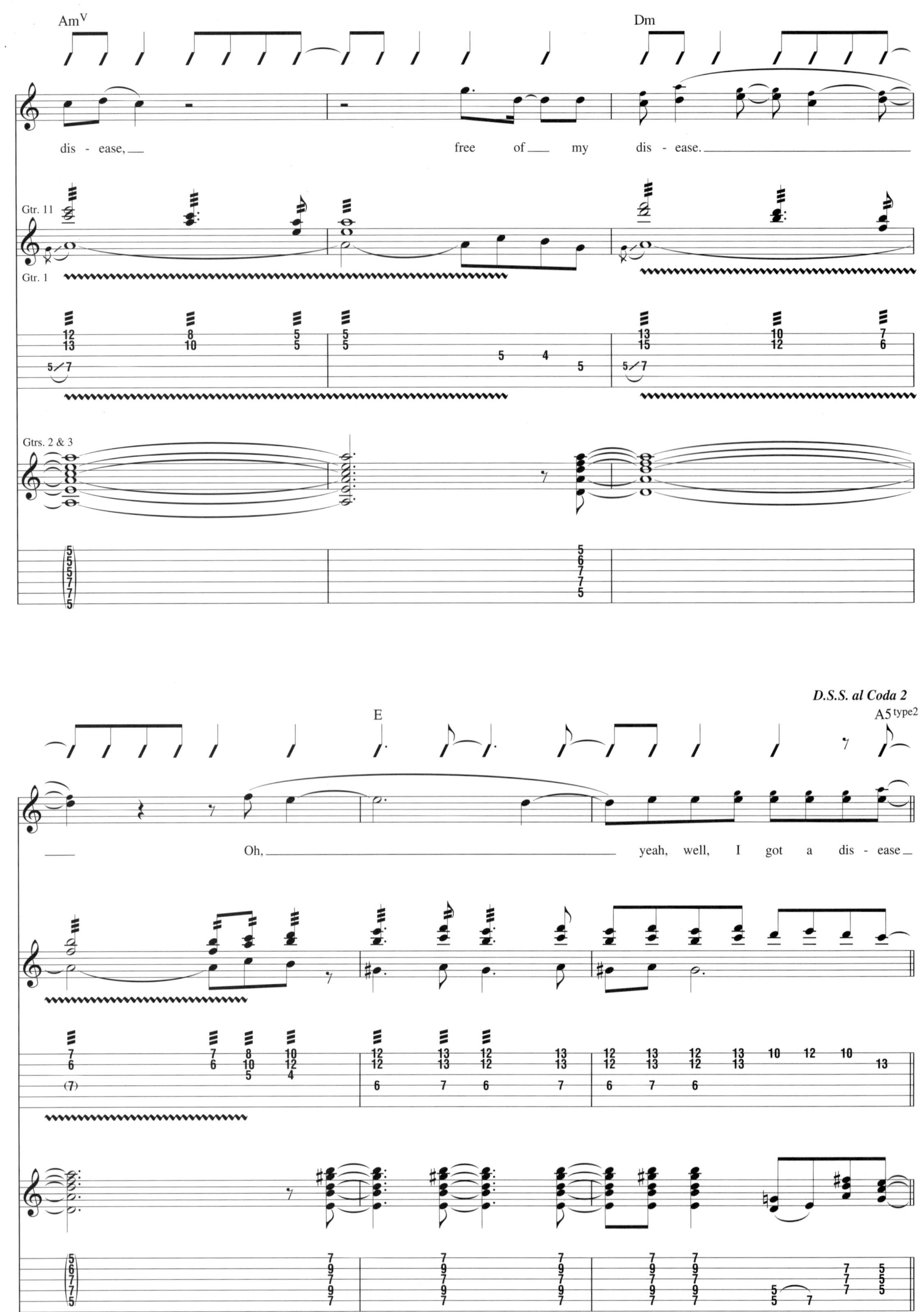

Am[V]
Dm
dis - ease,
free of my dis - ease.
Gtr. 11
Gtr. 1
Gtrs. 2 & 3
D.S.S. al Coda 2
E
A5 type2
Oh, yeah, well, I got a dis - ease

Coda 2
Gtrs. 2 & 3: w/ Rhy. Fig. 3 (last meas.)
Gtrs. 8 & 9: w/ Rhy. Fig. 3A (last meas.)
Gtrs. 2 & 3: w/ Rhy. Fig. 3 (1 1/2 times)
Gtrs. 8 & 9: w/ Rhy. Fig. 3A (1 1/2 times)
Dm
Yeah, well, I think that I'm sick, but leave me be while my world
Gtr. 1
is com - ing down on me.
E
Am
You taste like hon - ey, hon - ey, tell me can I be your hon - ey -
Dm
bee. Be strong, keep tell-ing my - self that it won't take long till
Gtrs. 2 & 3: w/ Rhy. Fill 2
Gtr. 4: w/ Rhy. Fill 2A
E5
Gtrs. 8 & 9
I'm free of my
(Free of my dis -
Outro
A5
E5
A5
E5
dis - ease, yeah, free of my dis - ease.
ease.)
Gtr. 12 (elec.)
w/ dist.
Gtr. 1

A5 E5 A5

Set me free of my dis - ease. Oo, oh, yeah.

E5

Free time

A5

rit.

rit.

grad. bend

1/2

rit.

Bright Lights

Words and Music by Rob Thomas

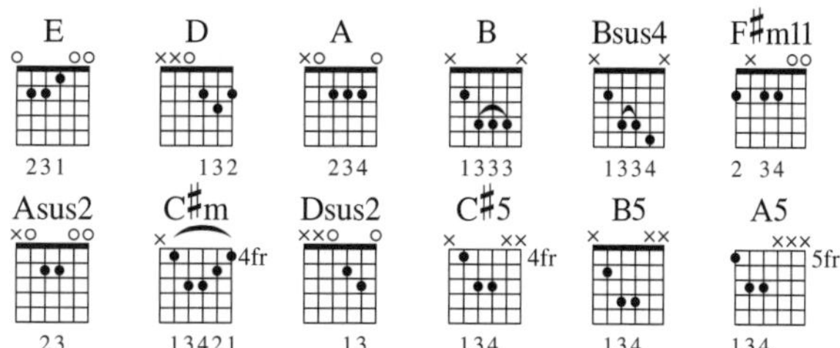

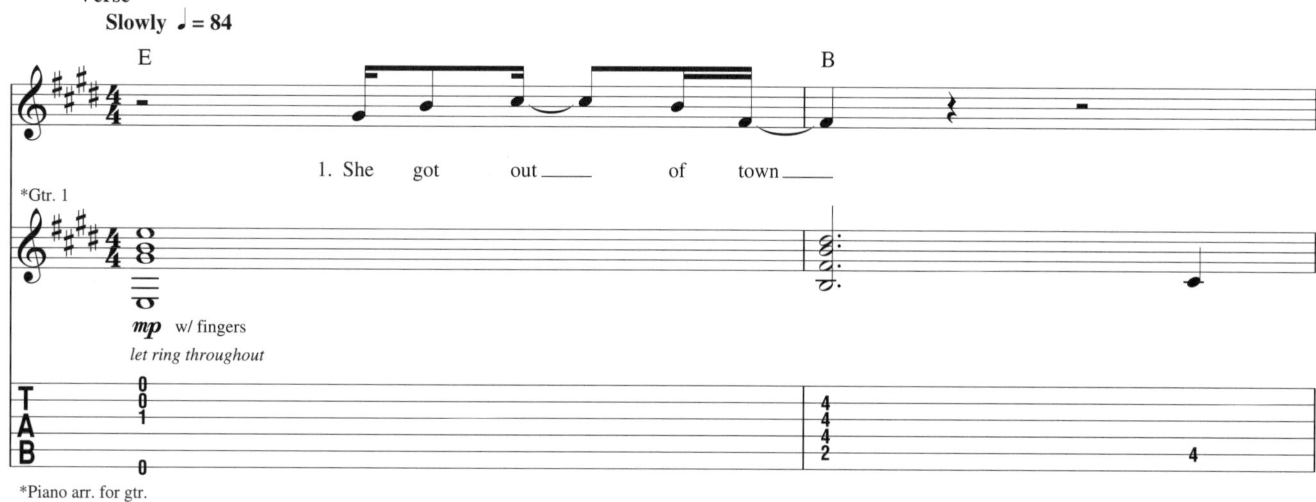

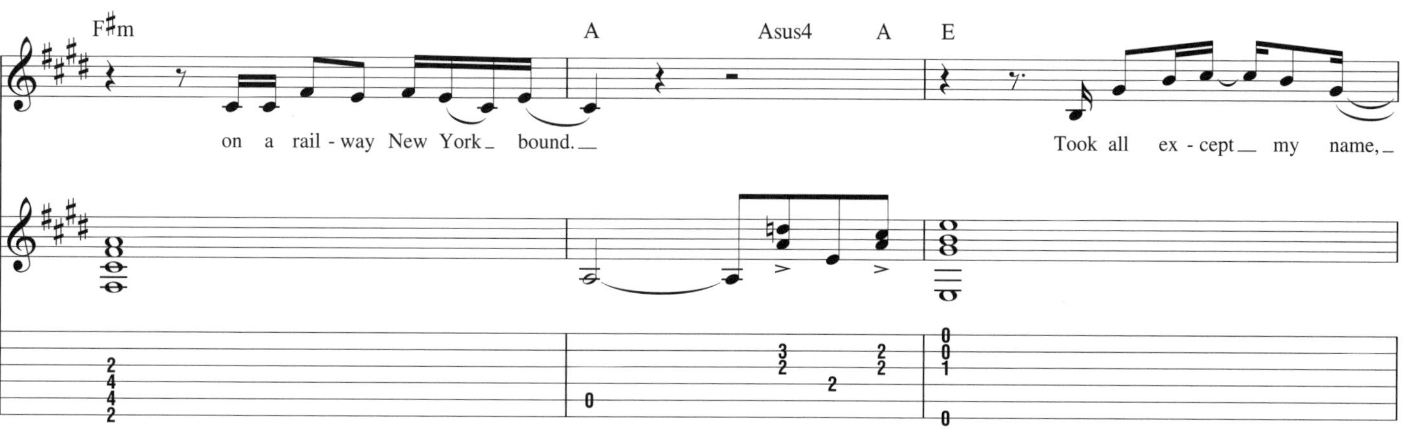

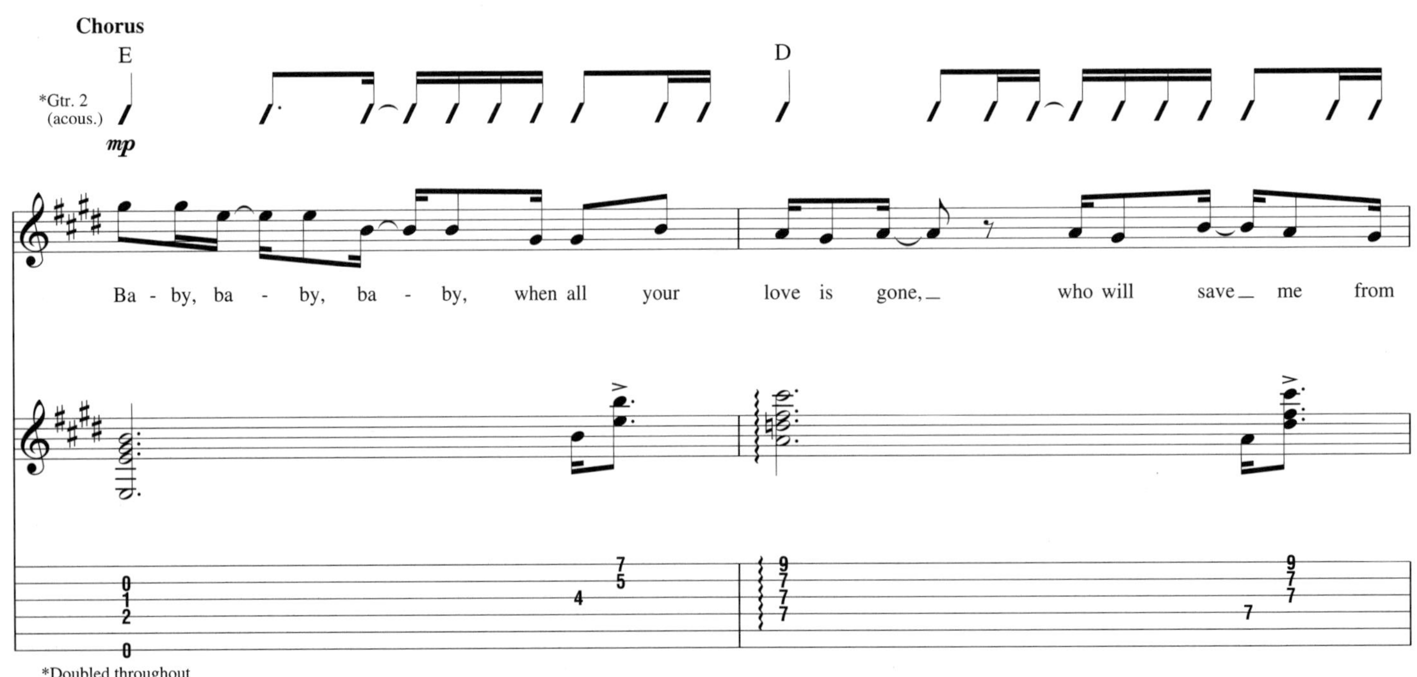

*Doubled throughout

A
E
all I'm up a - gainst out in this world? And
Gtr. 3 (elec.)
mp
w/ dist.
Gtr. 1
*Vol. swell
Gtr. 3 tacet
D
may - be, may - be, may - be you'll find some-thing that's e - nough to keep you, but if the
A
B
bright lights don't re - ceive you, you should turn your - self a - round and come on
Gtr. 1

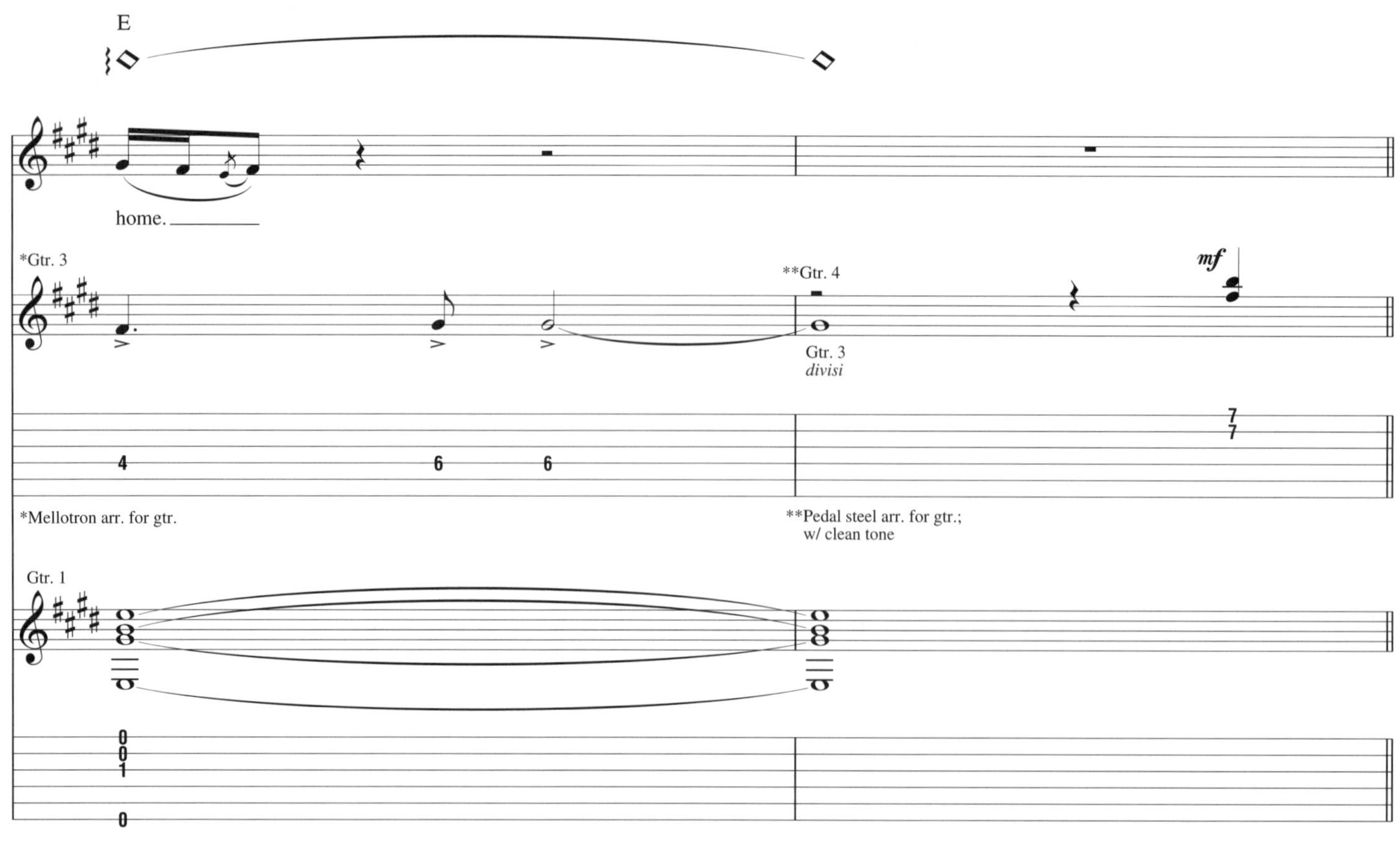

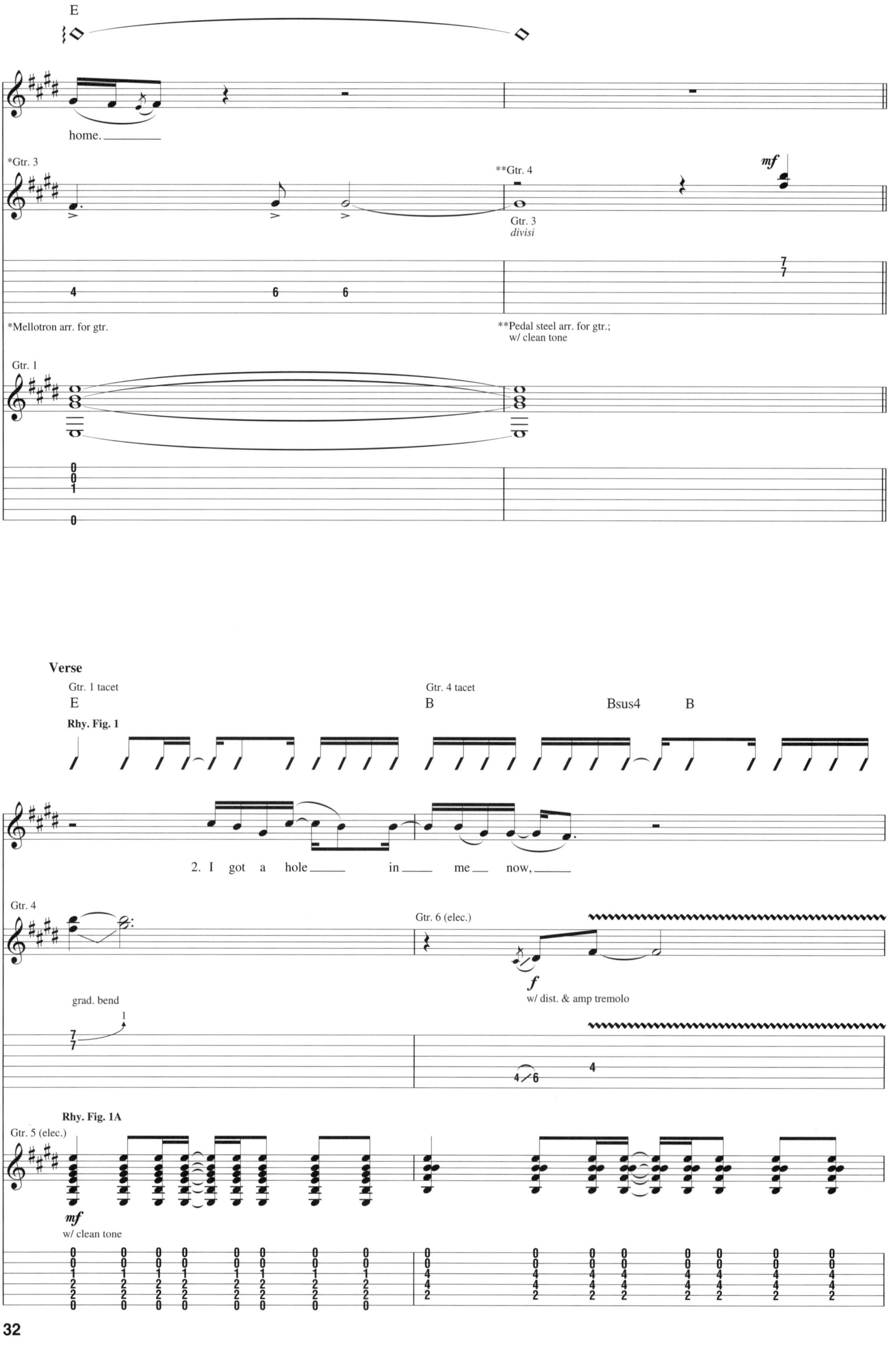

E
home.
*Gtr. 3
**Gtr. 4
mf
Gtr. 3
divisi
*Mellotron arr. for gtr.
**Pedal steel arr. for gtr.;
w/ clean tone
Gtr. 1
Verse
Gtr. 1 tacet
E
Gtr. 4 tacet
B
Bsus4
B
Rhy. Fig. 1
2. I got a hole in me now,
Gtr. 4
Gtr. 6 (elec.)
f
w/ dist. & amp tremolo
grad. bend
Rhy. Fig. 1A
Gtr. 5 (elec.)
mf
w/ clean tone

F#m11 Asus2

End Rhy. Fig. 1

yeah, I got a scar I can talk a - bout.

End Rhy. Fig. 1A

E B Bsus4 B

And she keeps a pic - ture of me

1/2

C♯m
B
Bsus4
A
in her a - part - ment in the ci - ty.

Gtrs. 2 & 5: w/ Rhy. Figs. 1 & 1A
E
B
Bsus4
B
Some things in this world, man, they don't make sense, and
Gtr. 6
1/2

F♯m11
Asus2
some things you don't need un - til they leave you, then they're things that you miss, you say.

Chorus
Gtr. 6 tacet
2nd time, Gtr. 12: w/ Fill 1
E
Dsus2
Rhy. Fig. 2
Gtrs. 2 & 5
Ba - by, ba - by, ba - by, when all your love is gone, who will save me from
Gtr. 7 (elec.)
mf
w/ clean tone
let ring
A
E
End Rhy. Fig. 2
all I'm up a - gainst out in this world?
And
Yeah, well
mp
Dsus2
may - be, may - be, may - be you'll find some-thing that's e-nough to keep you, but if the
Fill 1
Gtr. 12

Bridge

Gtrs. 2, 5 & 7 tacet

C♯5 B5 A B5

*Gtr. 8 (elec.)

f

w/ dist.

Let that cit - y take you in.

(Come on home.

Gtr. 9 (elec.)

mf

w/ dist.

1/2

9 9 11 9 9 9 12 9 9

9

Gtr. 10 (elec.)

mf

w/ dist.

Gtr. 11 (elec.)

divisi

mf

w/ dist.

1/2

1

9 9 11 9 9 9 9 9

9 9 12 9 9 12 9

11 9 11 9

*Doubled throughout

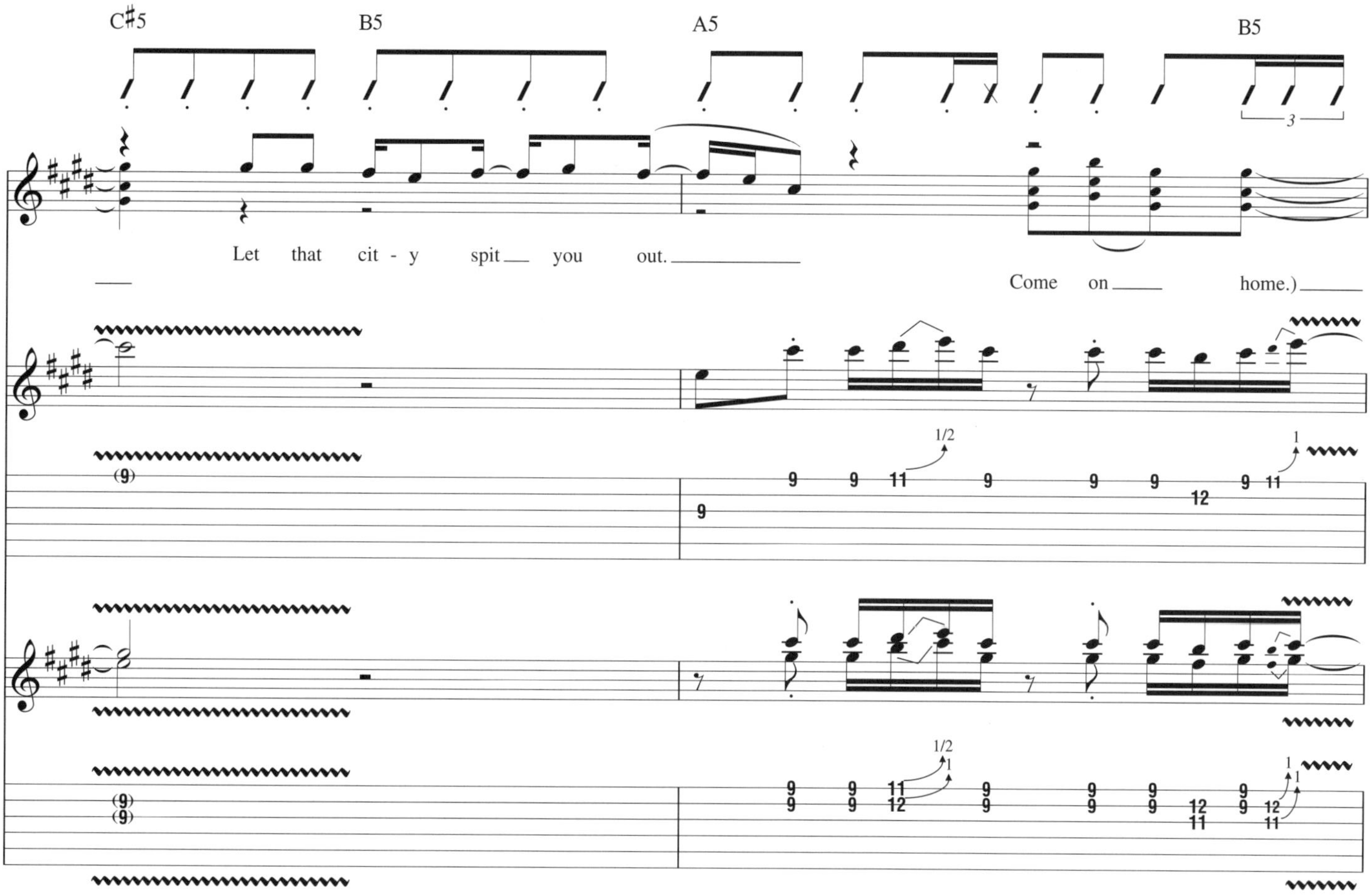

C♯5 B5 A5 B5

Let that cit - y spit you out.

Come on home.)

1/2

1

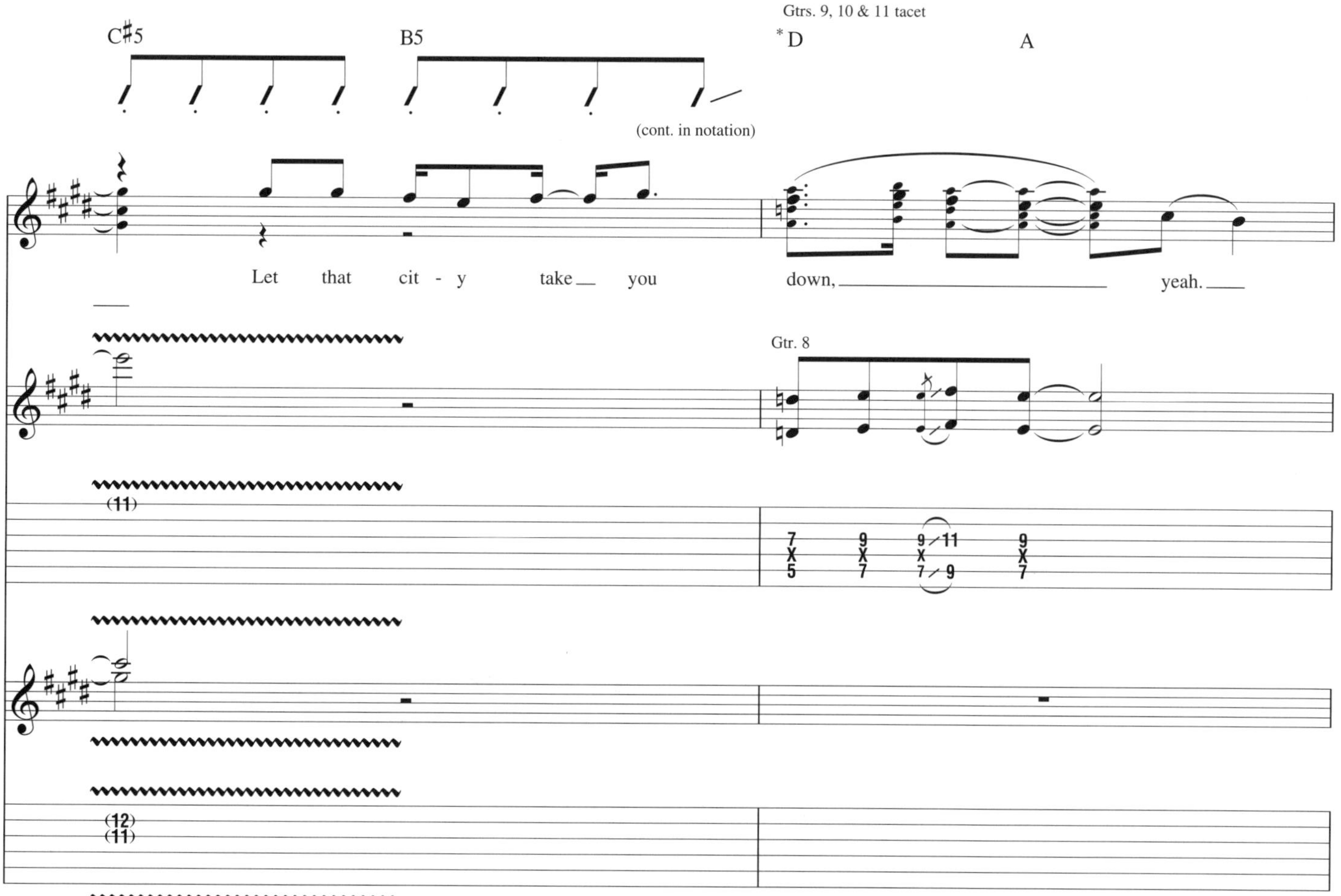

C♯5 B5

(cont. in notation)

Gtrs. 9, 10 & 11 tacet

*D A

Let that cit - y take you down, yeah.

Gtr. 8

*Chord symbols reflect overall harmony.

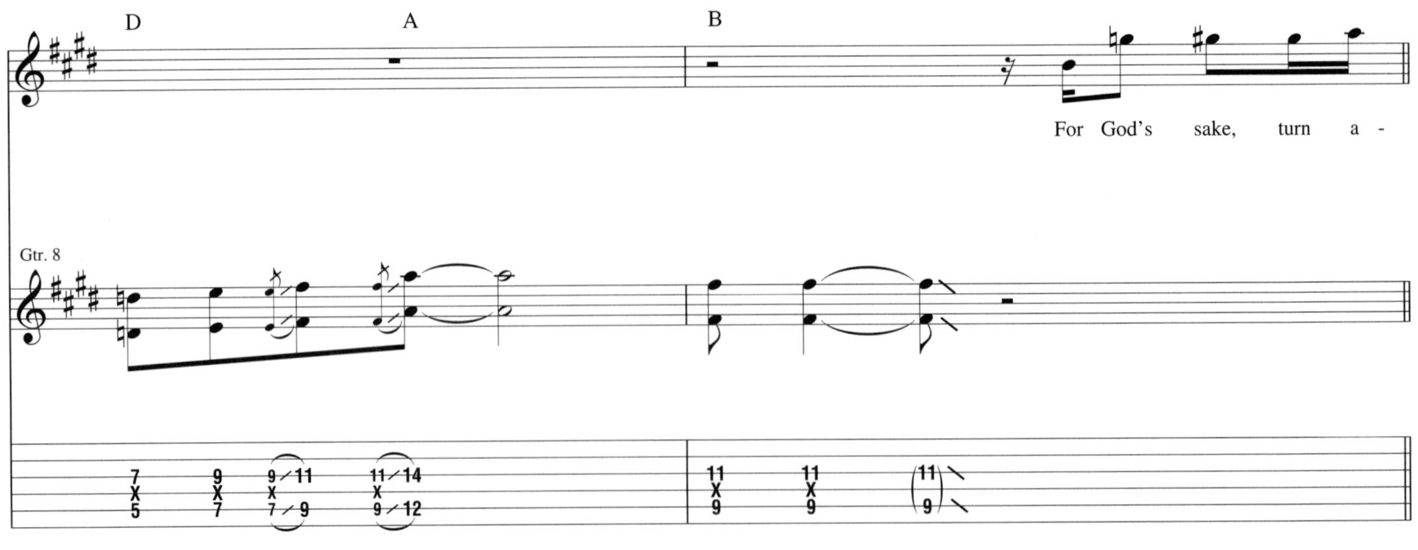
D
A
B
For God's sake, turn a -
Gtr. 8

Guitar Solo

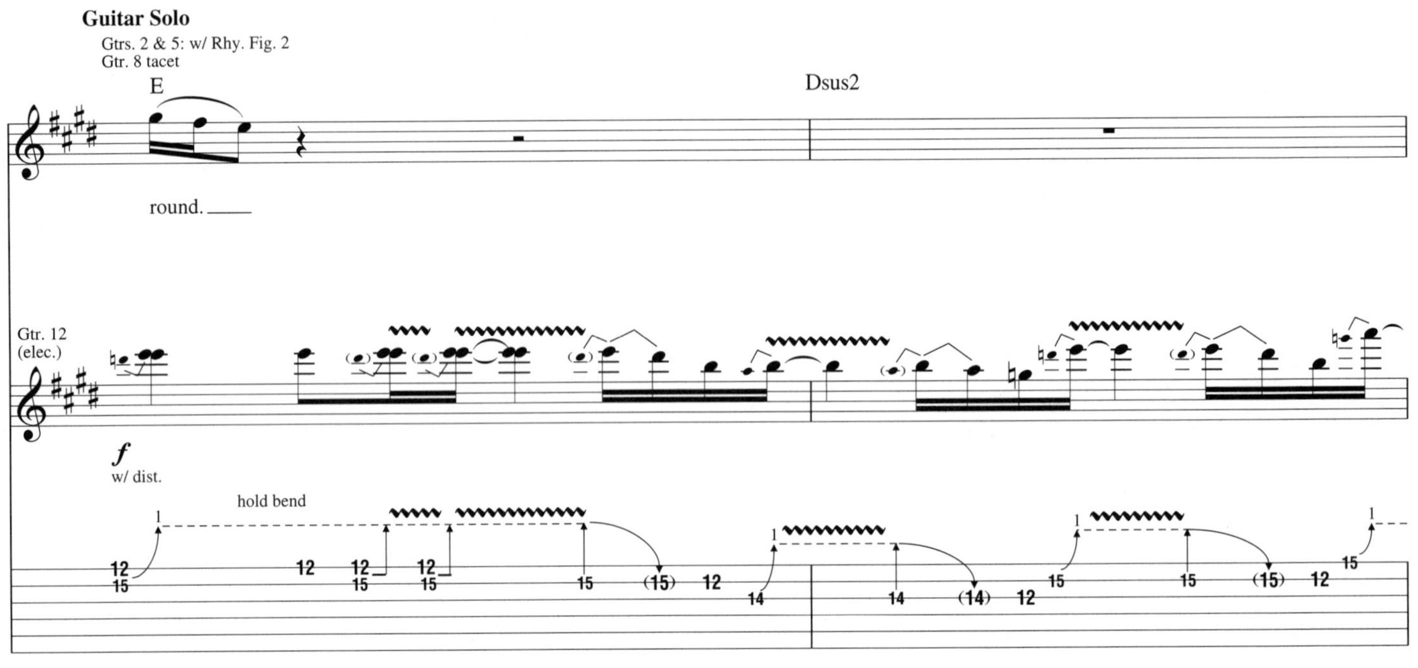
Gtrs. 2 & 5: w/ Rhy. Fig. 2
Gtr. 8 tacet
E
Dsus2
round.
Gtr. 12
(elec.)
f
w/ dist.
hold bend

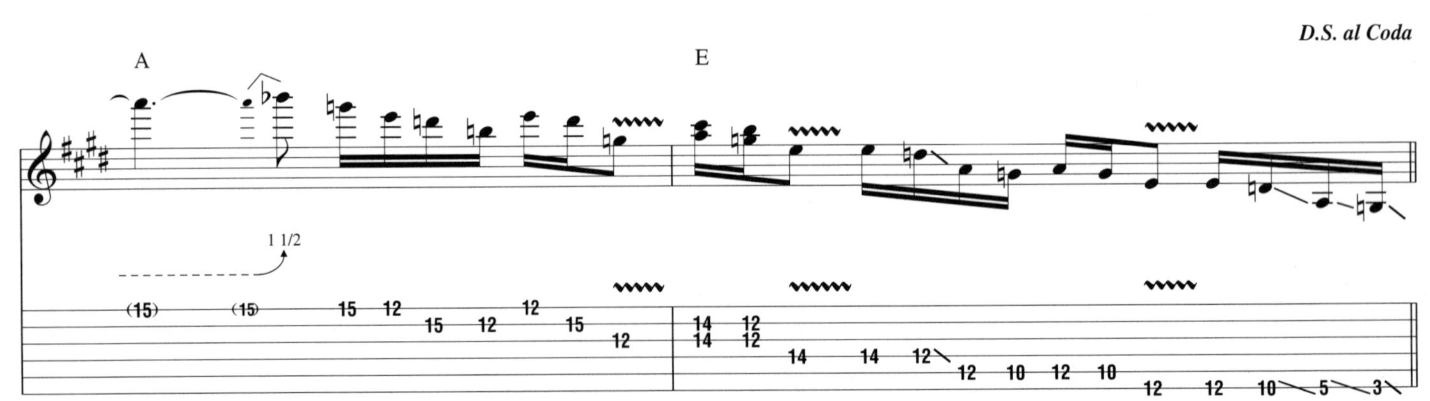
D.S. al Coda
A
E
1 1/2

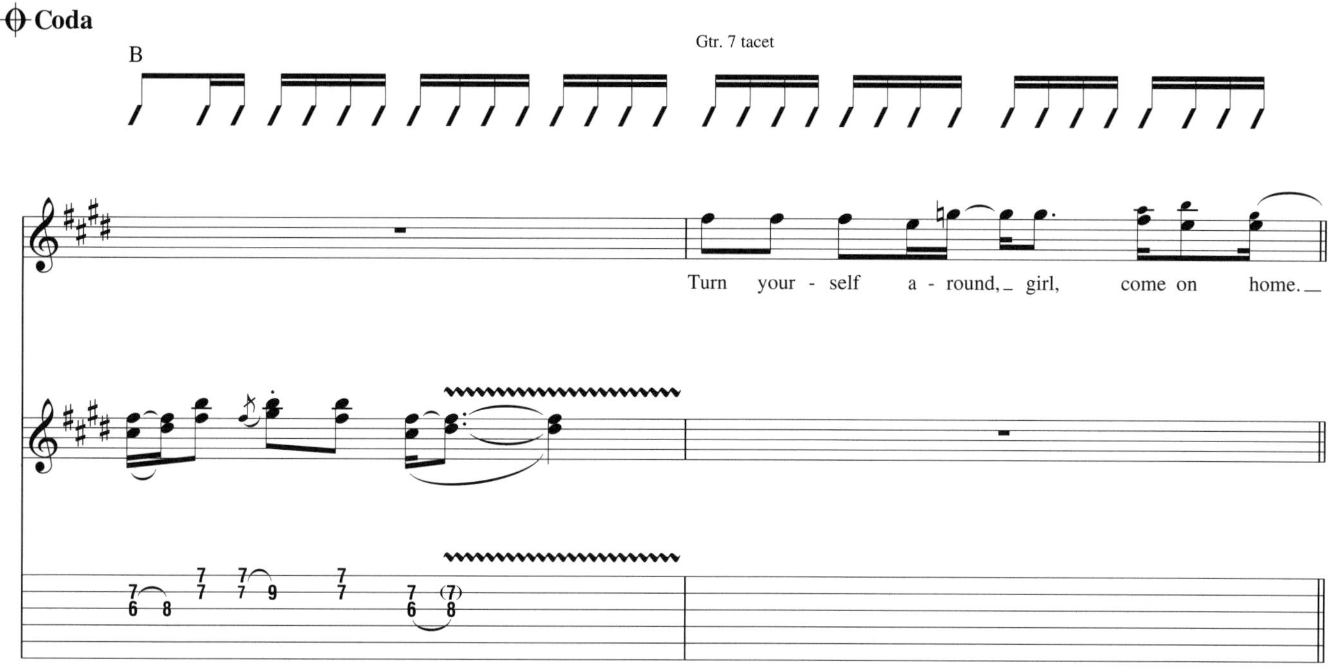

Outro

1.

E

Rhy. Fig. 3

A

End Rhy. Fig. 3

Yeah, come on home.

Riff A

End Riff A

Gtr. 12

let ring

let ring

Gtr. 12

1/2

1/2

let ring

*Gtr. 13 (elec.)

mf

w/ dist.

*Doubled throughout

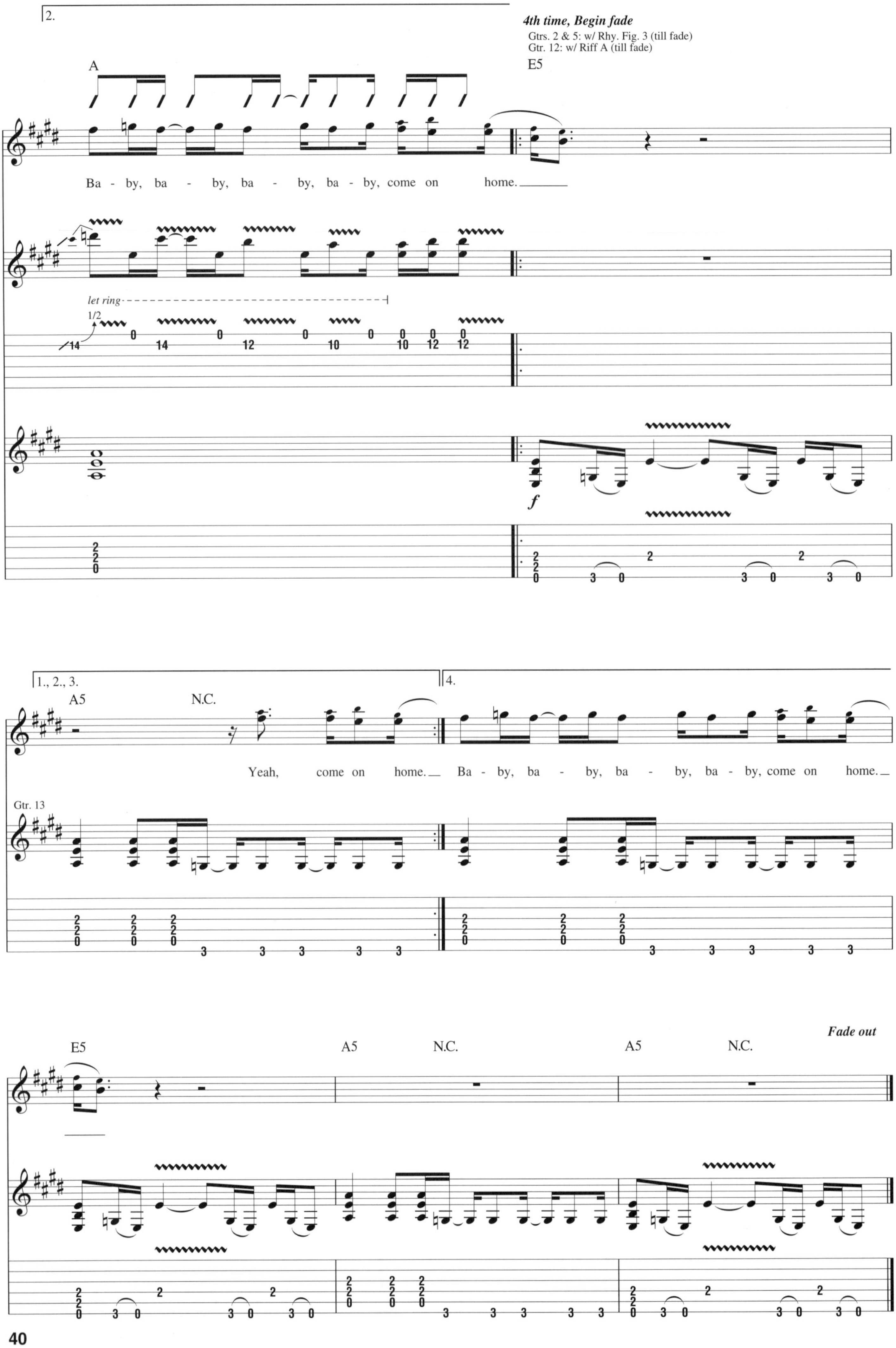

2.

4th time, Begin fade

Gtrs. 2 & 5: w/ Rhy. Fig. 3 (till fade)
Gtr. 12: w/ Riff A (till fade)

A — E5

Ba - by, ba - by, ba - by, ba - by, come on home.

let ring

1/2

Unwell

Words and Music by Rob Thomas

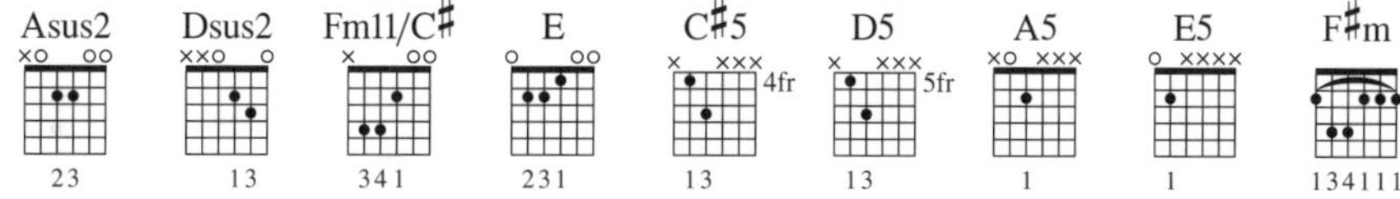

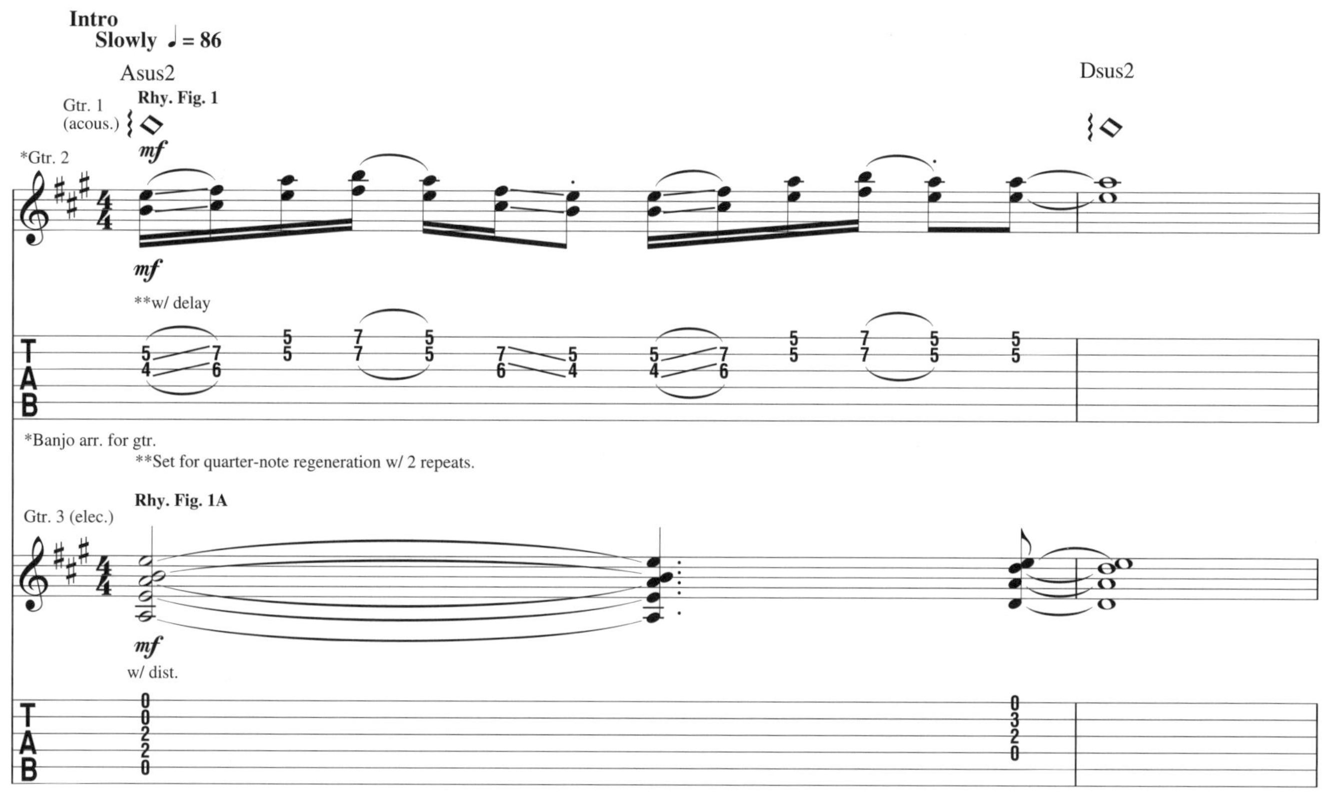

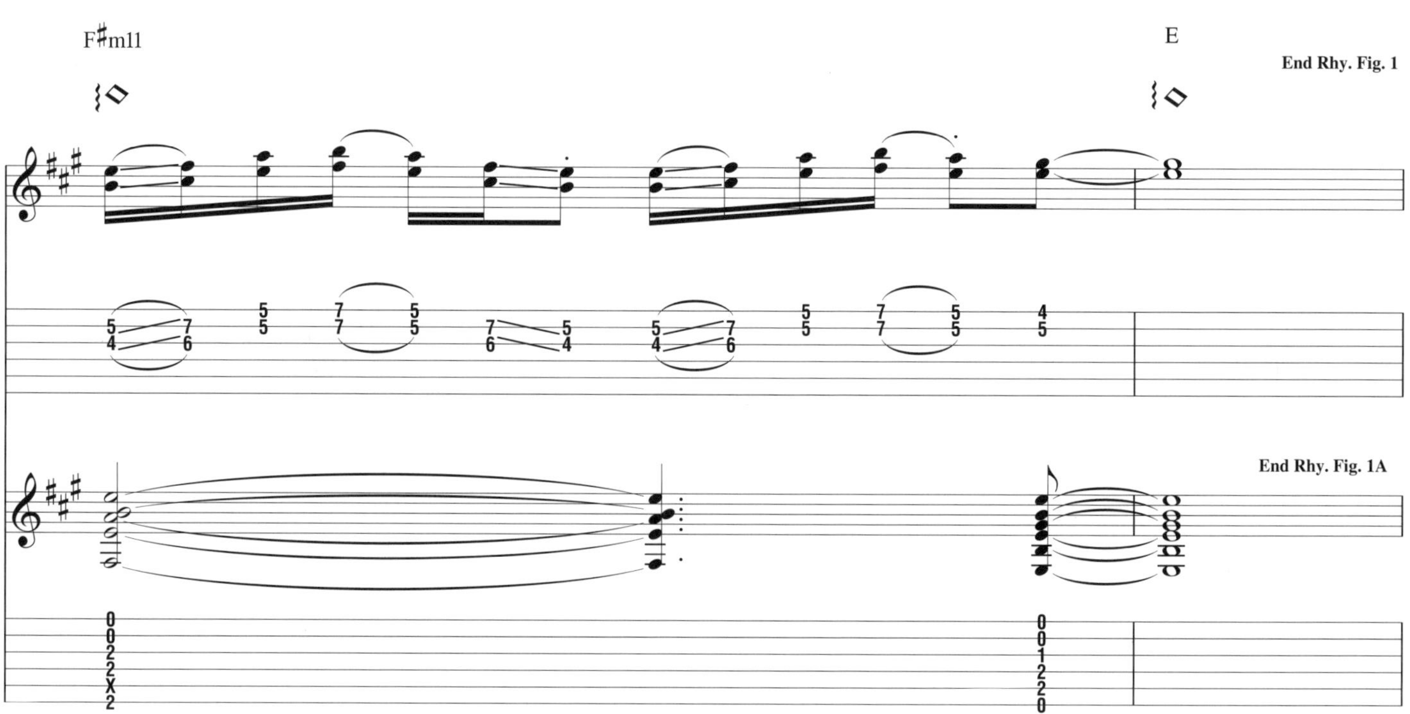

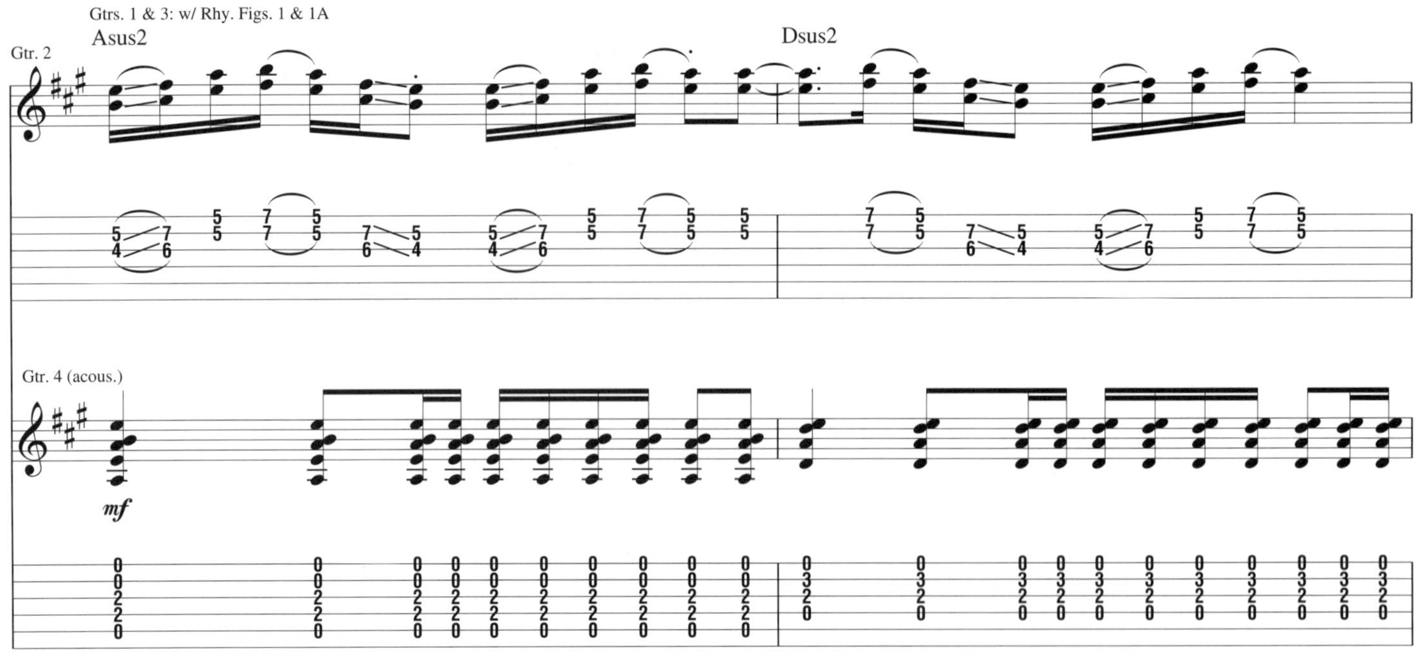

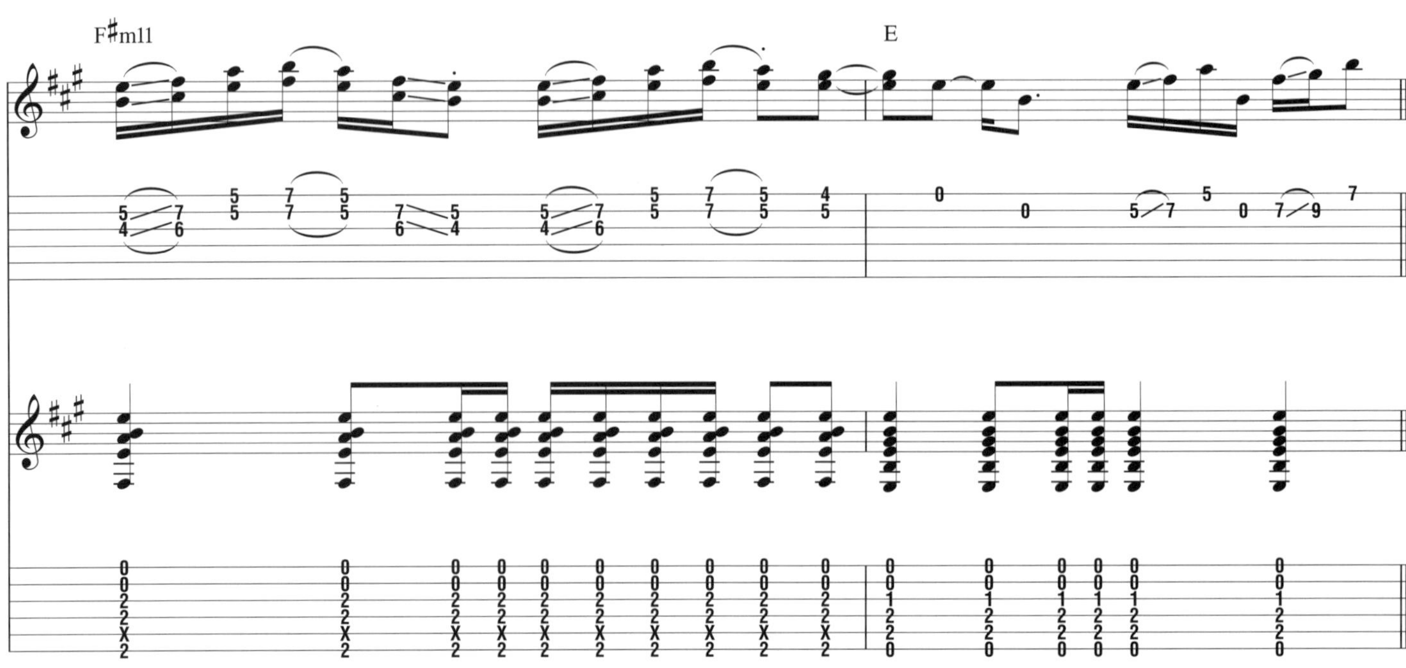

Verse

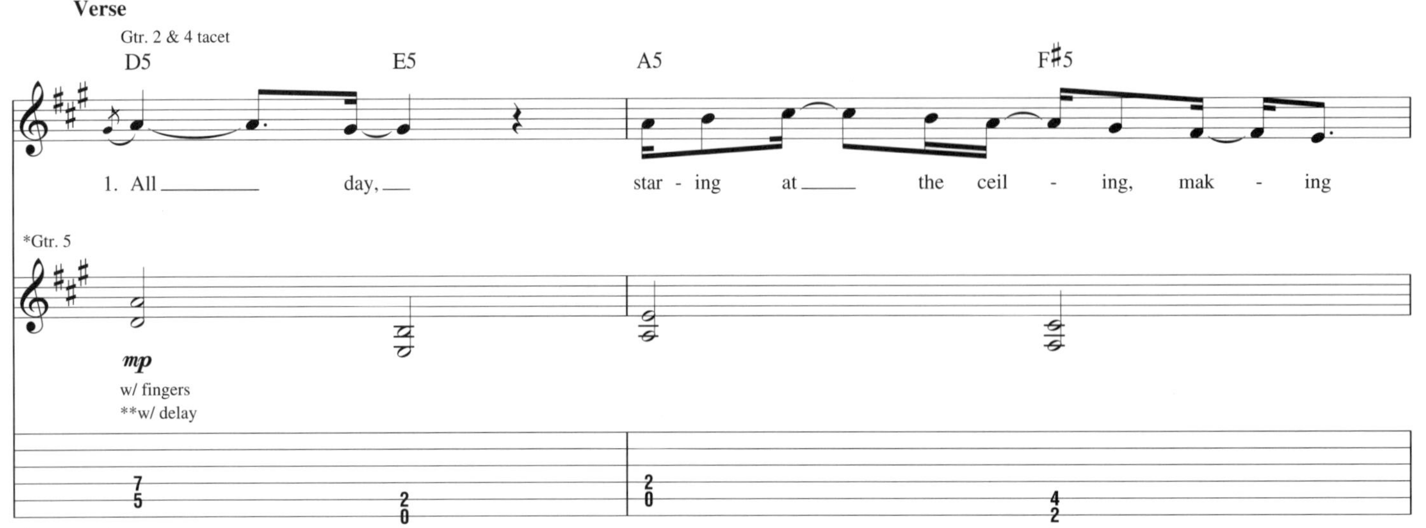

*Piano arr. for gtr.

**Set for quarter-note triplet regeneration w/ 2 repeats.

D5 E5 F♯5 D5 E5
friends with shad - ows on my wall. All night,
A5 F♯5 D5
hear - ing voic - es tell - ing me that I should get some sleep be - cause to - mor -
Pre-Chorus
E5 C♯5 D5
Gtr. 5
- row might be good for some - thing. Hold on,
w/ slide & reverb
mp
Gtr. 7 (elec.)
(cont. in slashes)
Gtr. 6 (elec.) divisi
mp
w/ clean tone
A5 E5 C♯5 D5
feel - ing like I'm head - ed for a break - down and

Chorus
Gtrs. 4 & 5 tacet
3rd time, Gtr. 8: w/ Fill 1
Gtr. 7 tacet
A5
E5
Asus2
*Gtrs. 1 & 4
mf
I don't know why. But I'm not cra - zy, I'm just a lit - tle un -
Gtr. 6
Gtr. 3
mf
*Composite arrangement
Dsus2
F♯m11/C♯
well. I know right now you can't tell, but stay a - while and may - be then you'll see
E
Asus2
a dif - f'rent side of me. I'm not cra - zy, I'm just a lit - tle im -
Fill 1
Gtr. 8

To Coda 1
To Coda 2

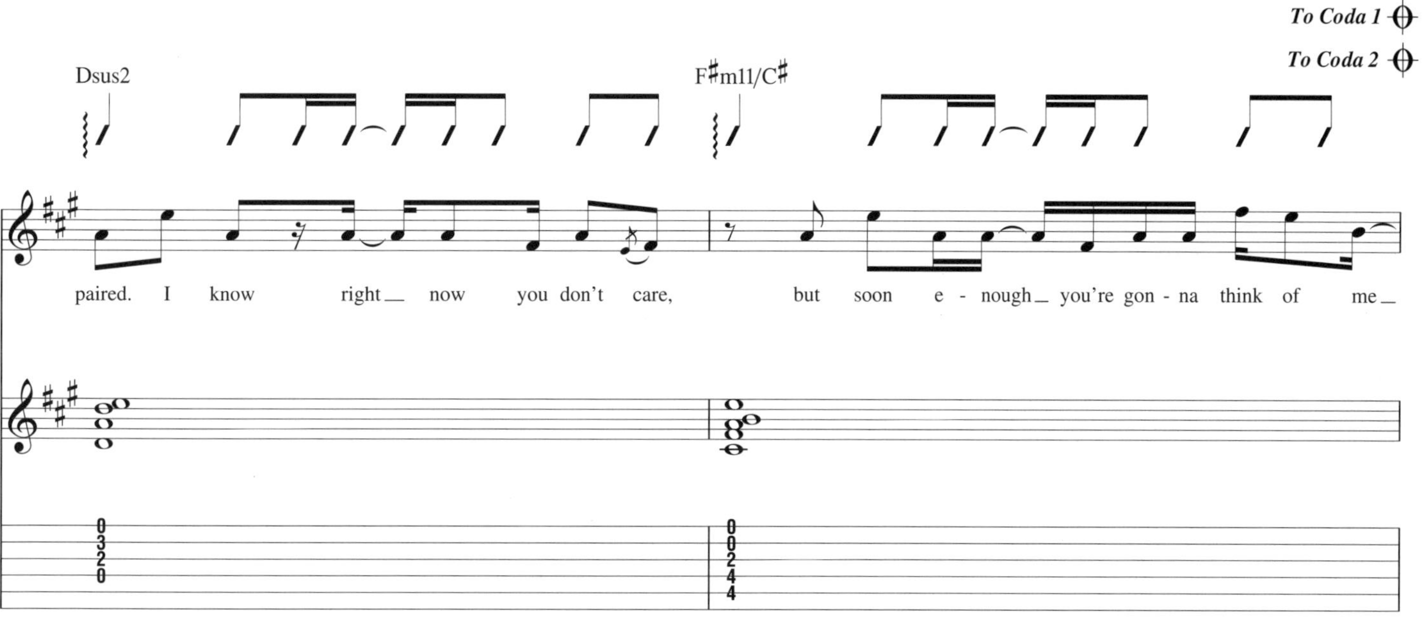

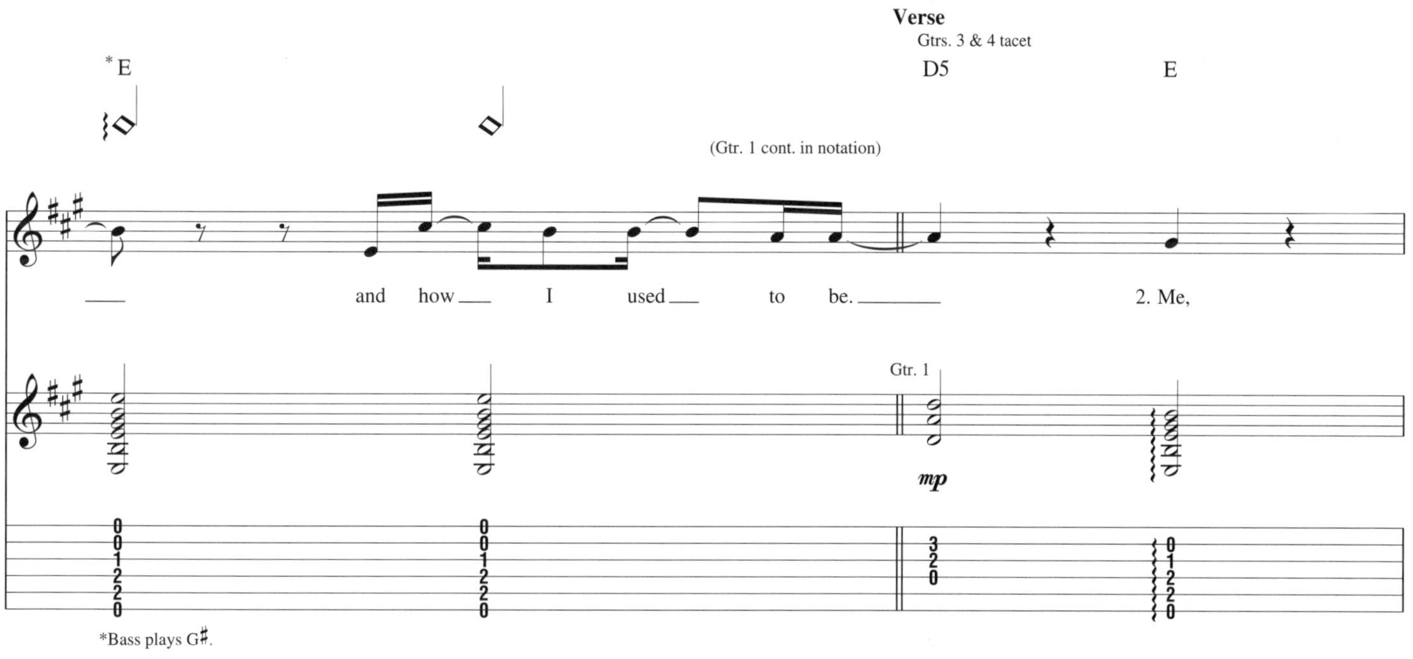

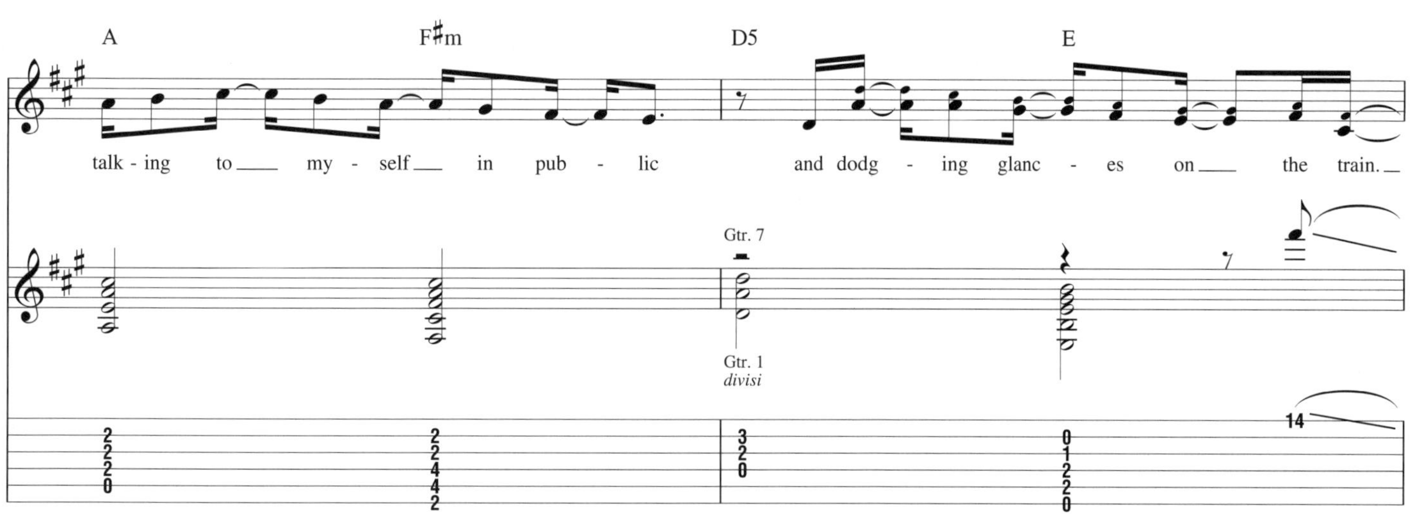

Gtr. 7 tacet
F#m11
D5
E
A
F#m
And I know, I know they've all been talk - ing 'bout me.
Gtr. 1
let ring

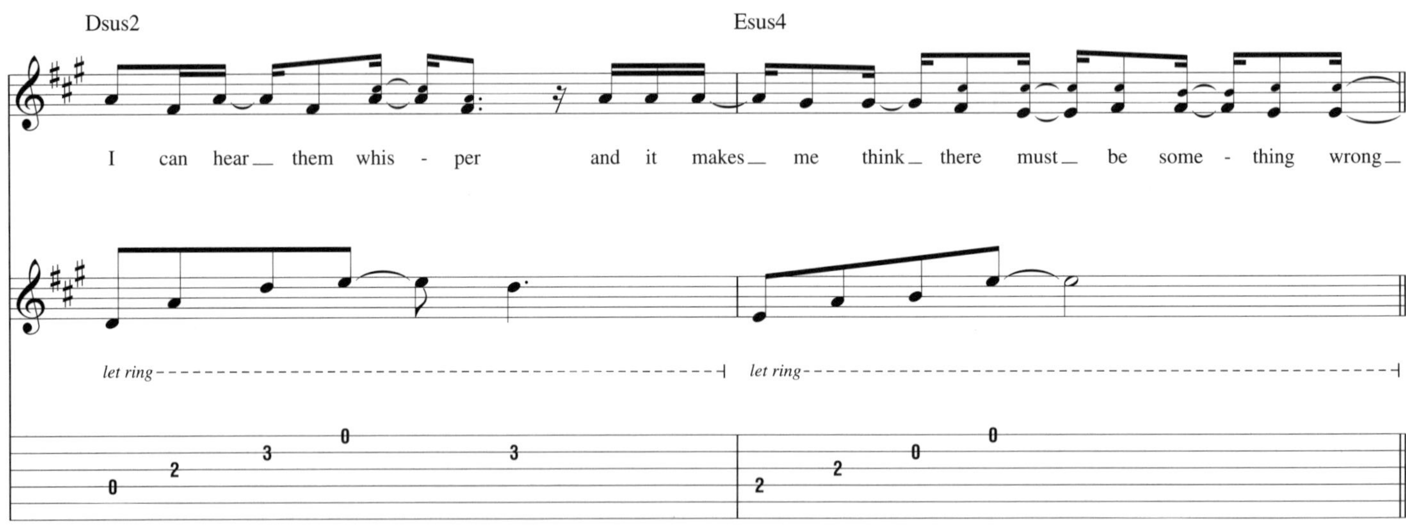
Dsus2
Esus4
I can hear them whis - per and it makes me think there must be some - thing wrong
let ring
let ring

Pre-Chorus

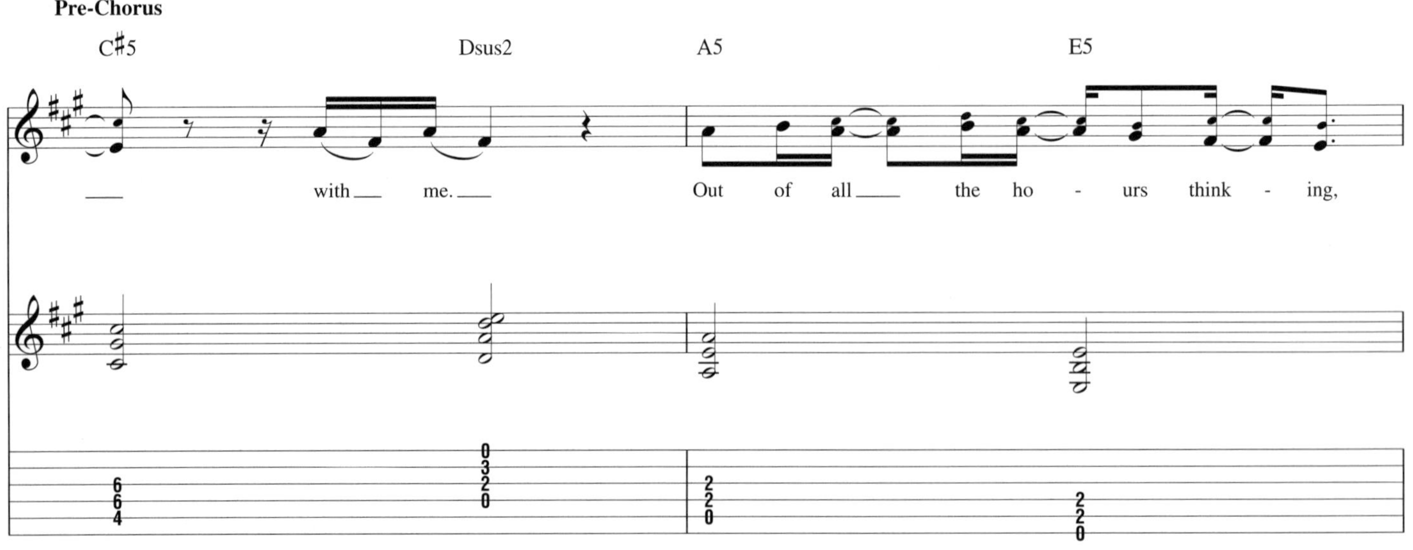
C#5
Dsus2
A5
E5
with me. Out of all the ho - urs think - ing,

D.S. al Coda 1
C♯m7
Dsus2
A5
E5
some - how
(some - how...)
I've lost my mind.
But
let ring
(cont. in slashes)

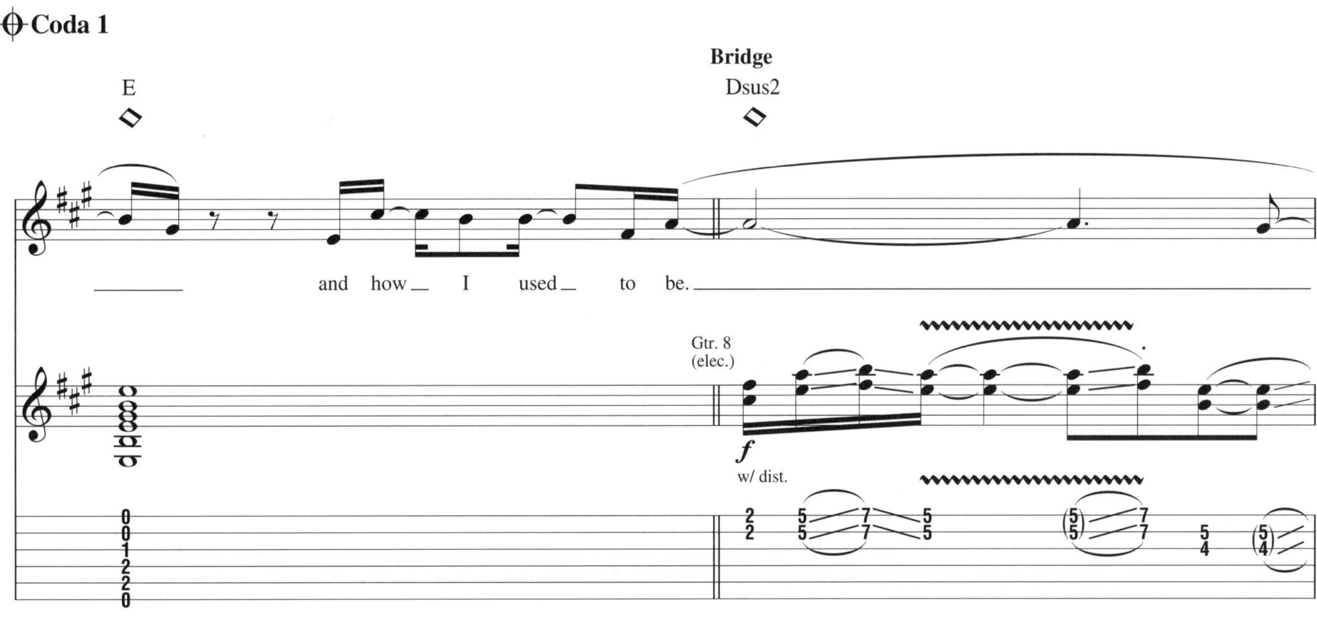
Coda 1
Bridge
E
Dsus2
and how I used to be.
Gtr. 8
(elec.)
f
w/ dist.

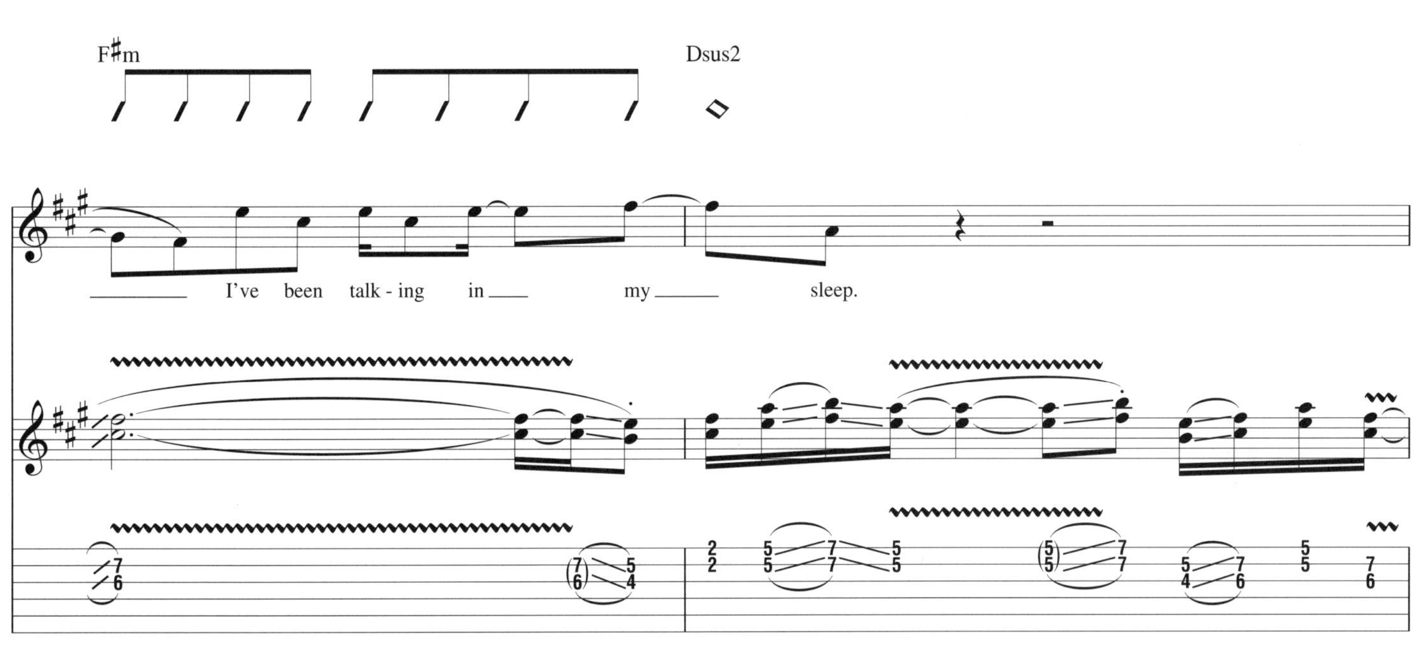
F♯m
Dsus2
I've been talk - ing in my sleep.

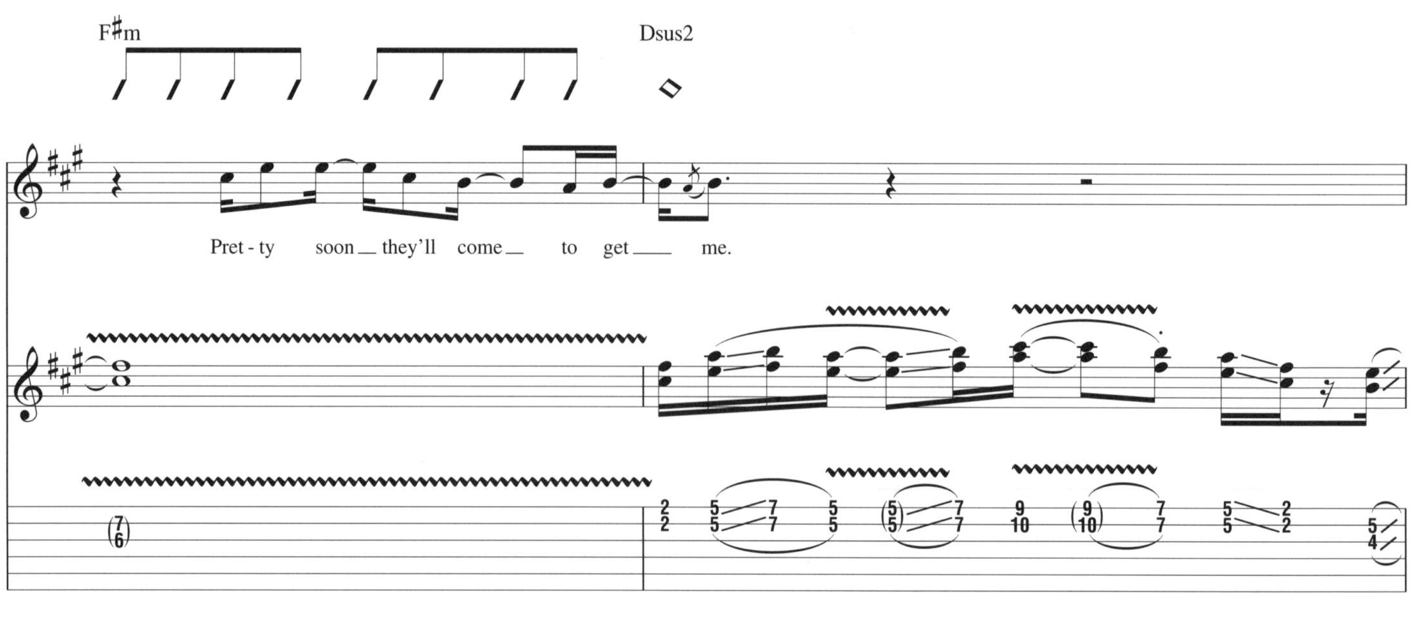
F#m
Dsus2
Pret - ty soon they'll come to get me.

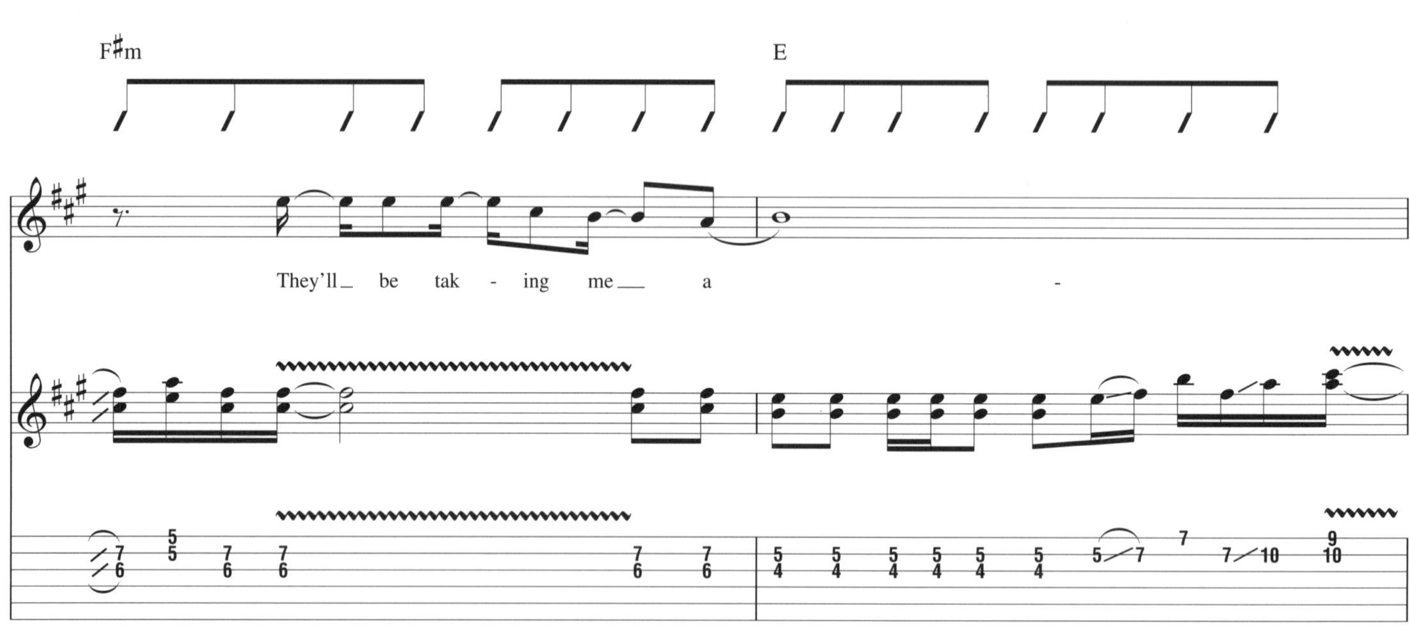
F#m
E
They'll be tak - ing me a -

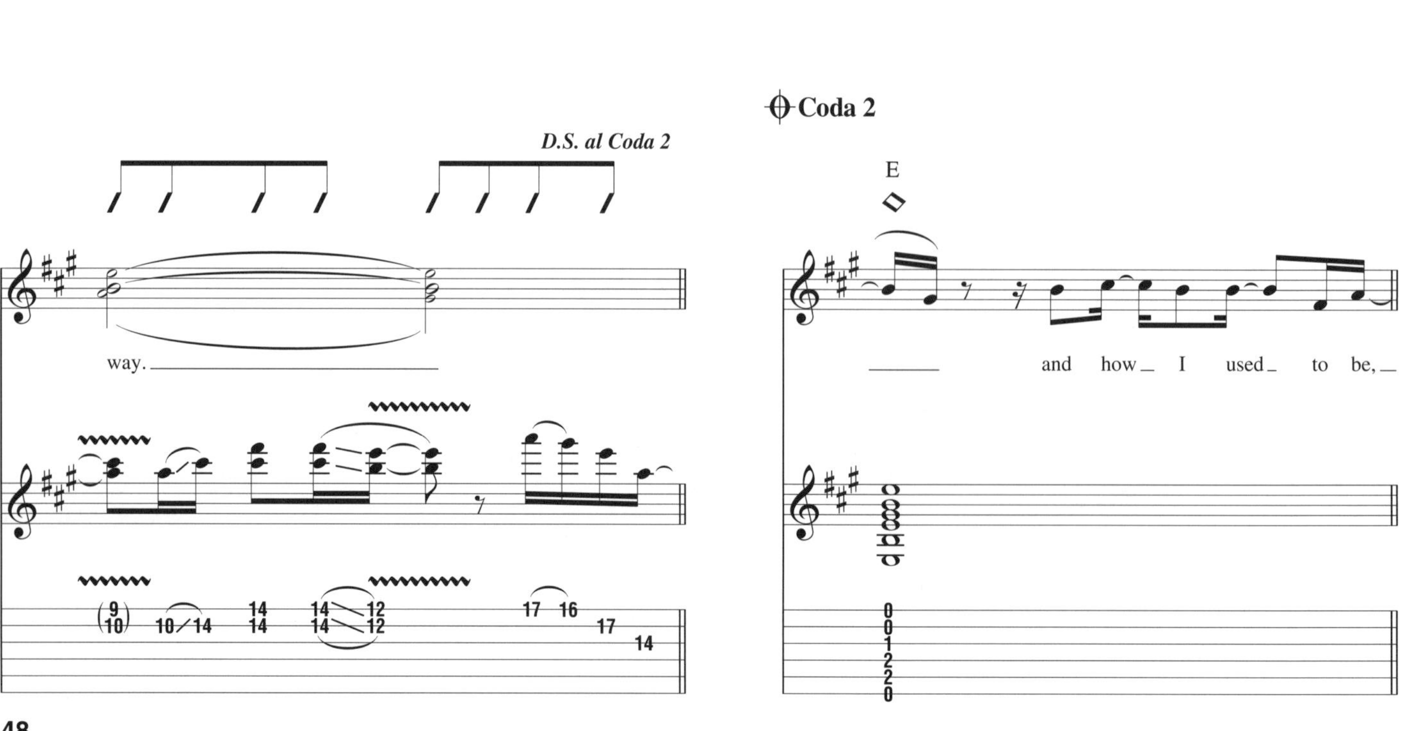
Coda 2
D.S. al Coda 2
E
way.
and how I used to be,

Outro

Gtrs. 1 & 3: w/ Rhy. Figs. 1 & 1A (3 times)

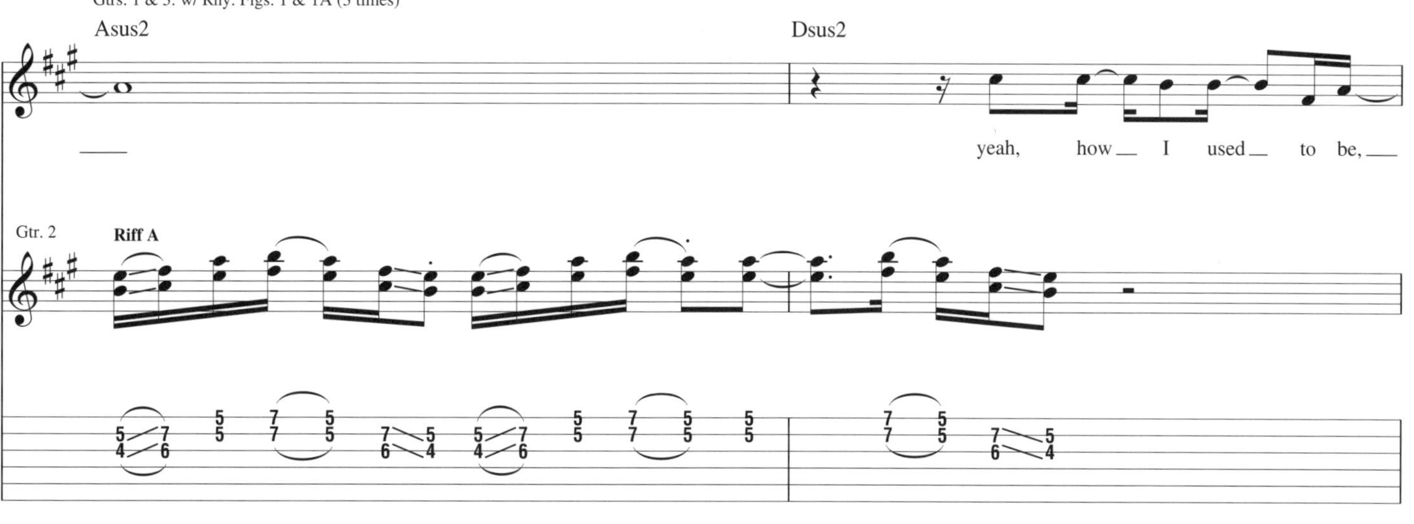
Asus2
Dsus2
yeah, how I used to be,
Gtr. 2
Riff A

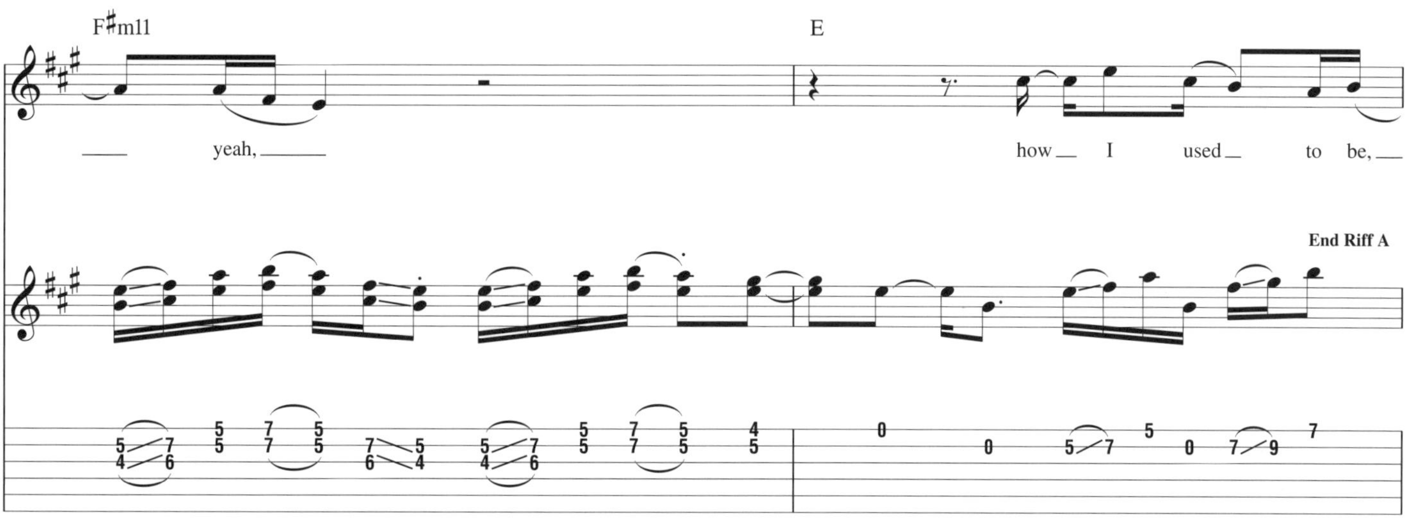
F♯m11
E
yeah,
how I used to be,
End Riff A

Gtr. 2: w/ Riff A
Asus2
Dsus2
oh, yeah.
Well, I'm just a lit - tle un -

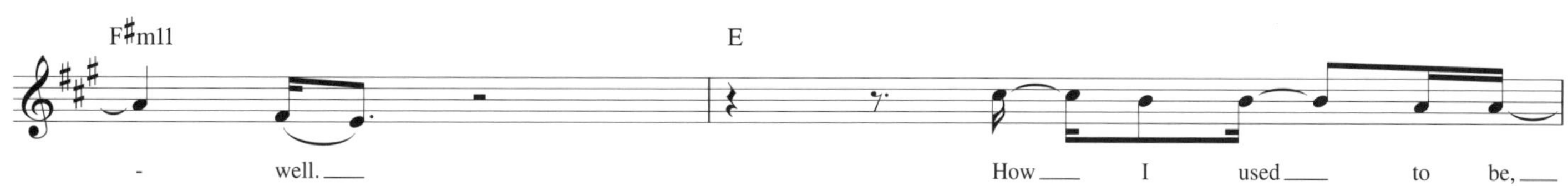
F♯m11
E
- well.
How I used to be,

Begin fade
Asus2
Dsus2
how I used to be,
(A lit - tle un - well.
Gtr. 2

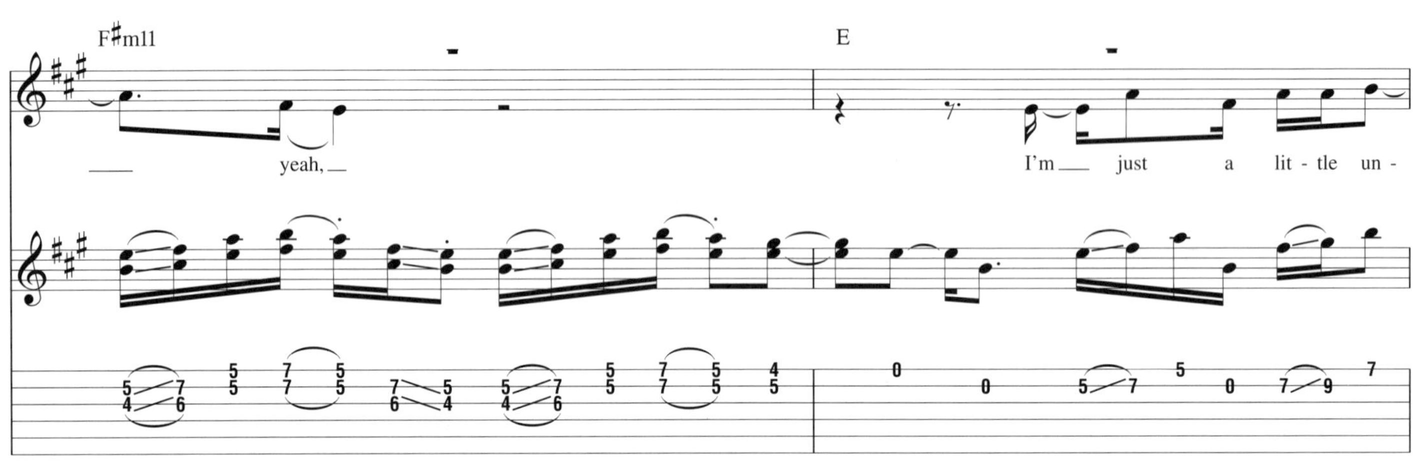
F♯m11
E
yeah,
I'm just a lit - tle un -

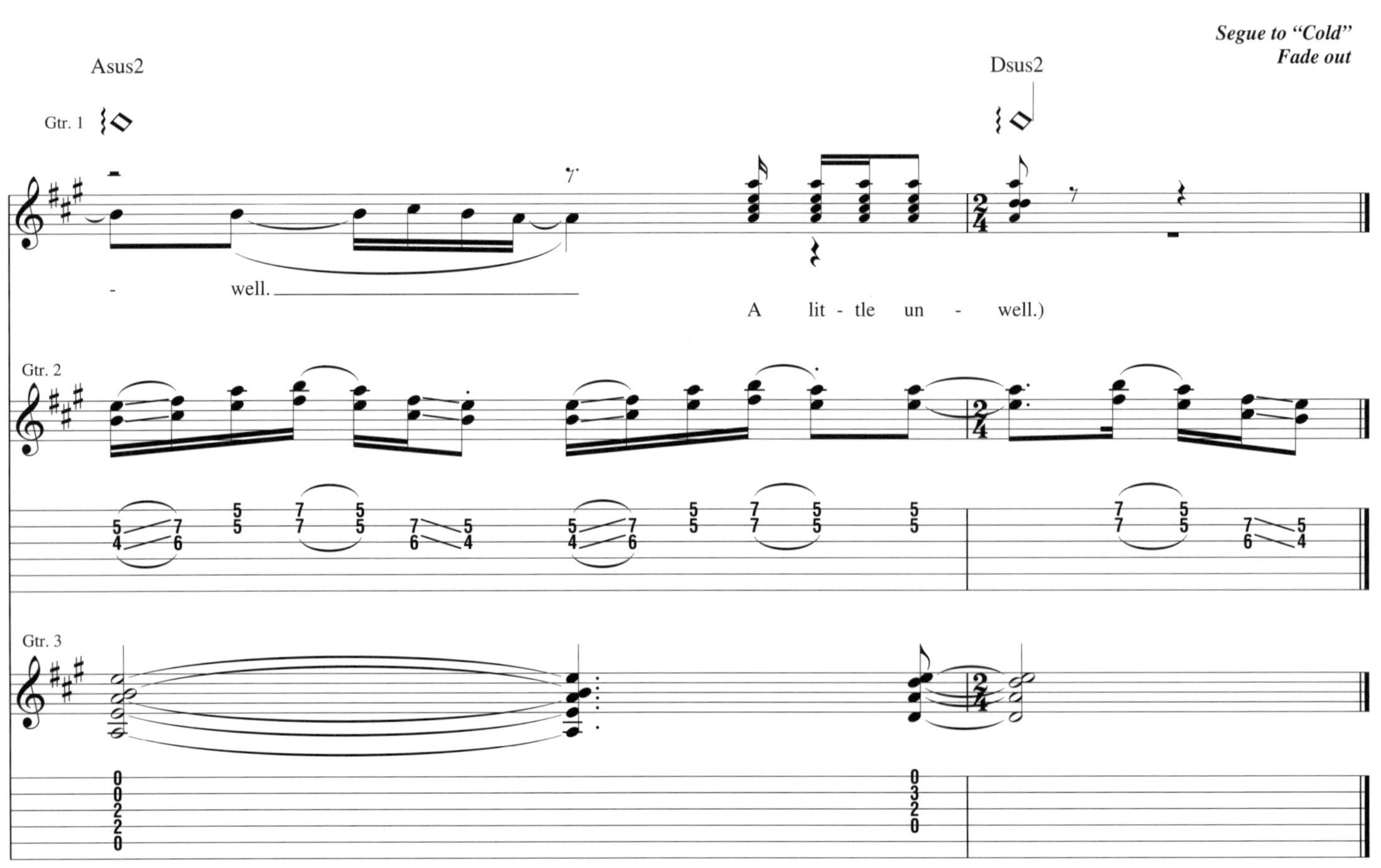
Segue to "Cold"
Fade out
Asus2
Dsus2
Gtr. 1
- well.
A lit - tle un - well.)
Gtr. 2
Gtr. 3

Cold

Words and Music by Rob Thomas and Matt Serletic

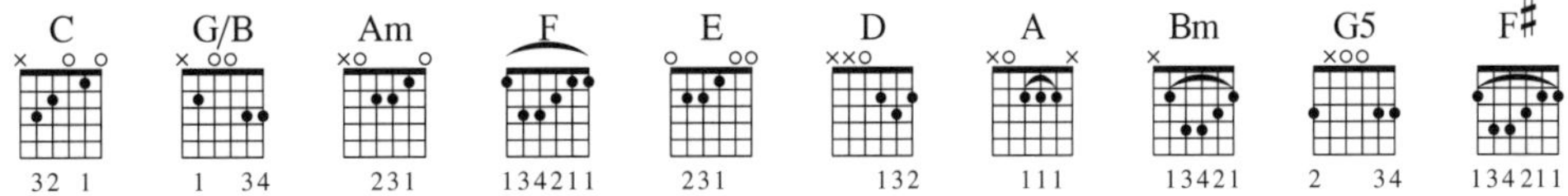

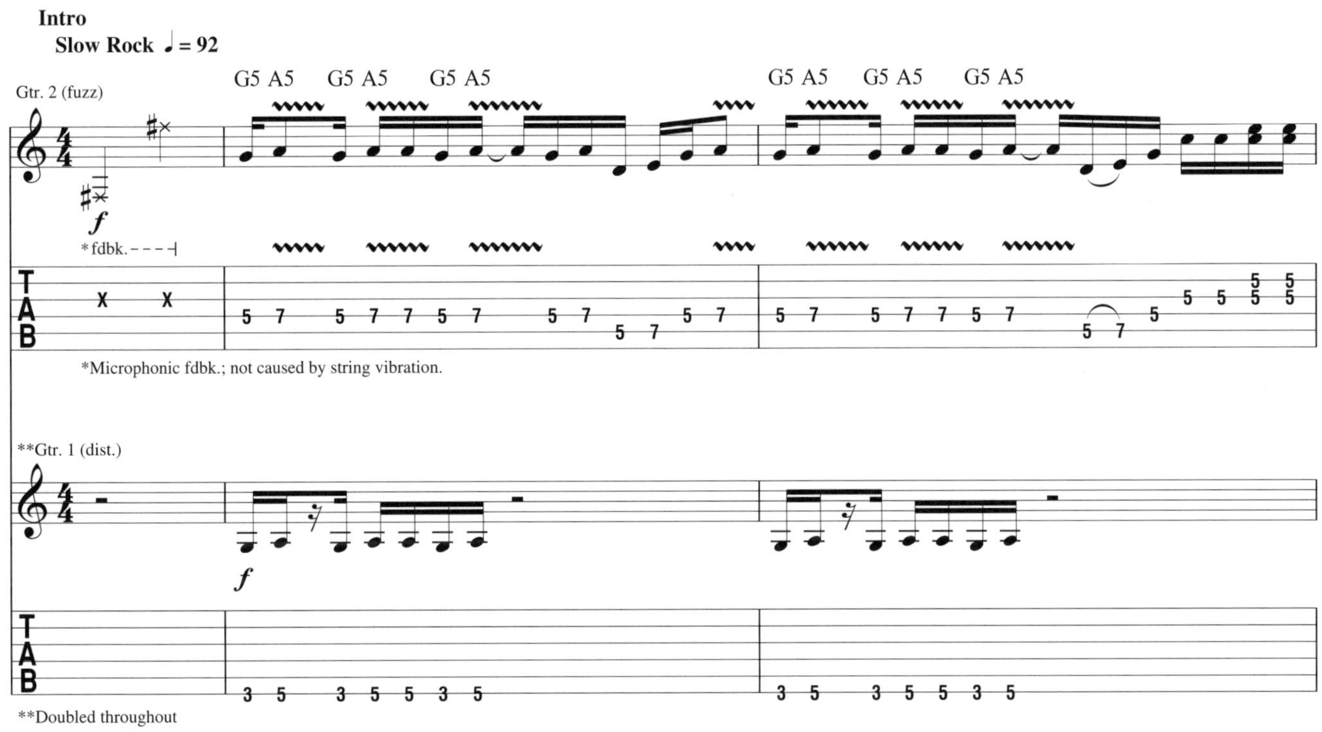

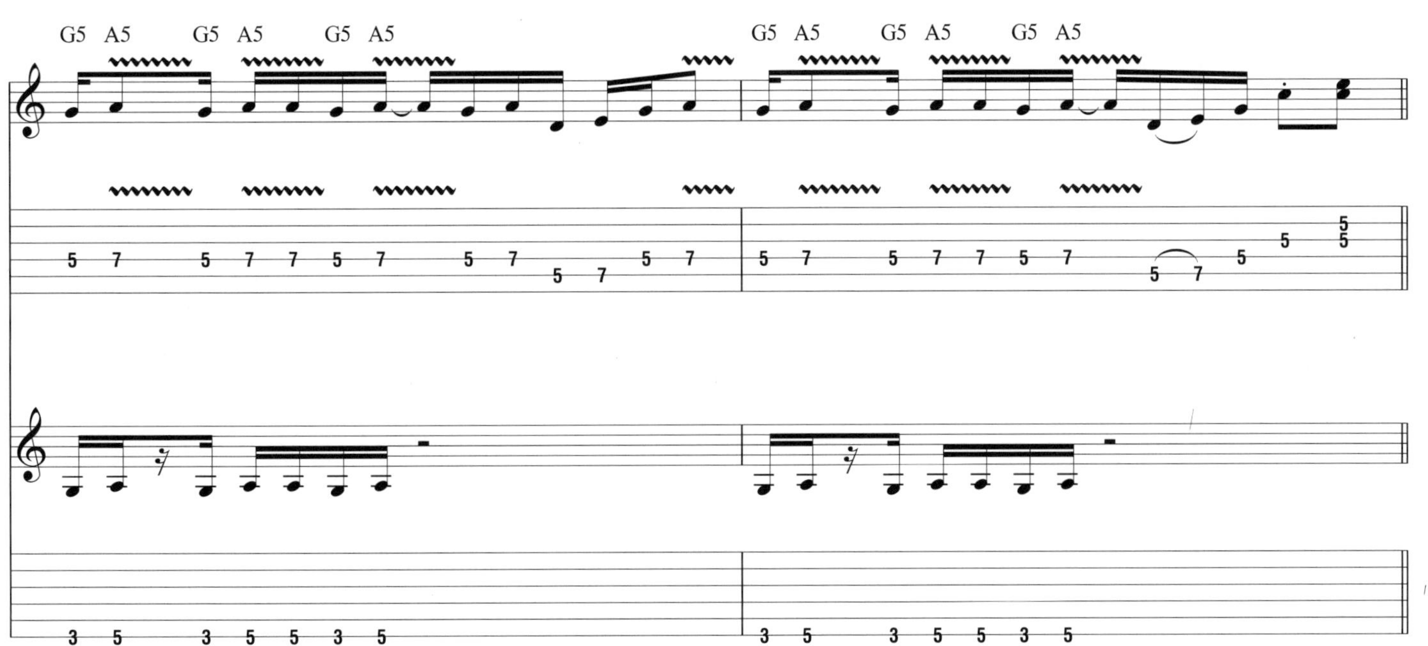

Verse
Gtr. 2 tacet
2nd time, Gtr. 8 tacet
2nd time, Gtr. 9: w/ Riff B (3 times)
2nd time, Gtr. 10: w/ Riff C (3 times)
*Am
G/A
1. I will do with - out
2. Yeah, you will go with - out
**Gtr. 3
Rhy. Fig. 1
mp
**Elec. piano arr. for gtr.
Gtr. 1
Riff A
mp
P.M.
*Chord symbols reflect overall harmony.
Am6
Gtrs. 1 & 3 tacet
Fsus2
C/F
the spac - es in be - tween
the bet - ter part of me.
Gtr. 4 (clean)
End Rhy. Fig. 1
Rhy. Fill 1
End Rhy. Fill 1
mp
w/ chorus
End Riff A
Gtr. 5 (clean)
w/ delay
Riff B
Gtr. 9 (clean)
w/ delay & chorus
let ring
Riff C
Gtr. 10 (dist.)

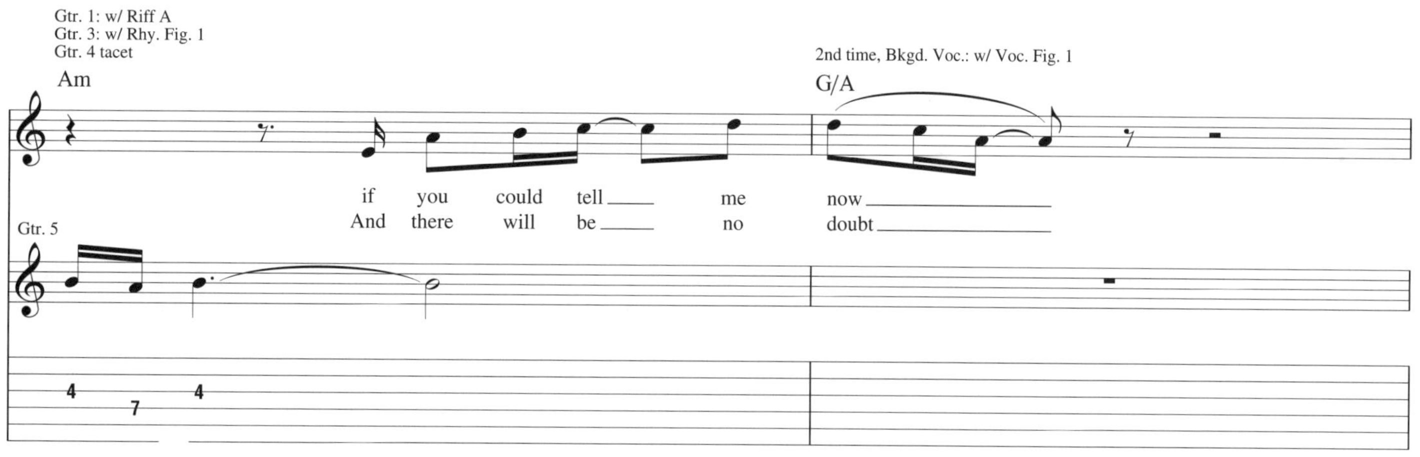
Gtr. 1: w/ Riff A
Gtr. 3: w/ Rhy. Fig. 1
Gtr. 4 tacet
Am
2nd time, Bkgd. Voc.: w/ Voc. Fig. 1
G/A
if you could tell me now
And there will be no doubt
Gtr. 5
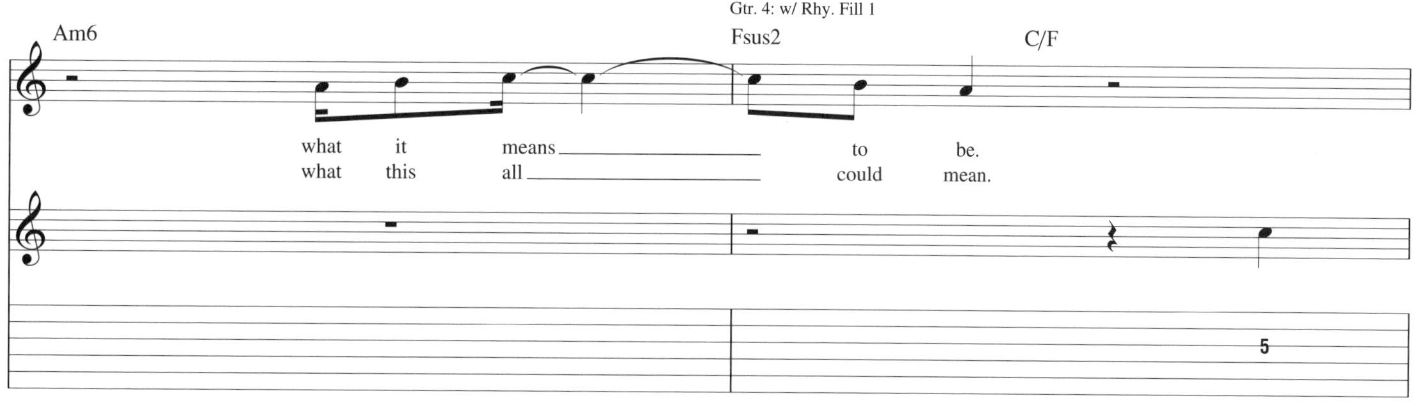
Am6
Gtr. 4: w/ Rhy. Fill 1
Fsus2
C/F
what it means to be.
what this all could mean.
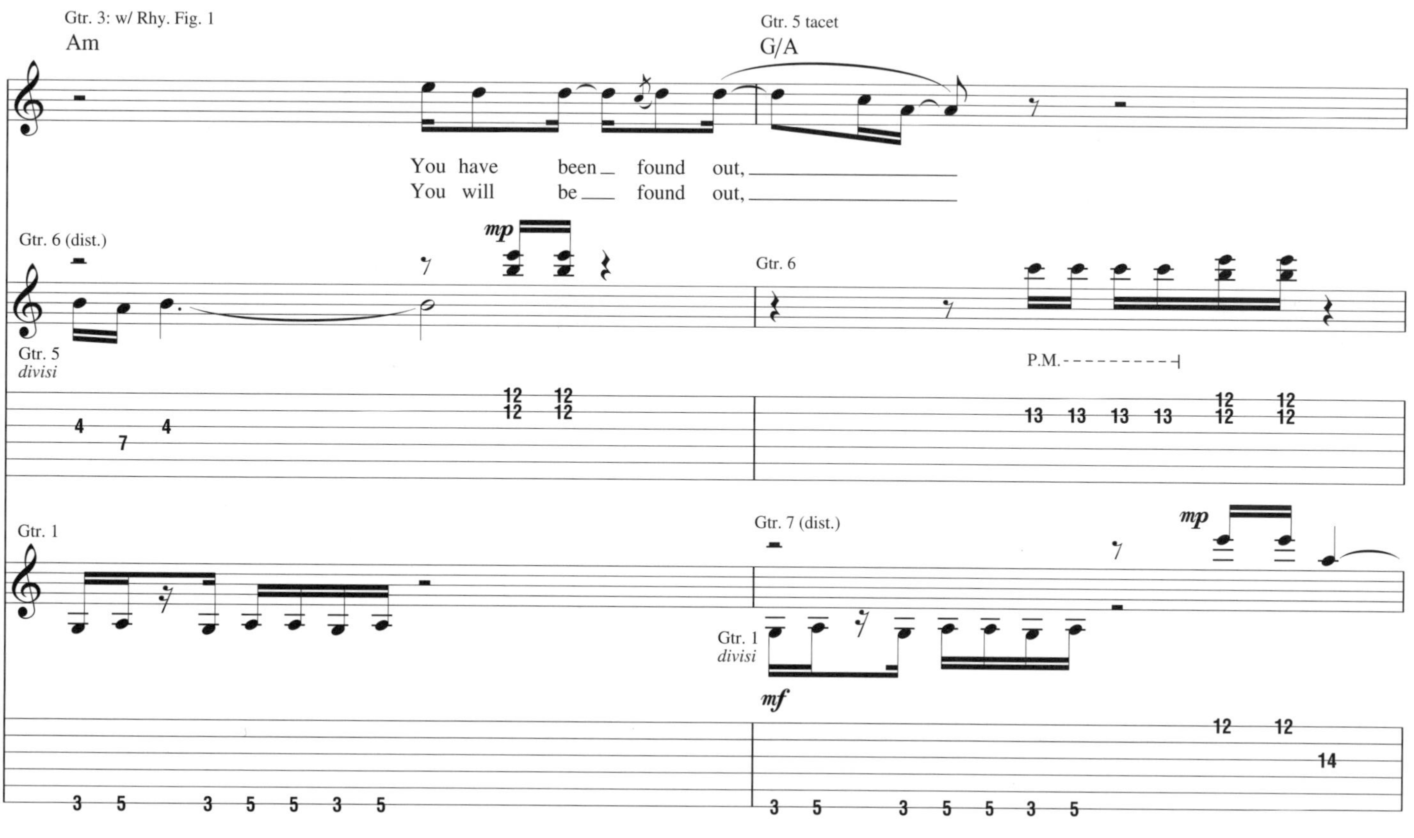
Gtr. 3: w/ Rhy. Fig. 1
Am
Gtr. 5 tacet
G/A
You have been found out,
You will be found out,
Gtr. 6 (dist.)
Gtr. 5
divisi
Gtr. 6
P.M.
Gtr. 1
Gtr. 7 (dist.)
Gtr. 1
divisi

Voc. Fig. 1
(There will be no doubt.)

Gtr. 6 tacet
Am6
Fsus2
C/F
Gsus4
I have been de - ceived by the one that I need. Tell
I can - not be - lieve in
Gtr. 4
(Gtr. 1 cont. in slashes)

Chorus

Gtrs. 4 & 7 tacet
C
G/B
Gtr. 1
f
me why you got - ta be so cold. How'd you get so high? Why you keep - ing me low?
Gtr. 8 (clean)
mf

Am
F
You don't know, You don't know. And tell
You don't know, you don't know.
let ring
let ring
let ring

C
G/B
E
(2nd time, cont. in notation)
me how we're gon - na make it last; you're read - y to fly, I'm read - y to crash.

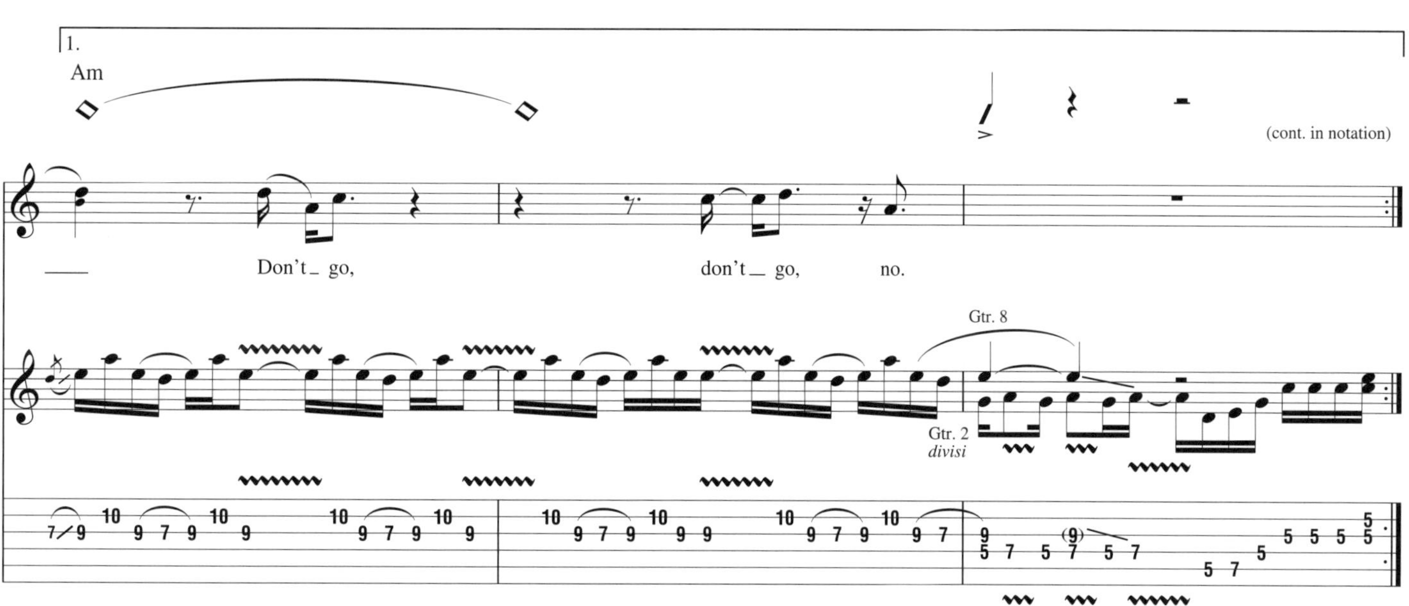
1.
Am
(cont. in notation)
Don't go, don't go, no.
Gtr. 8
Gtr. 2
divisi

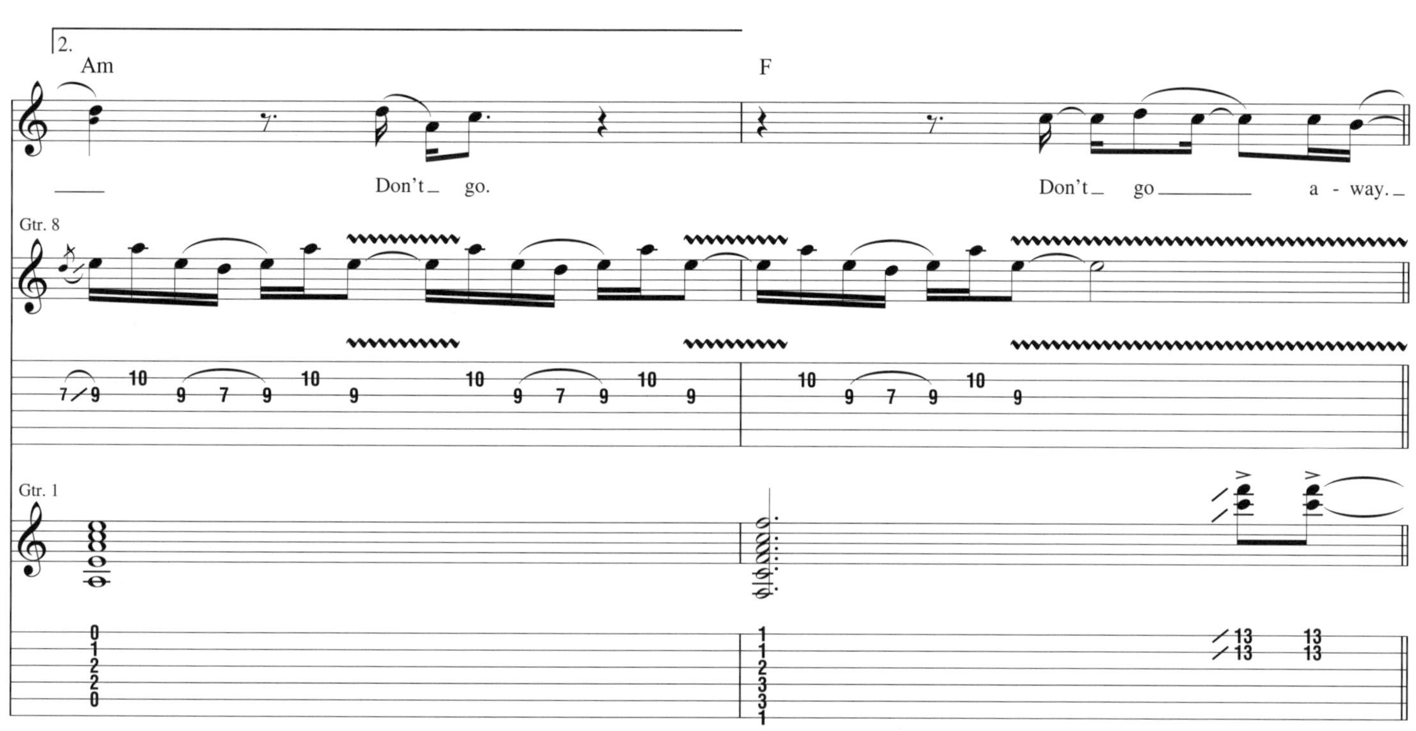
2.
Am
F
Don't go. Don't go a - way.
Gtr. 8
Gtr. 1

Interlude
Gtr. 8 tacet
Am
D7
Gtr. 2
*Gtr. 11
mf
*Organ arr. for gtr.
Gtr. 1
Rhy. Fill 2
End Rhy. Fill 2
Gtr. 1 tacet
Am
Gtr. 1: w/ Rhy. Fill 2
D7
Gtr. 2
Gtr. 11
Am
Gtr. 1: w/ Rhy. Fill 2
G/A
Gtr. 12 (dist.)
f
Gtr. 2 divisi
Gtr. 11

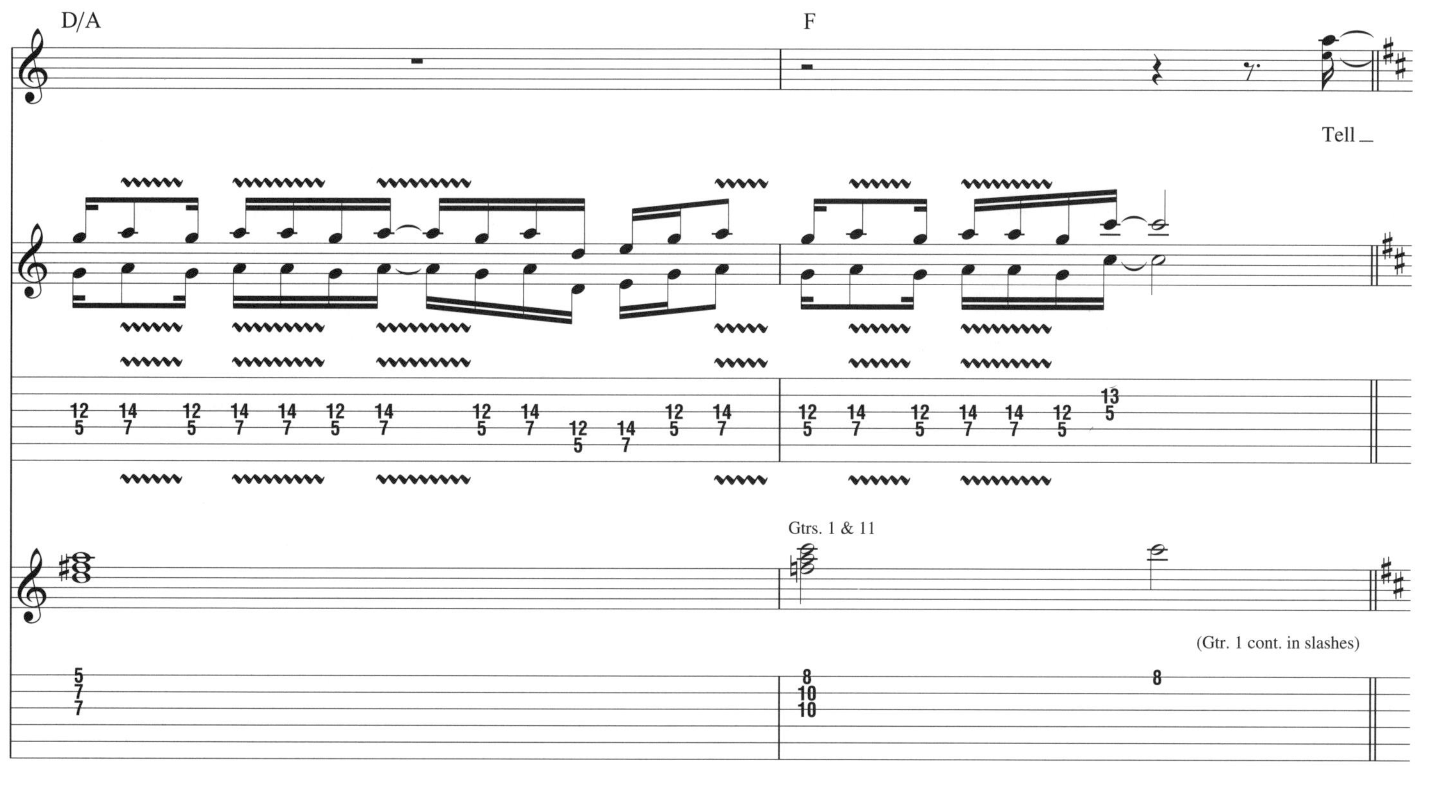

Outro-Chorus

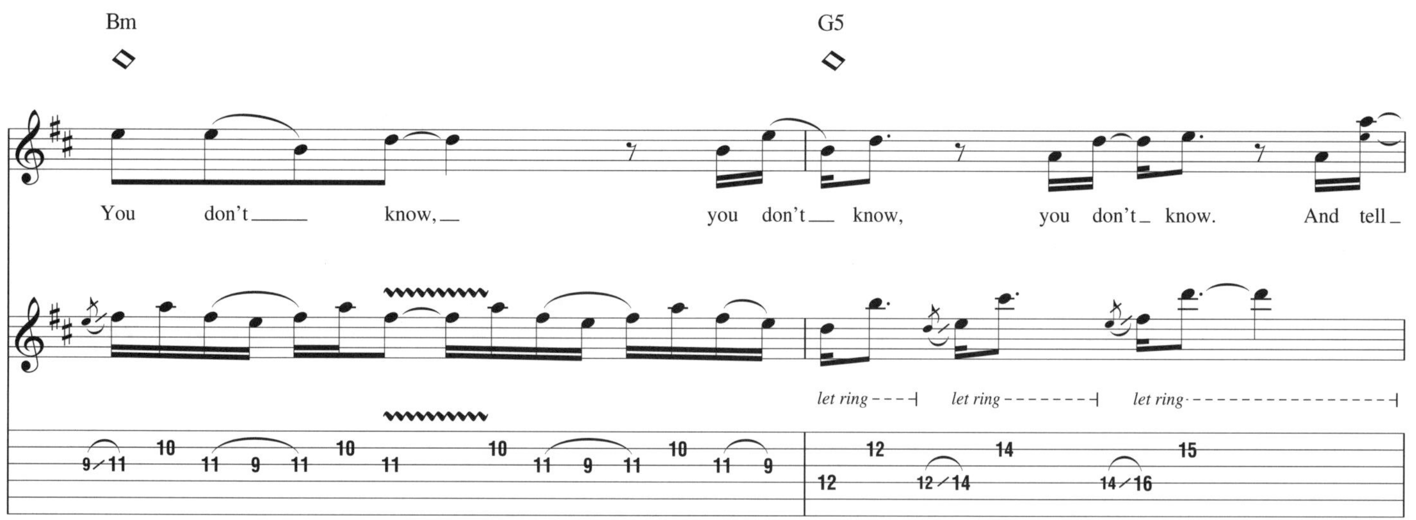

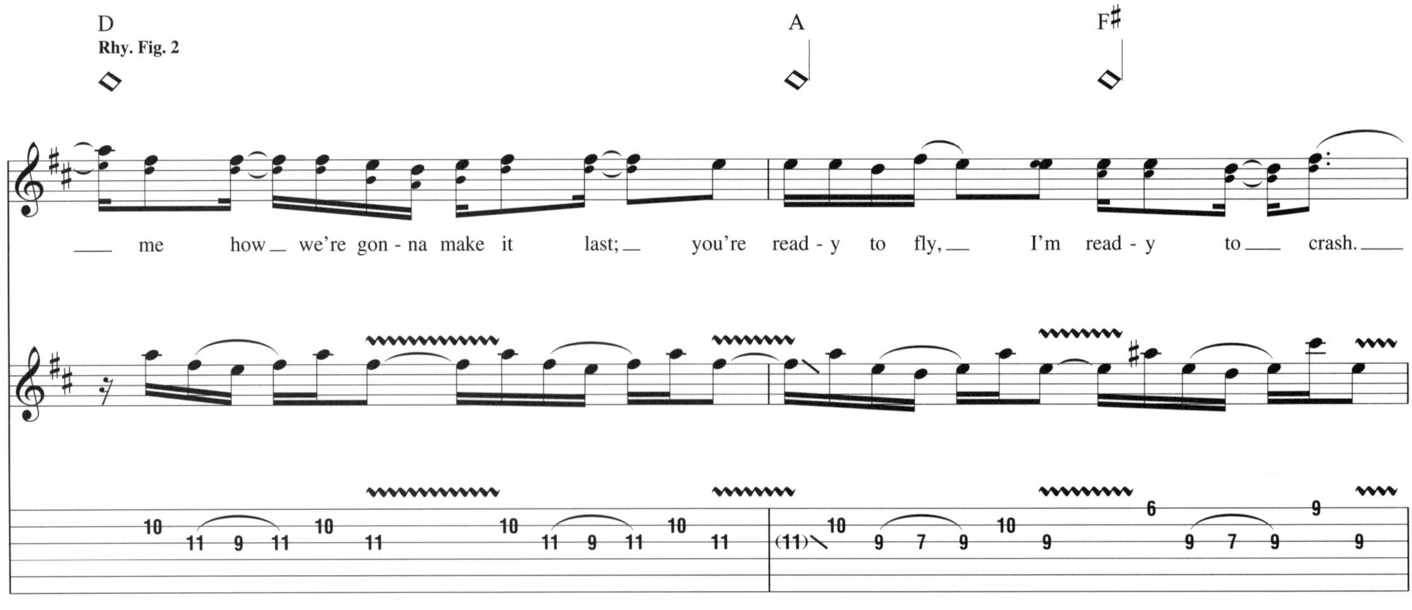
D
Rhy. Fig. 2
A
F♯
me how we're gon - na make it last; you're read - y to fly, I'm read - y to crash.

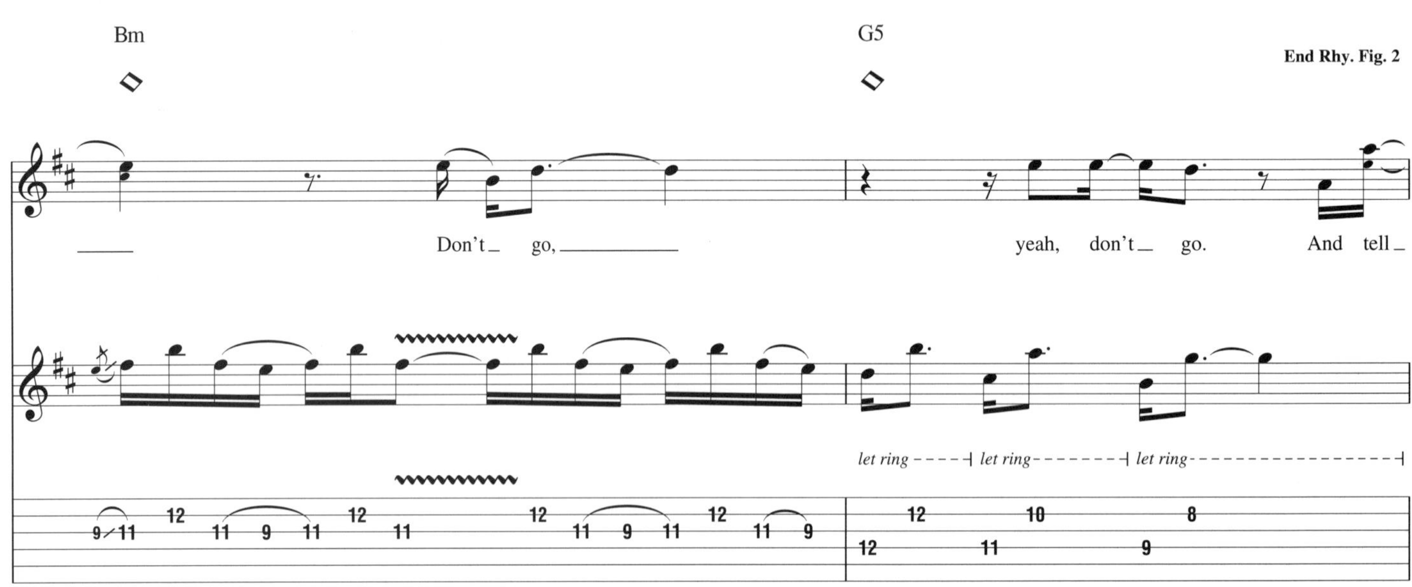
Bm
G5
End Rhy. Fig. 2
Don't go, yeah, don't go. And tell
let ring
let ring
let ring

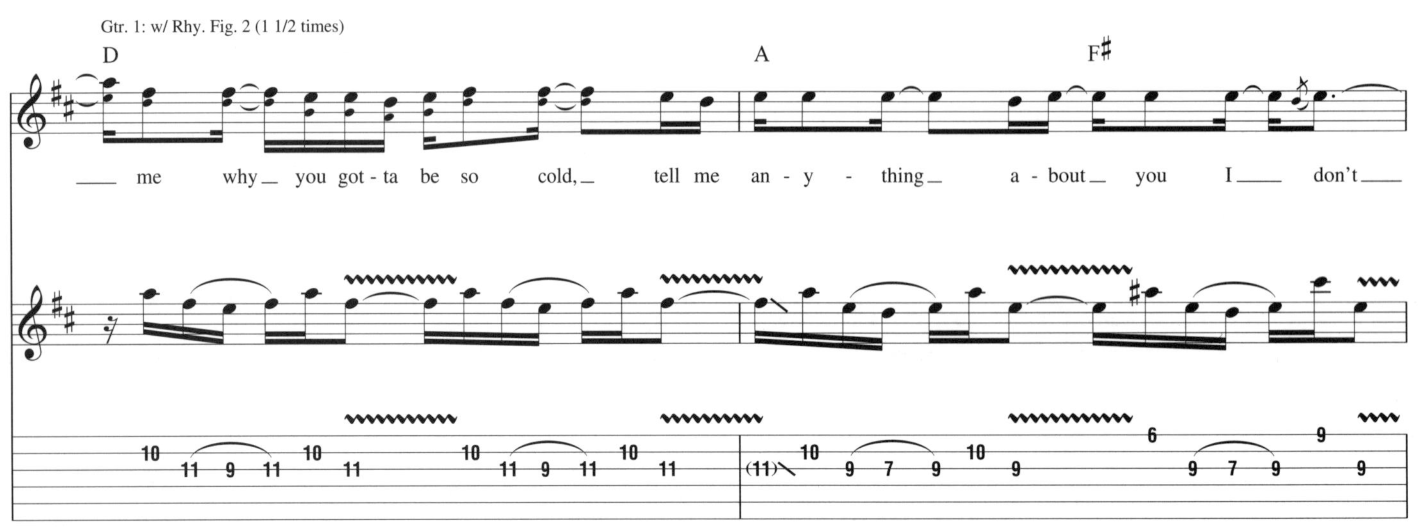
Gtr. 1: w/ Rhy. Fig. 2 (1 1/2 times)
D
A
F♯
me why you got - ta be so cold, tell me an - y - thing a - bout you I don't

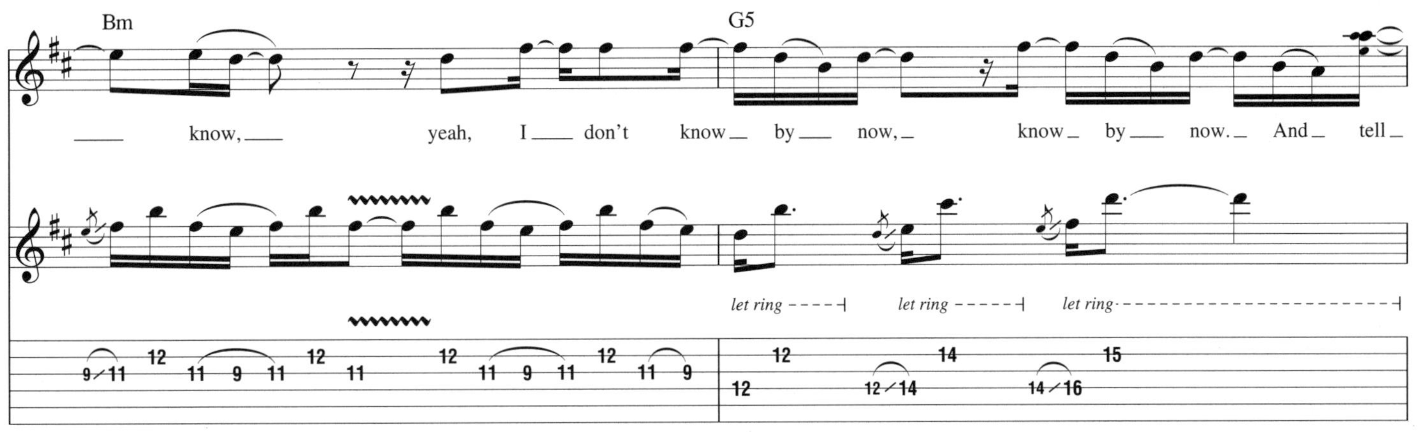
Bm
G5
know, yeah, I don't know by now, know by now. And tell
let ring
let ring
let ring

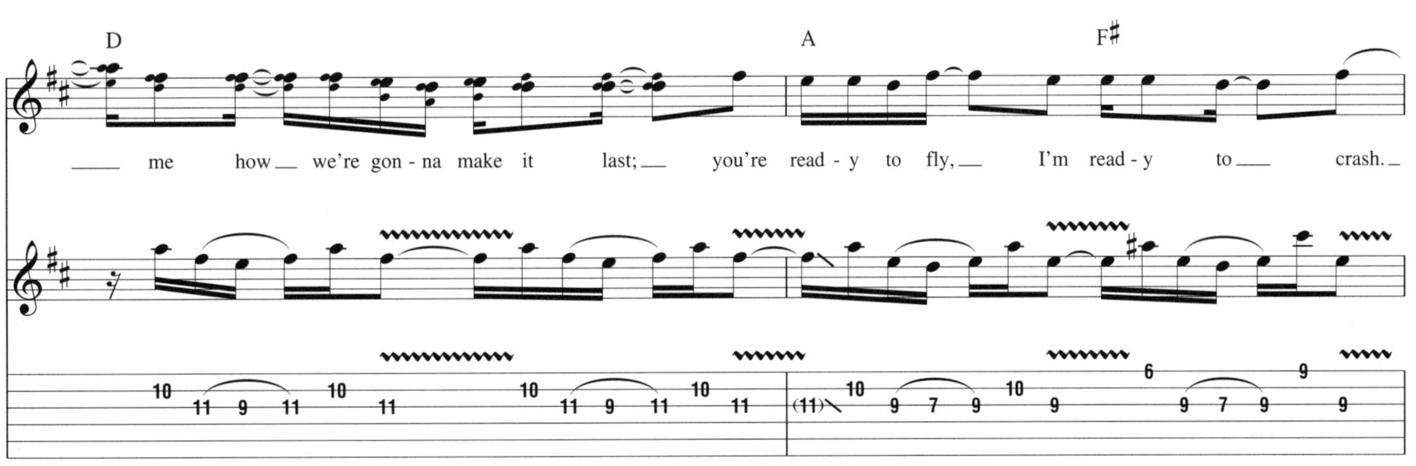
D
A
F♯
me how we're gon - na make it last; you're read - y to fly, I'm read - y to crash.

Bm
Gtr. 1
(cont. in notation)
Don't go, yeah, don't go.

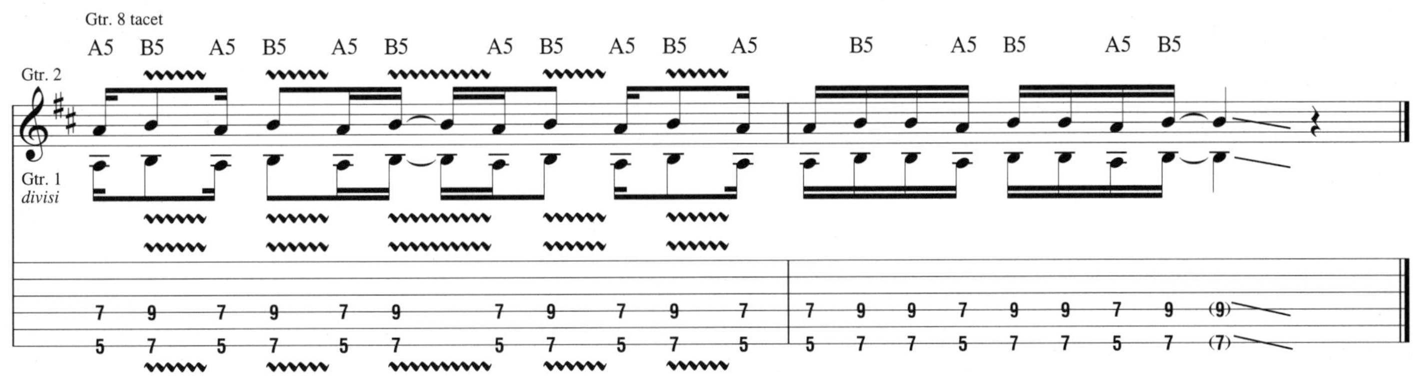
Gtr. 8 tacet
A5 B5 A5 B5 A5 B5 A5 B5 A5 B5 A5 B5 A5 B5 A5 B5
Gtr. 2
Gtr. 1
divisi

All I Need

Words and Music by Rob Thomas

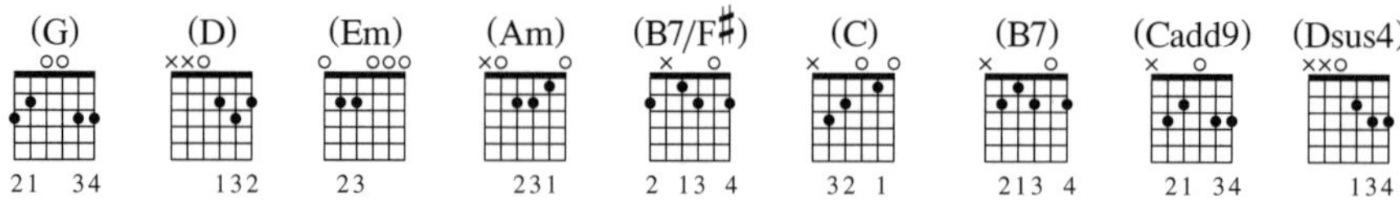

Capo I

*Symbols in parentheses represent chord names respective to capoed guitar. Symbols above reflect actual sounding chord. Capoed fret is "0" in tab.

**Gtr. 2 (acous.) played *mp*

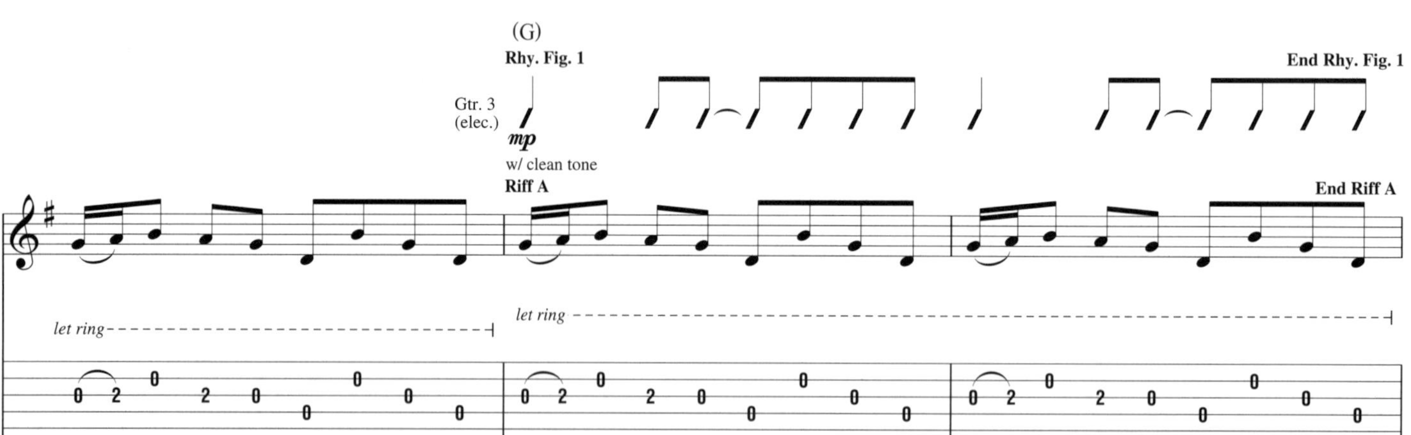

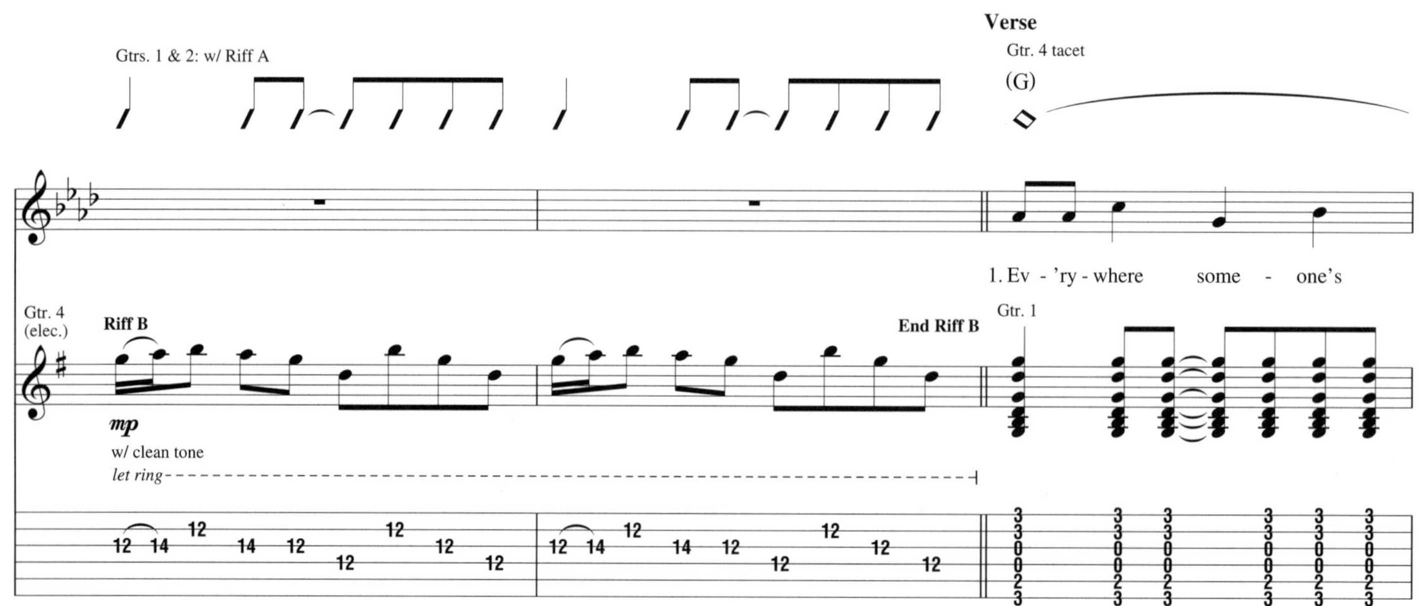

Gtr. 3 tacet
Fm
(Em)
get - ting o - ver; ev - e - ry - bod - y cries and some - times
(cont. in slashes)
(Am)
Gtr. 1
(D)
you can still lose e - ven if you real - ly try.
Gtr. 5 (acous.)
Riff C
mf
let ring
Gtr. 5 tacet
(G)
Rhy. Fig. 2
Gtrs. 1 & 2
Talk - ing 'bout the dream like the dream is o - ver;
Gtr. 5
End Riff C
let ring
Gtr. 3
Riff D
let ring

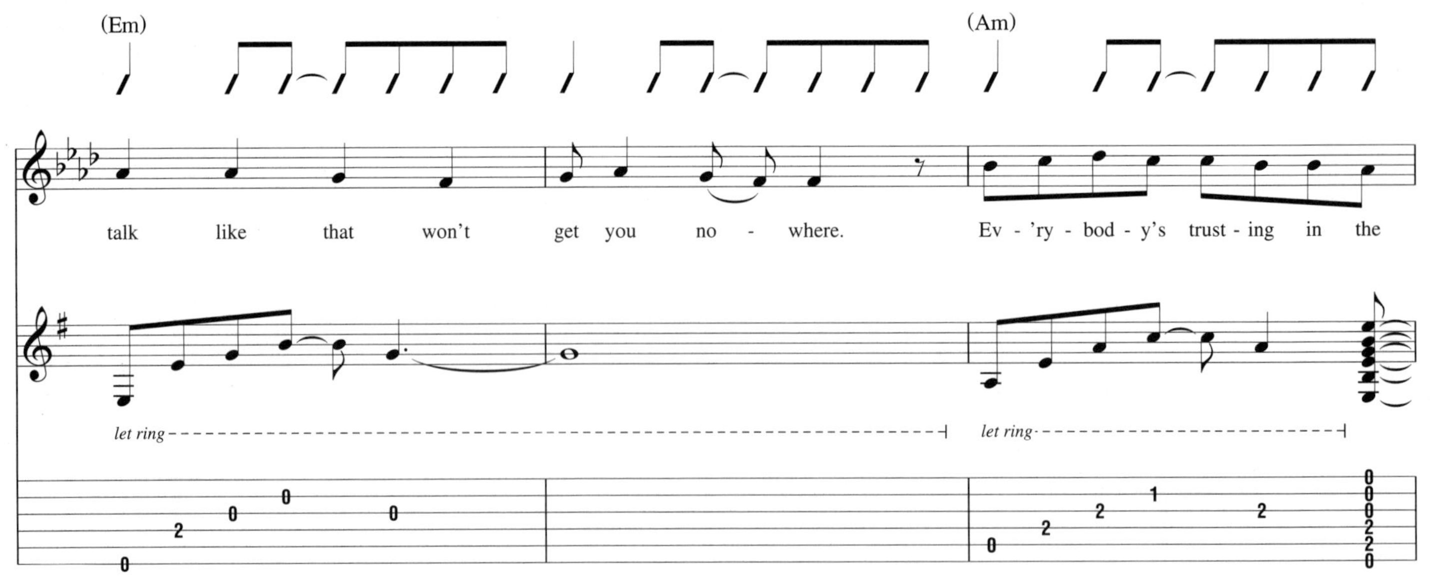

(Em) Eb5 (D5) Eb5/Db (D5/C) Eb5/C (D5/B) Eb5/Bb (D5/A)

End Rhy. Fig. 2

Gtrs. 1 & 2

(cont. in notation)

heart like the heart don't lie. And

Gtr. 6 (elec.)

Riff E2 **End Riff E2**

mp

w/ clean tone

let ring

Gtr. 5

Riff E1 **End Riff E1**

let ring

End Riff D **Riff E** **End Riff E**

Gtrs. 1, 2 & 3

Gtr. 3

let ring

(cont. in slashes)

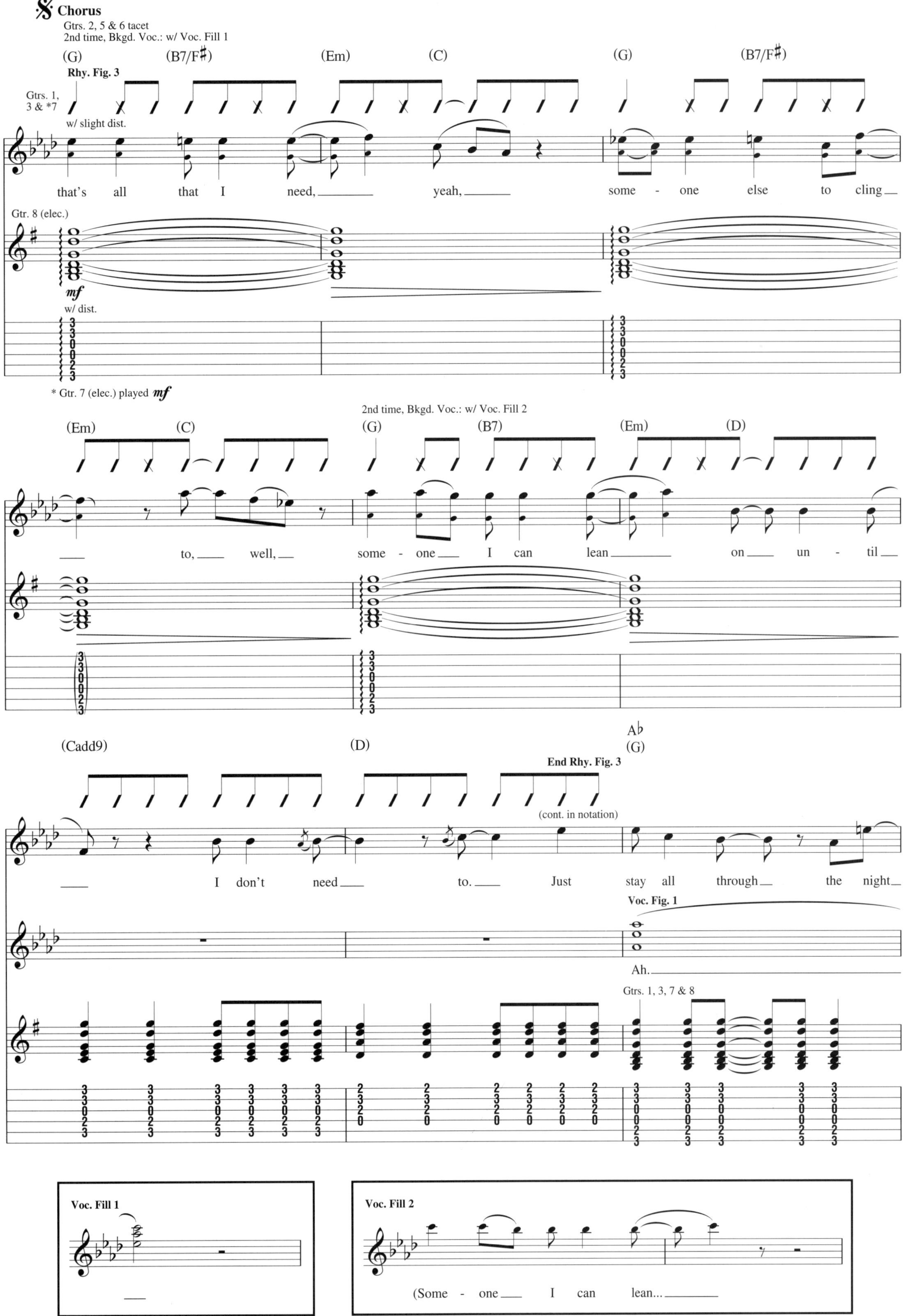
Chorus
Gtrs. 2, 5 & 6 tacet
2nd time, Bkgd. Voc.: w/ Voc. Fill 1
(G) (B7/F♯) (Em) (C) (G) (B7/F♯)
Rhy. Fig. 3
Gtrs. 1, 3 & *7
w/ slight dist.
that's all that I need, yeah, some - one else to cling
Gtr. 8 (elec.)
mf
w/ dist.
* Gtr. 7 (elec.) played mf
2nd time, Bkgd. Voc.: w/ Voc. Fill 2
(Em) (C) (G) (B7) (Em) (D)
to, well, some - one I can lean on un - til
(Cadd9) (D) A♭ (G)
End Rhy. Fig. 3
(cont. in notation)
I don't need to. Just stay all through the night
Voc. Fig. 1
Ah.
Gtrs. 1, 3, 7 & 8
Voc. Fill 1
Voc. Fill 2
(Some - one I can lean...

C7
(B7)
Fm
(Em)
D♭
(C)
and in the morn - ing, let me down. 'Cause
End Voc. Fig. 1
To Coda
Gtrs. 7 & 8 tacet
A♭
(G)
C7
(B7)
(Cadd9)
(D)
(Cadd9)
Gtrs. 7 & 8
(cont. in notation)
that's all that I need right now.
Gtrs. 1 & 3
(Gtr. 1 cont. in bottom staff)
E♭ E♭sus2 E♭ A♭
(D) (Dsus2) (D) (G)
Verse
(G)
Gtr. 2
2. Ev - 'ry - where some - one's get - ting o - ver;
Gtr. 3
w/ clean tone
let ring
Gtrs. 1, 7 & 8

Gtrs. 7 & 8 tacet
(Em)
(Am)
Gtr. 2
ev - e - ry - bod - y's lied to some - one. Peo - ple still use other
Gtr. 3
(Ev - e - ry - bod - y's lied.)
let ring
Gtr. 1
mp
w/ clean tone
Gtr. 5: w/ Riff C
(D)
peo - ple with a crook - ed smile. And
let ring
Gtrs. 1 & 2: w/ Rhy. Fig. 2
Gtr. 3: w/ Riff D
A♭
(G)
Fm
(Em)
all a - round the world, there's a sink - ing feel - ing; out there right now some - one's real - ly down
D.S. al Coda
Gtrs. 1, 2 & 3: w/ Riff E
Gtr. 5: w/ Riff E1
Gtr. 6: w/ Riff E2
B♭m
(Am)
Fm
(Em)
E♭5
(D5)
E♭5/D♭
(D5/C)
E♭5/C
(D5/B)
E♭5/B♭
(D5/A)
on them - selves and don't know why, ev - e - ry night. And
(Ah.)

Coda

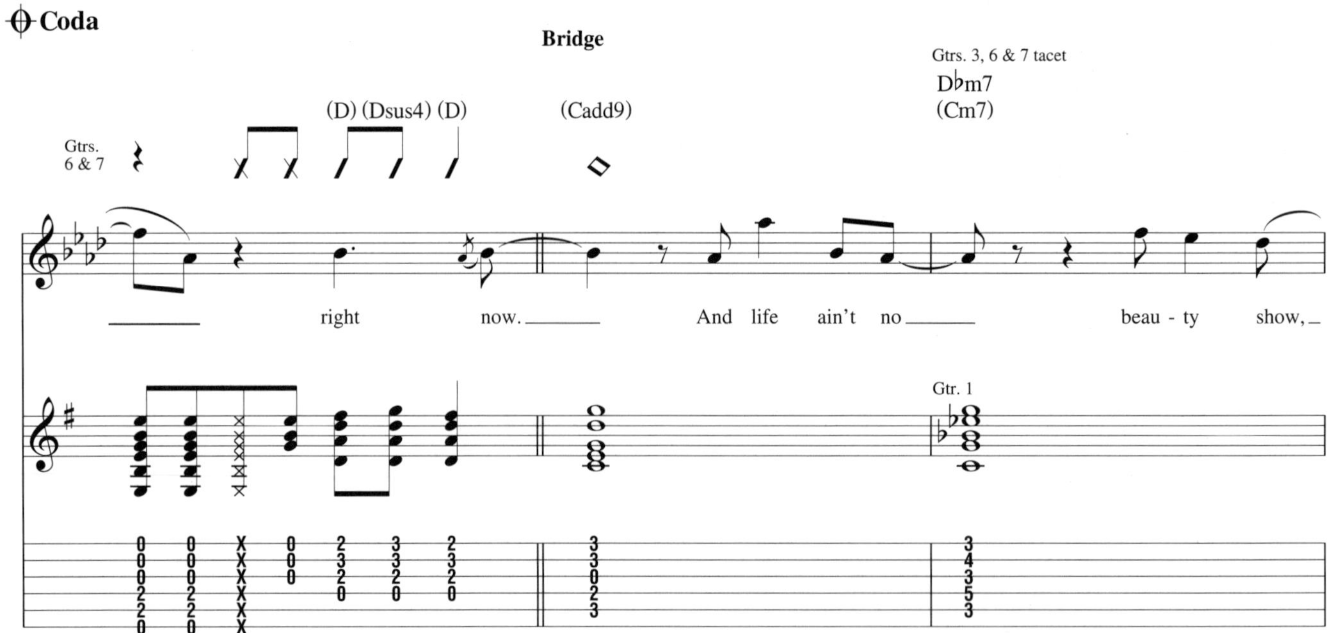
Bridge
Gtrs. 3, 6 & 7 tacet
(D) (Dsus4) (D)
(Cadd9)
D♭m7
(Cm7)
Gtrs. 6 & 7
right now. And life ain't no beau - ty show,
Gtr. 1
0 0 X 0 2 3 2
0 0 X 0 3 3 3
0 0 X 0 2 2 2
2 2 X 0 0 0
2 2 X
0 0 X
3 3 0 2 3
3 4 3 5 3

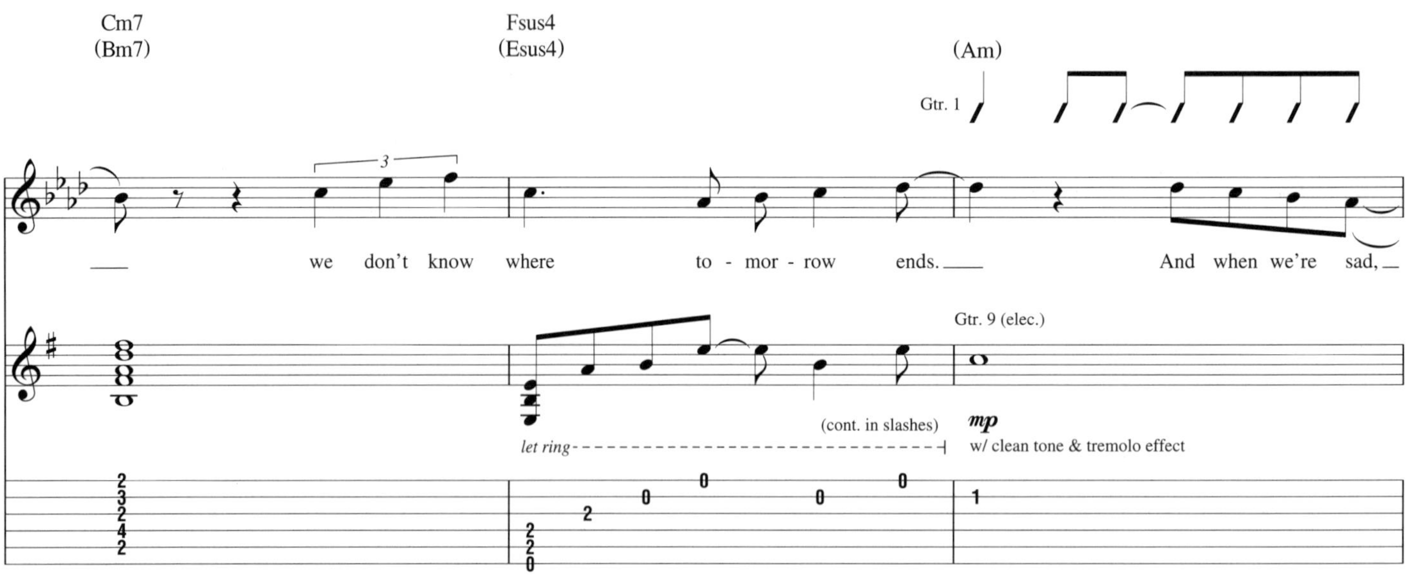
Cm7
(Bm7)
Fsus4
(Esus4)
(Am)
Gtr. 1
we don't know where to - mor - row ends. And when we're sad,
Gtr. 9 (elec.)
(cont. in slashes)
let ring
mp
w/ clean tone & tremolo effect
2 3 2 4 2
2 2 0 2 0 0 0 0
1

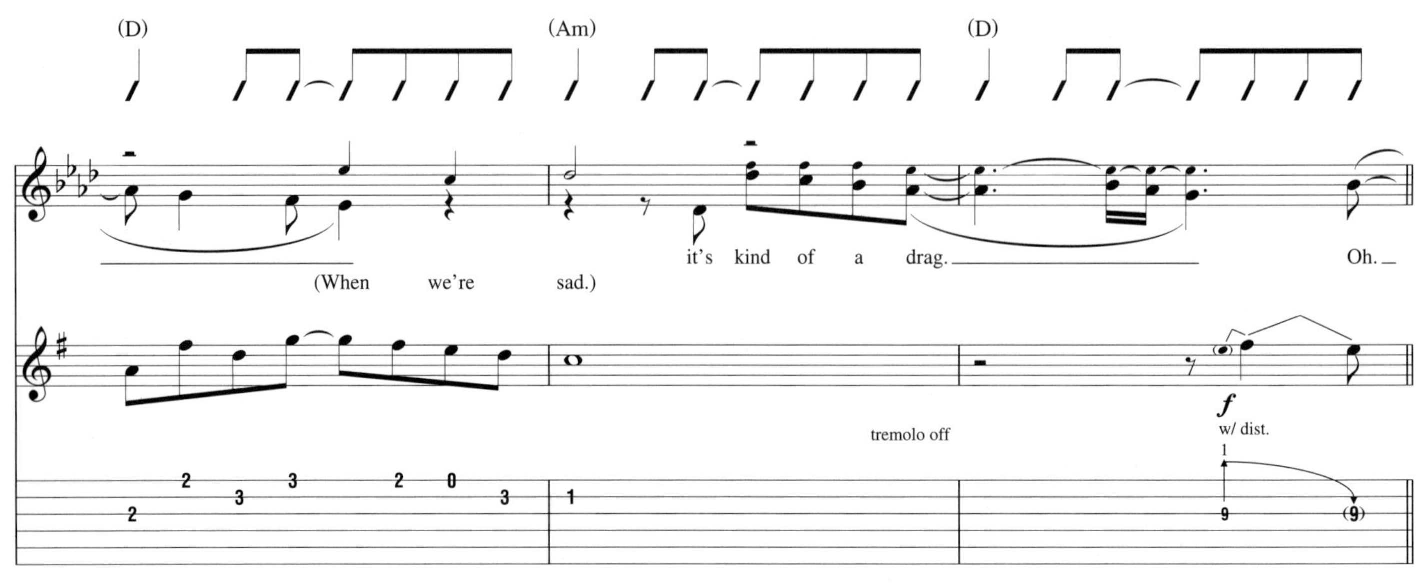
(D)
(Am)
(D)
(When we're sad.)
it's kind of a drag. Oh.
tremolo off
f
w/ dist.
2 3 3 2 0 3
1
1
9 (9)

Guitar Solo
Gtrs. 1, 3, 7 & 8: w/ Rhy. Fig. 3
A♭ (G) C7/G (B7/F♯) Fm (Em) D♭ (C)
let ring
hold bend
A♭ (G) C7 (B7) Fm (Em) E♭ (D) D♭add9 (Cadd9)
E♭ (D)
Bkgd. Voc.: w/ Voc. Fig. 1
Gtrs. 1, 3, 7 & 8
(cont. in notation)
Gtr. 9 tacet
C7 (B7)
Well, just stay all through the night and in the morn -
- ing, let me down.
Fm (Em) D♭ (C) Dm7♭5 (C♯m7♭5)
Yeah, 'cause

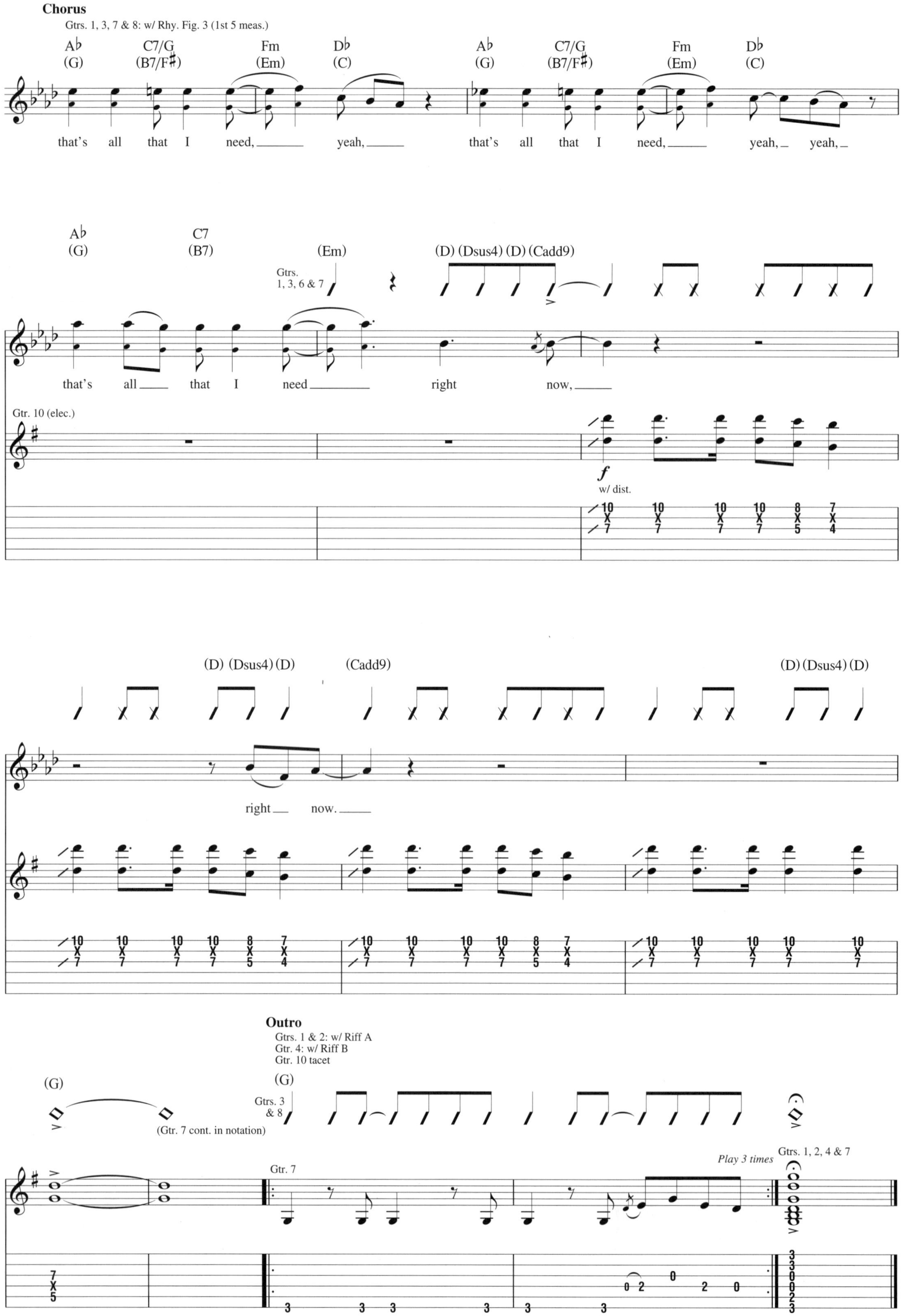

Chorus

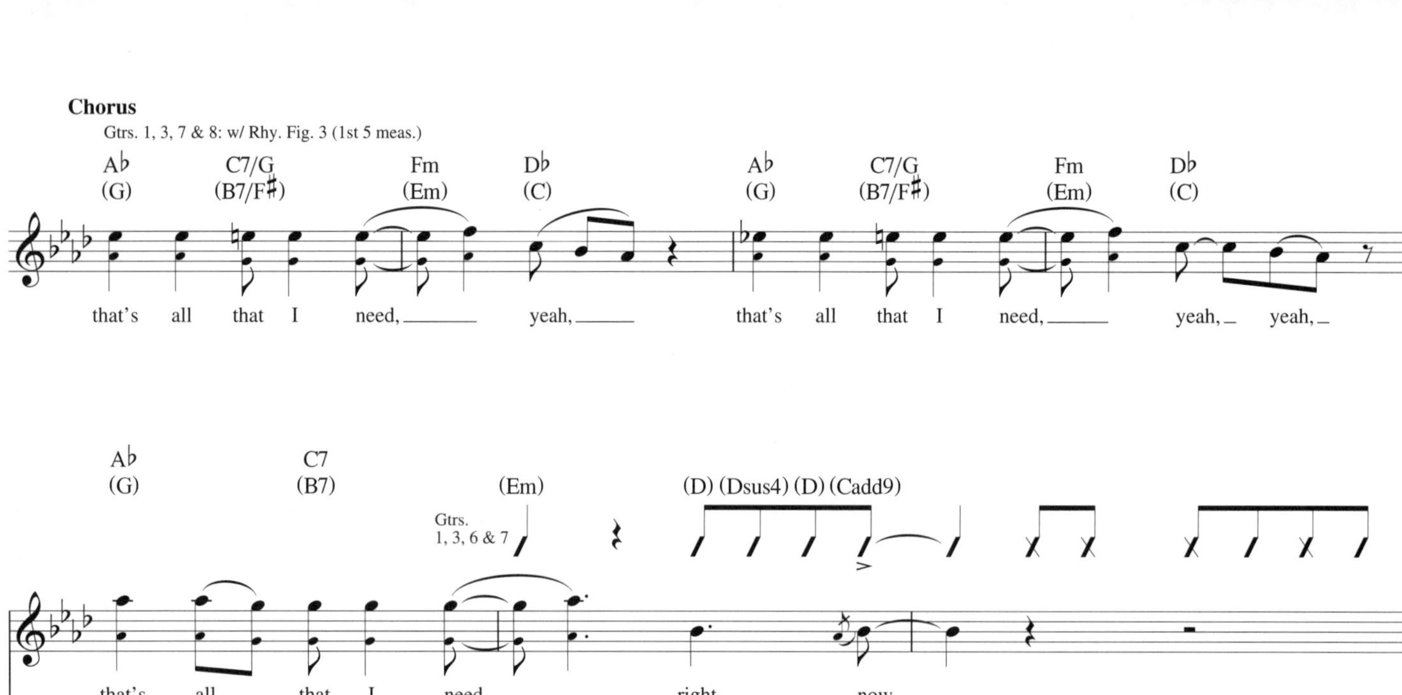

(D) (Dsus4) (D) (Cadd9) (D) (Dsus4) (D)

right now.

Outro

Gtrs. 1 & 2: w/ Riff A
Gtr. 4: w/ Riff B
Gtr. 10 tacet

(G) (G)

Gtrs. 3 & 8

(Gtr. 7 cont. in notation)

Gtr. 7

Play 3 times

Gtrs. 1, 2, 4 & 7

Hand Me Down

Words and Music by Rob Thomas

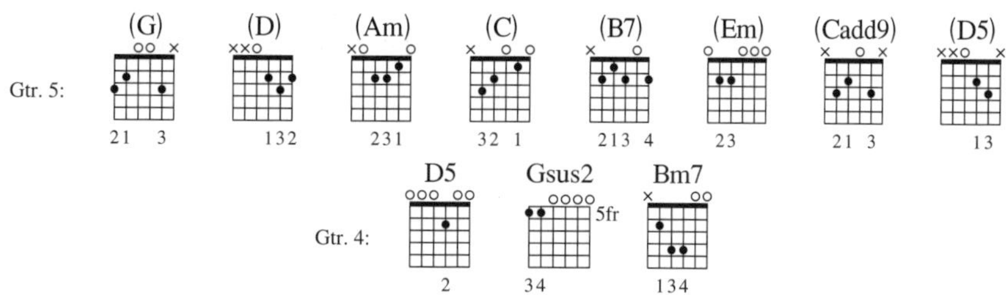

Gtrs. 1-3, 7-9; Tune down 1/2 step:
(low to high) E♭-A♭-D♭-G♭-B♭-E♭

Gtrs. 4 & 6; DADGAD tuning, down 1/2 step:
(low to high) D♭-A♭-D♭-G♭-A♭-D♭

Gtr. 5; Capo VII, Tune down 1/2 step:
(low to high) E♭-A♭-D♭-G♭-B♭-E♭

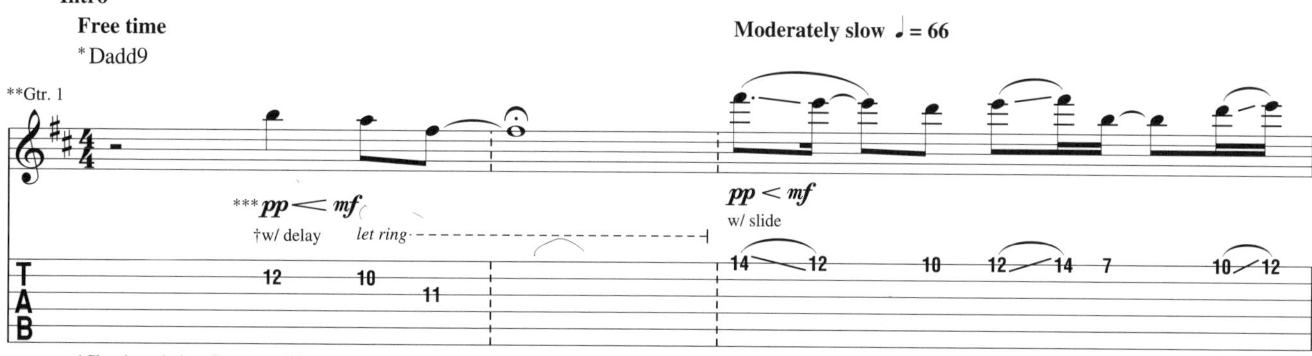

*Chord symbols reflect overall harmony.
**Pedal steel arr. for gtr.
***Vol. swell.
†Set for infinite repeat hold

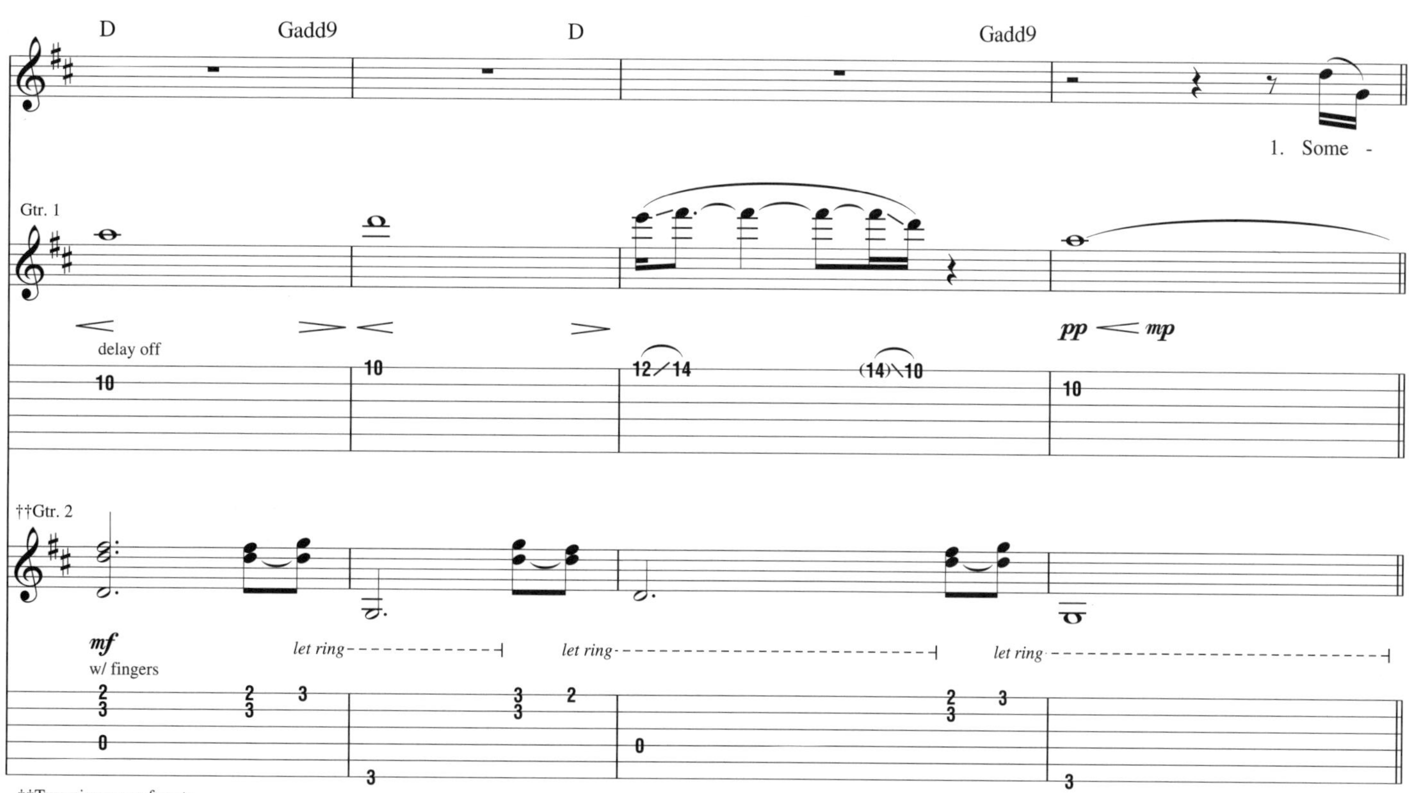

††Two pianos arr. for gtr.

Verse
Gtr. 2 tacet
D
day they'll find your small - town world on a big - town av - e - nue,
Gtr. 1
(10)

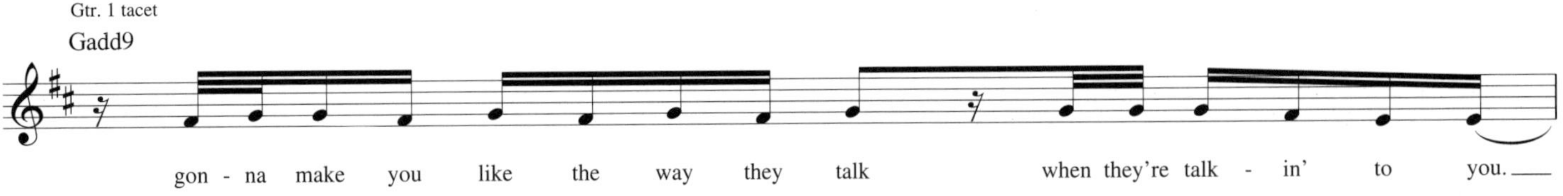
Gtr. 1 tacet
Gadd9
gon - na make you like the way they talk when they're talk - in' to you.

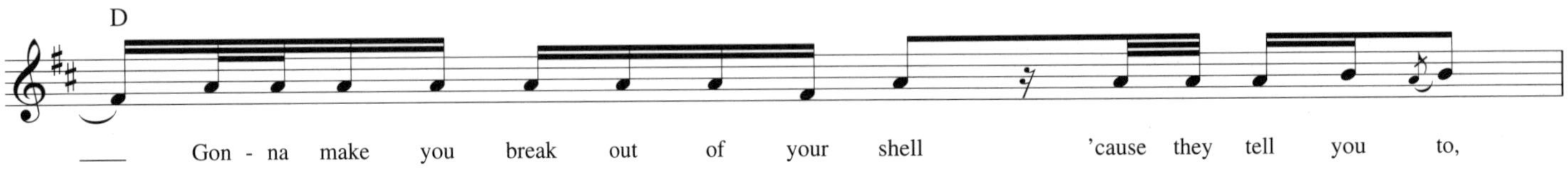
D
Gon - na make you break out of your shell 'cause they tell you to,

Gadd9
Bm7
3
gon - na make you like the way they lie bet - ter than the truth.
Gtr. 2
let ring
3
3
2

Gadd9
They'll tell you ev - 'ry - thing you want - ed some - one else to say,
let ring
let ring
2
3
3
2

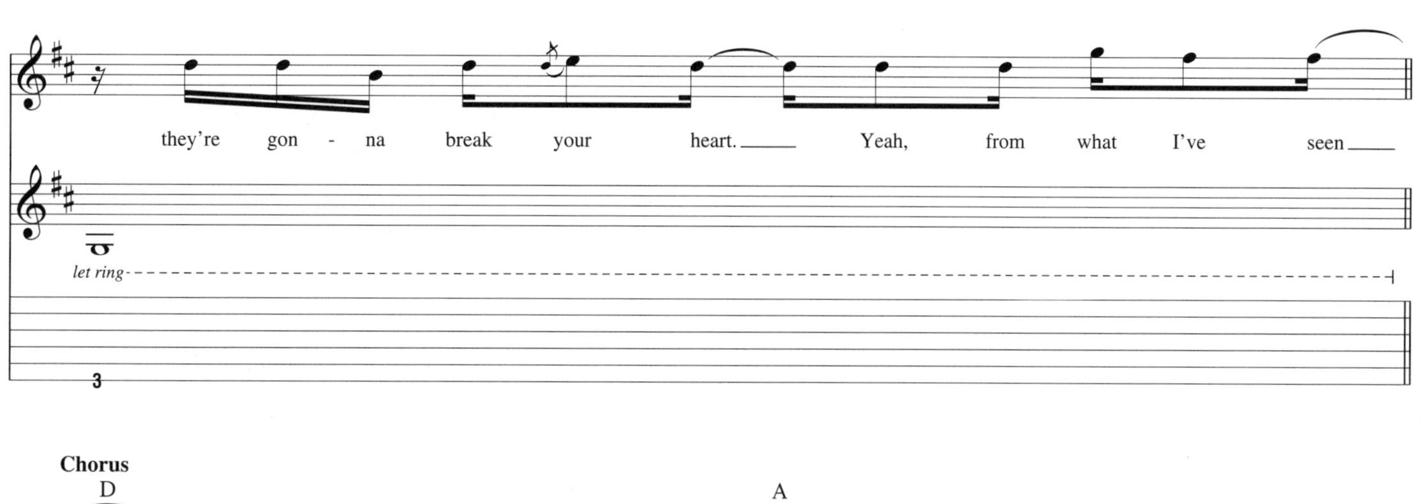
they're gon - na break your heart.
Yeah, from what I've seen
let ring

Chorus

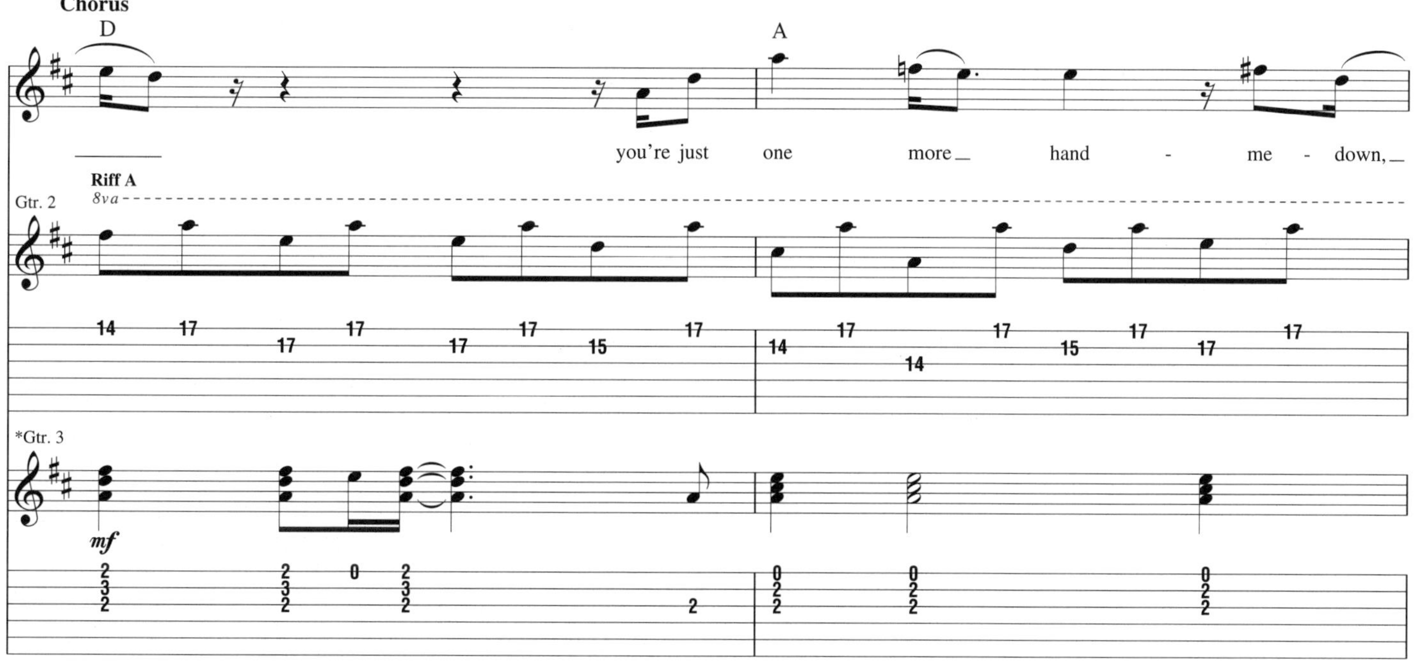
D
A
you're just one more hand - me - down,
Riff A
Gtr. 2
8va
*Gtr. 3
mf

*Elec. piano arr. for gtr.

Em
Em7
G
and no one's tried to give you what you need.
Gtr. 2
8va
Gtr. 1
let ring
Gtr. 3

Gtr. 1 tacet
D
A
F♯
So, lay all your trou - bles down,
End Riff A
Gtr. 2
8va
14 17 14 17 17 17 15 17
14 17 17 17 17 18 17 18
Gtr. 3
2 3 2 2 3 2 0 2 3 2 5
0 2 2 0 2 2 0 2 3 0 2 3 0 2 3

Bm
Gadd9
I am with you now. 2. Some -
loco
Gtr. 1
Gtr. 2
divisi
16 14 12 17
12
Gtr. 3
let ring
3 4 4 4 3
3 2 5

Verse
Gtrs. 1 & 3 tacet
D5
Gtr. 4 (acous.)
mp
bod - y ought - ta take you in try to make you love a - gain,
Gtr. 2
let ring

Gsus2
try to make you like the way they feel when they're un - der your skin.
let ring
let ring

D5
Nev - er once do you think that they would lie when they're hold - in' you,
let ring
let ring

Gsus2
then you won - der why they have - n't called when they said they'd call
let ring
let ring
3 3 2 3

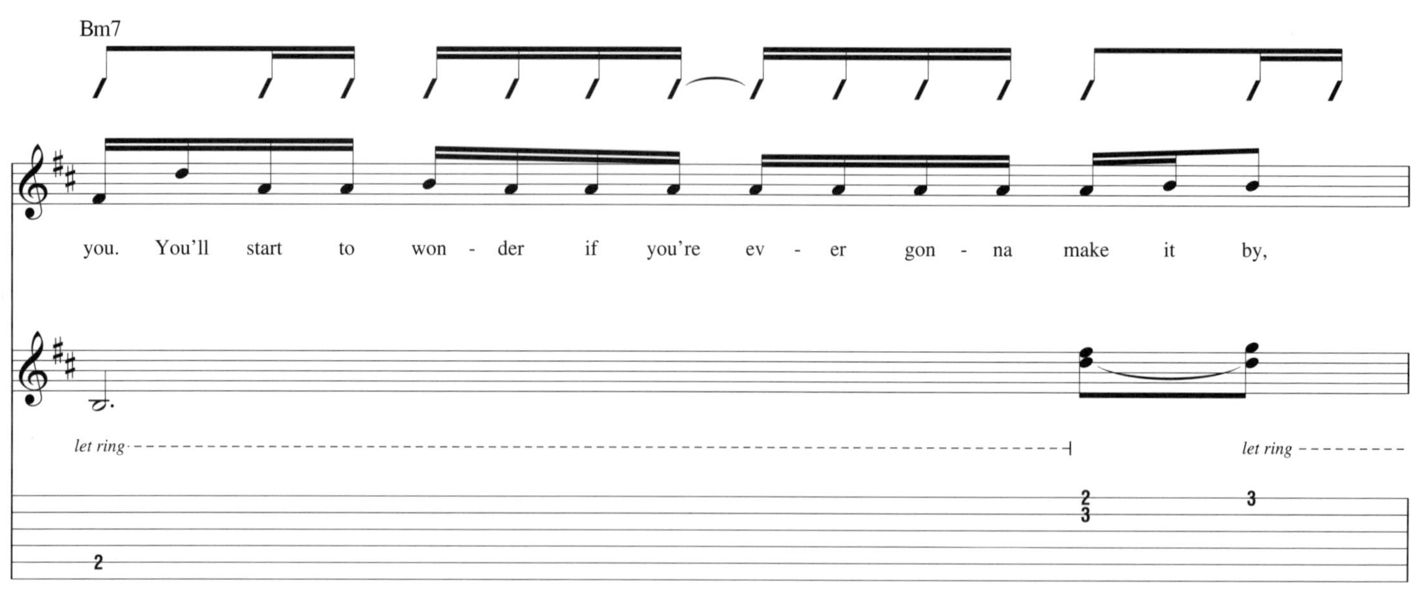
Bm7
you. You'll start to won - der if you're ev - er gon - na make it by,
let ring
let ring
2 3 3 2

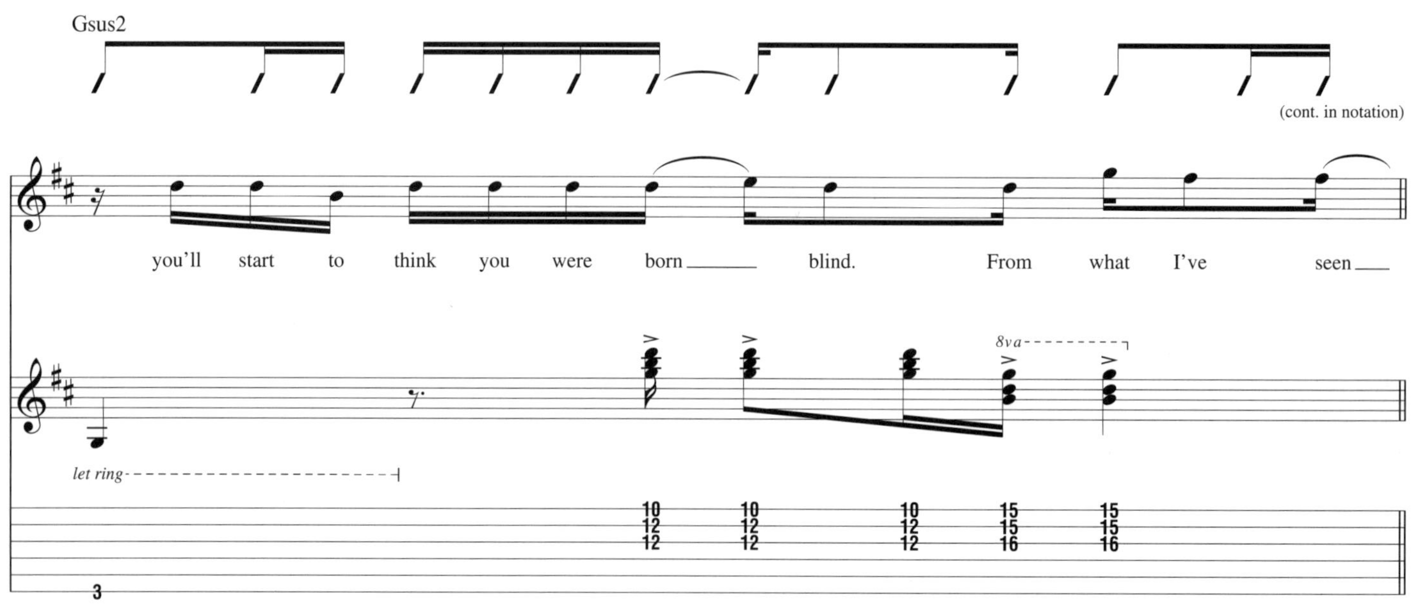
Gsus2
(cont. in notation)
you'll start to think you were born blind. From what I've seen
8va
let ring
10 12 12 10 12 12 10 12 12 15 15 16 15 15 16 3

Chorus

Gtr. 2: w/ Riff A

*(G) (D)

Gtr. 5 (acous.)

mp

you're just one more hand - me - down,

Gtr. 1

Gtr. 3 **Rhy. Fig. 1**

Gtr. 4

*Symbols in parentheses reflect chords respective to capoed gtr. and do not reflect actual pitch.

(Am) (C)

'cause no one's tried to give you what you need.

steady gliss.

(G) (D) (B7)

So, lay all your trou-bles down,

End Rhy. Fig. 1

let ring

Gtr. 1 tacet
(Em)

Gtr. 4 tacet
(C)

I am with you now. I'm here for the

Gtr. 3

let ring

Gtr. 4

Gtr. 6 (elec.)

mf
w/ dist. & slide

Gtr. 2

8va

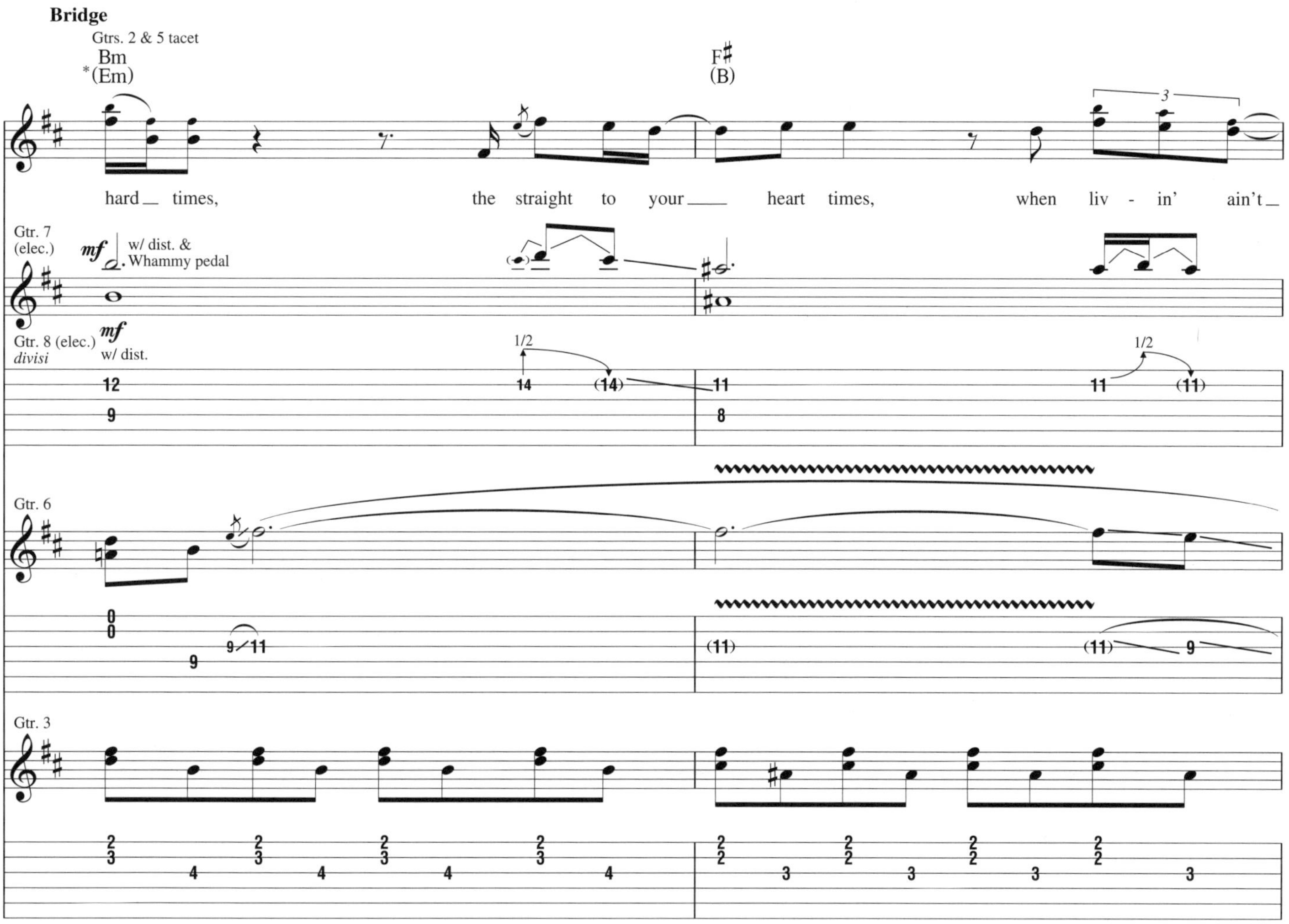

Bridge

Gtrs. 2 & 5 tacet

Bm *(Em) F♯ (B)

hard _ times, the straight to your _ heart times, when liv - in' ain't _

Gtr. 7 (elec.) mf w/ dist. & Whammy pedal

Gtr. 8 (elec.) divisi mf w/ dist.

1/2 1/2

Gtr. 6

Gtr. 3

*Symbols in parentheses represent chord names respective to capoed gtr. Symbols above represent actual sounding chords.

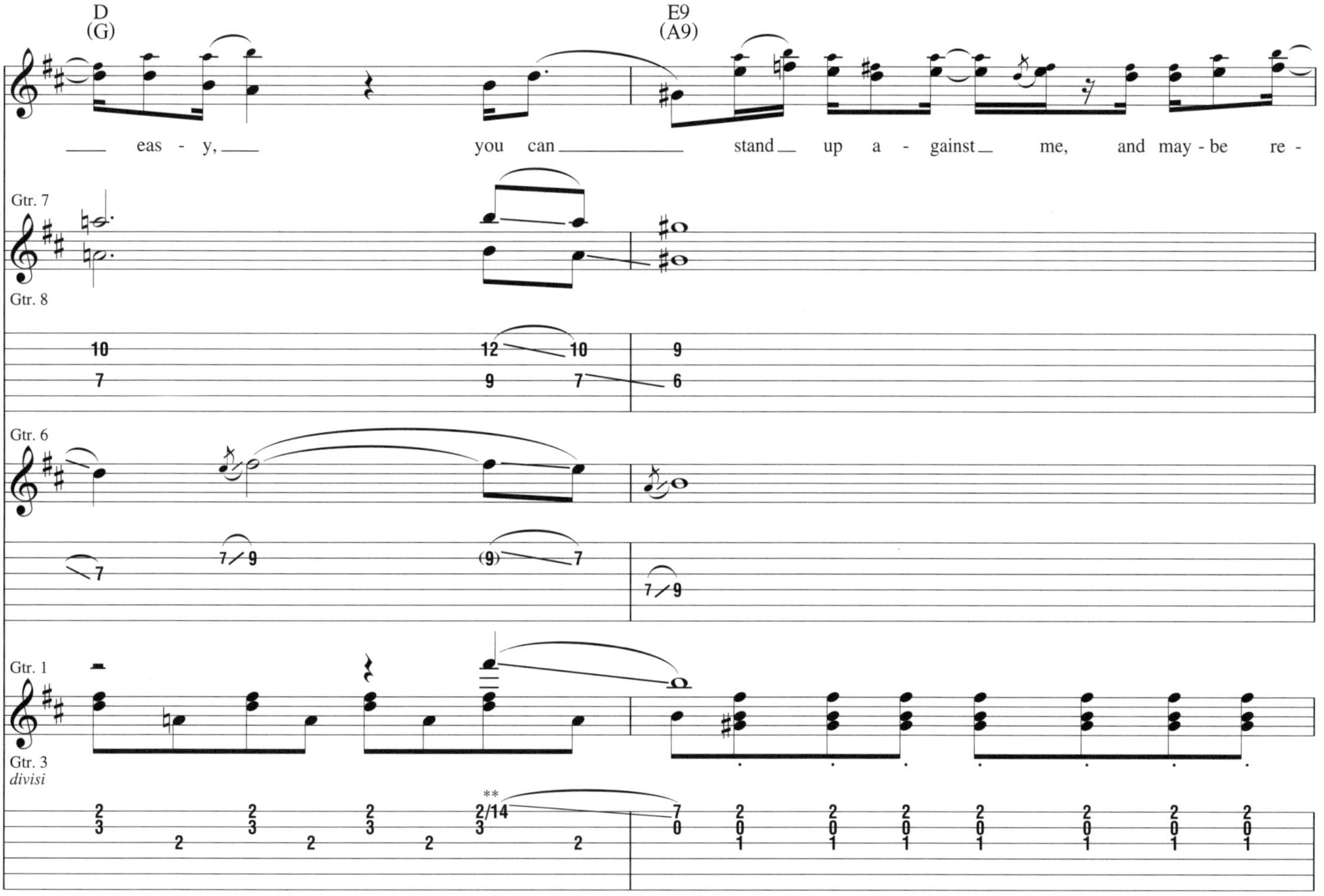

D (G) E9 (A9)

_ eas - y, _ you can _ stand _ up a - gainst _ me, and may - be re -

Gtr. 7

Gtr. 8

Gtr. 6

Gtr. 1

Gtr. 3 divisi

**Gtr. 1 to right of slash in tab.

Gtr. 1 tacet
Em9
(Am9)
A
(D)
G
(C)
- ly on me, and cry on me, yeah.
Gtr. 7
Gtr. 8
Gtr. 6
Gtr. 3
Guitar Solo
Gtr. 6 tacet
D
(G)
Dsus4 D
(Gsus4) (G)
A
(D)
Oh, no,
Gtr. 9 (elec.)
mf
w/ slight dist. & delay
1/2
Gtr. 7
Gtr. 8
divisi
Gtr. 3
let ring

Gtrs. 7 & 8 tacet
Em
(Am)
G
(C)
no, no.
3. Some -
Gtr. 9
Gtr. 6
dist. off
w/ dist.
let ring
Gtr. 3
Verse
Gtrs. 3 & 6 tacet
D
(G)
Dsus4
(Gsus4)
day they'll o - pen up your world,
shake it down to the draw - in' board,
Gtr. 9
Gtr. 1
Gtr. 9 tacet
D
(G)
Dsus4
(Gsus4)
do their best to change you.
They still can't e - rase you. From what I've seen
Gtr. 1
steady gliss.

Chorus

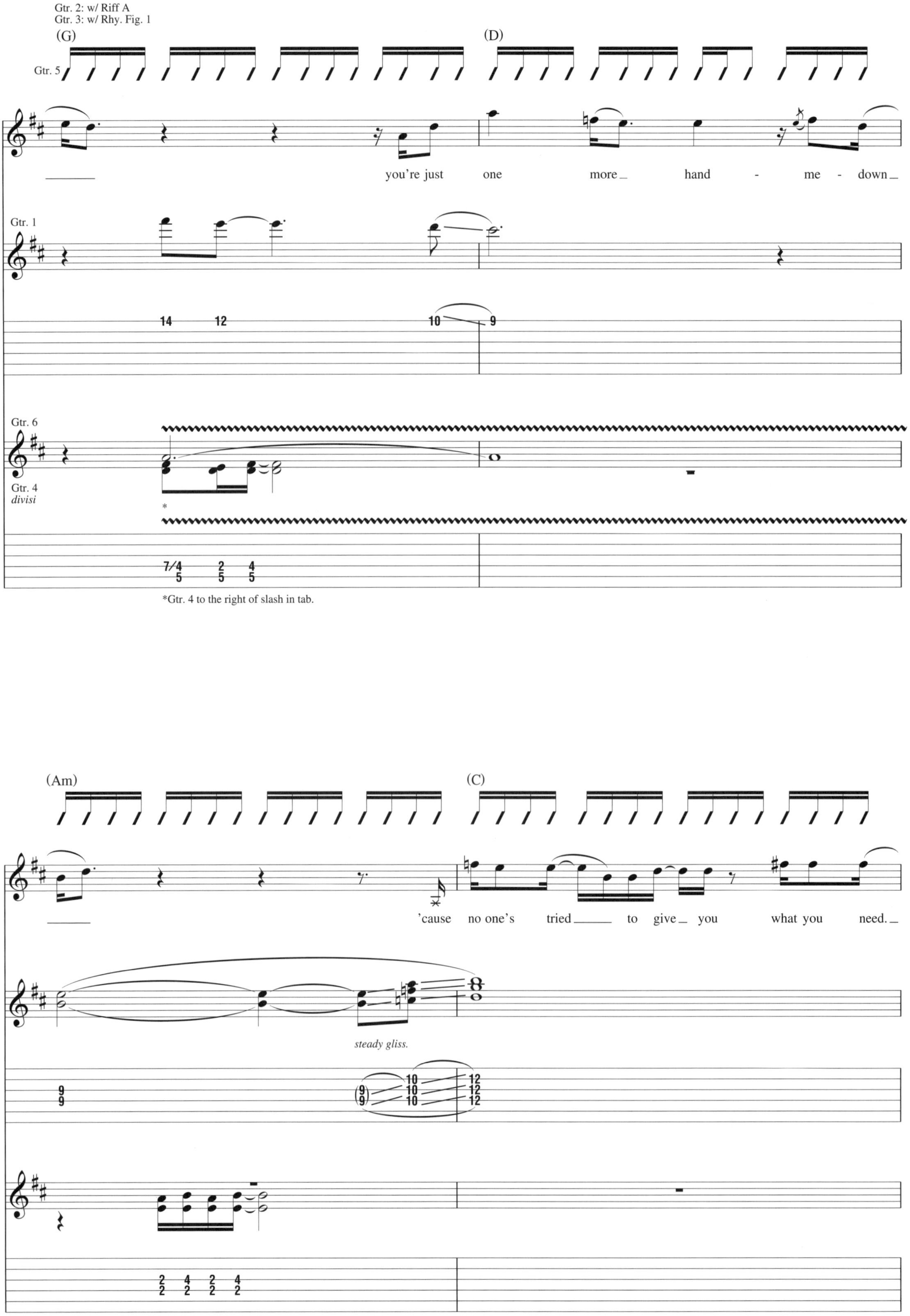

Gtr. 2: w/ Riff A
Gtr. 3: w/ Rhy. Fig. 1

(G) (D)

Gtr. 5

you're just one more hand - me - down

Gtr. 1

14 12 10 9

Gtr. 6

Gtr. 4
divisi

7/4 2 4
5 5 5

*Gtr. 4 to the right of slash in tab.

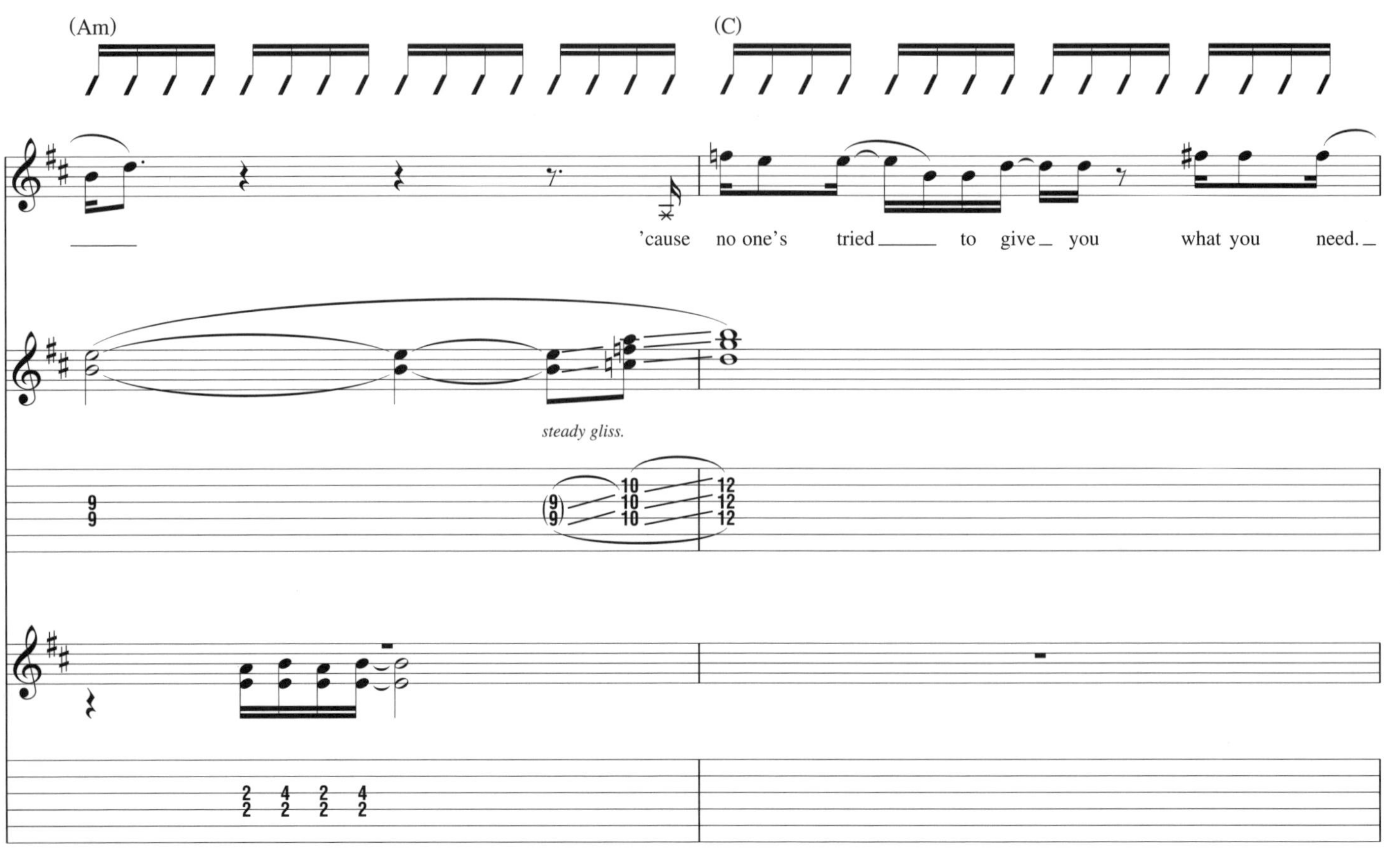

(G)
Gtr. 1 tacet
(D)
(B7)
So, lay all your_ trou - bles___ down,_
(Em)
(C)
I am with you now,_ lay___ them_ down_ on___ me._
Gtr. 2
8va
Gtr. 6
Gtr. 4
Gtr. 3

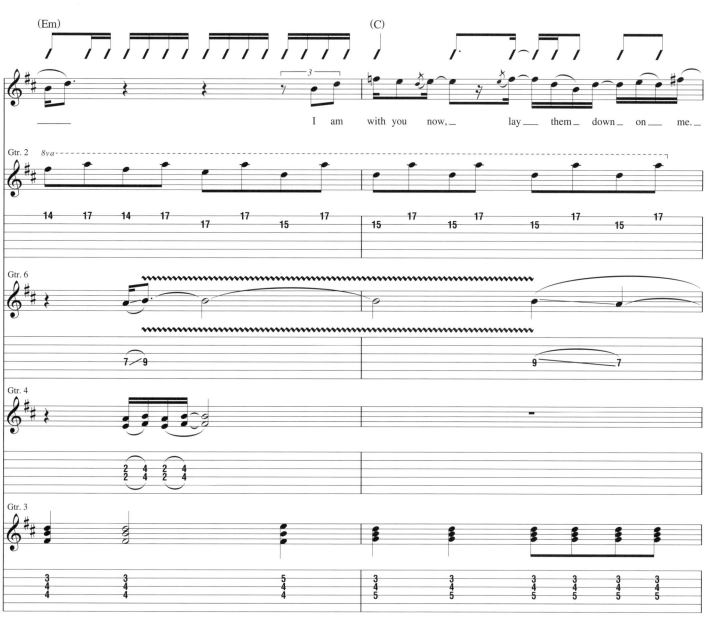

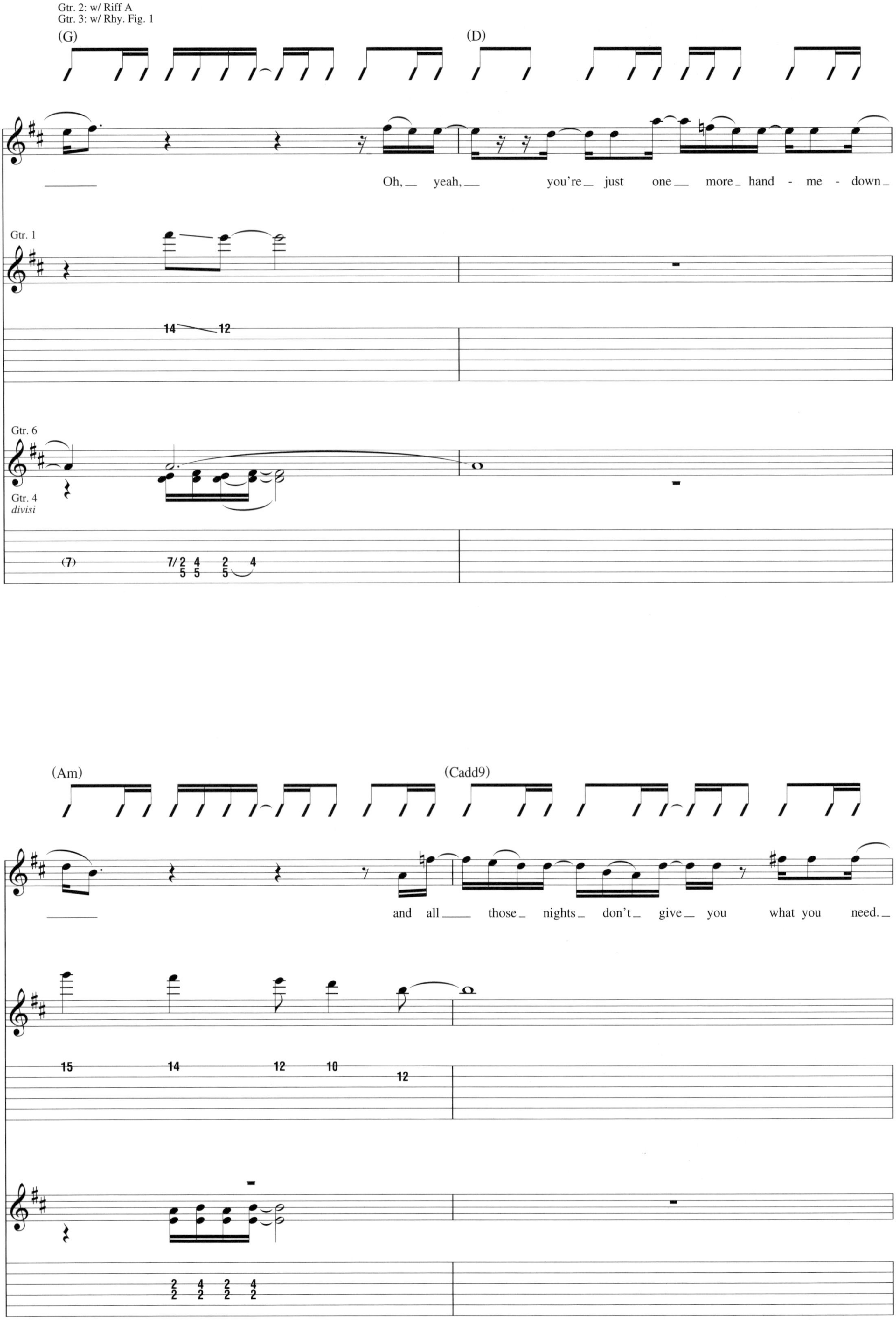

Gtr. 2: w/ Riff A
Gtr. 3: w/ Rhy. Fig. 1

(G) (D)

Oh, yeah, you're just one more hand - me - down

Gtr. 1

14 12

Gtr. 6

Gtr. 4
divisi

(7) 7/2 4 2 4
5 5 5

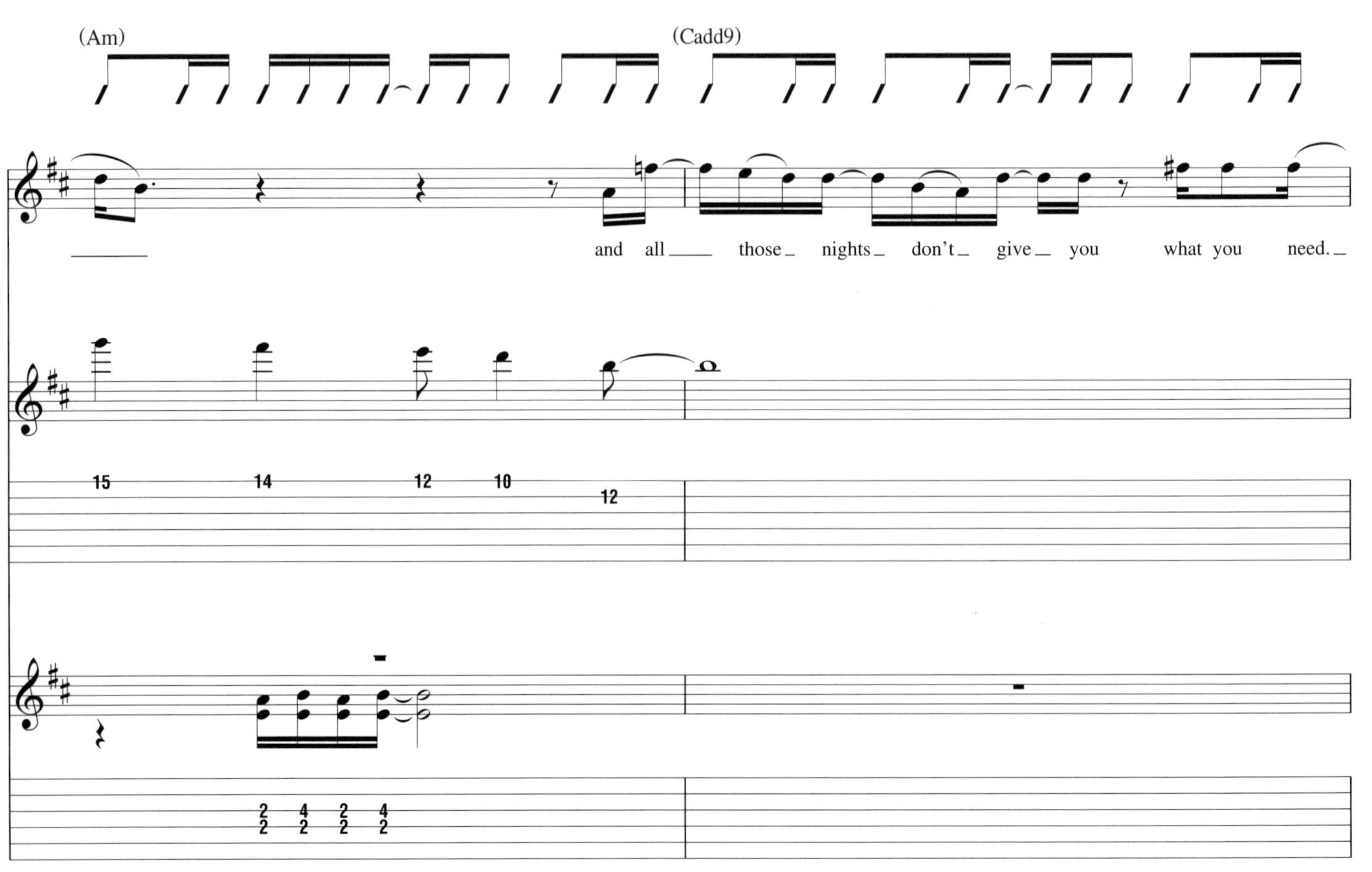

(Em)

on me.

Gtr. 2 *8va*

Gtr. 4

Gtr. 1

Gtr. 6 *divisi*

Outro

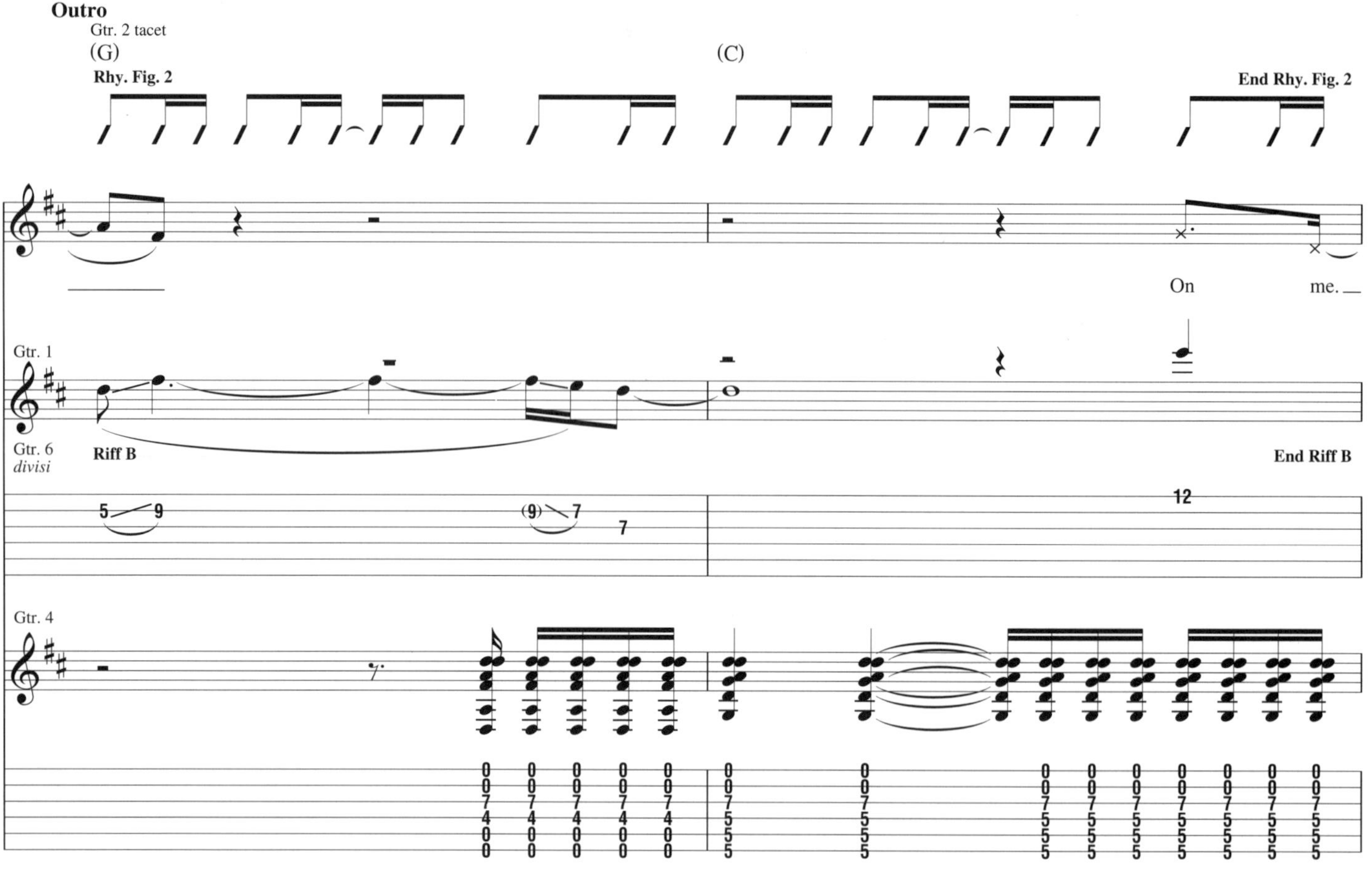

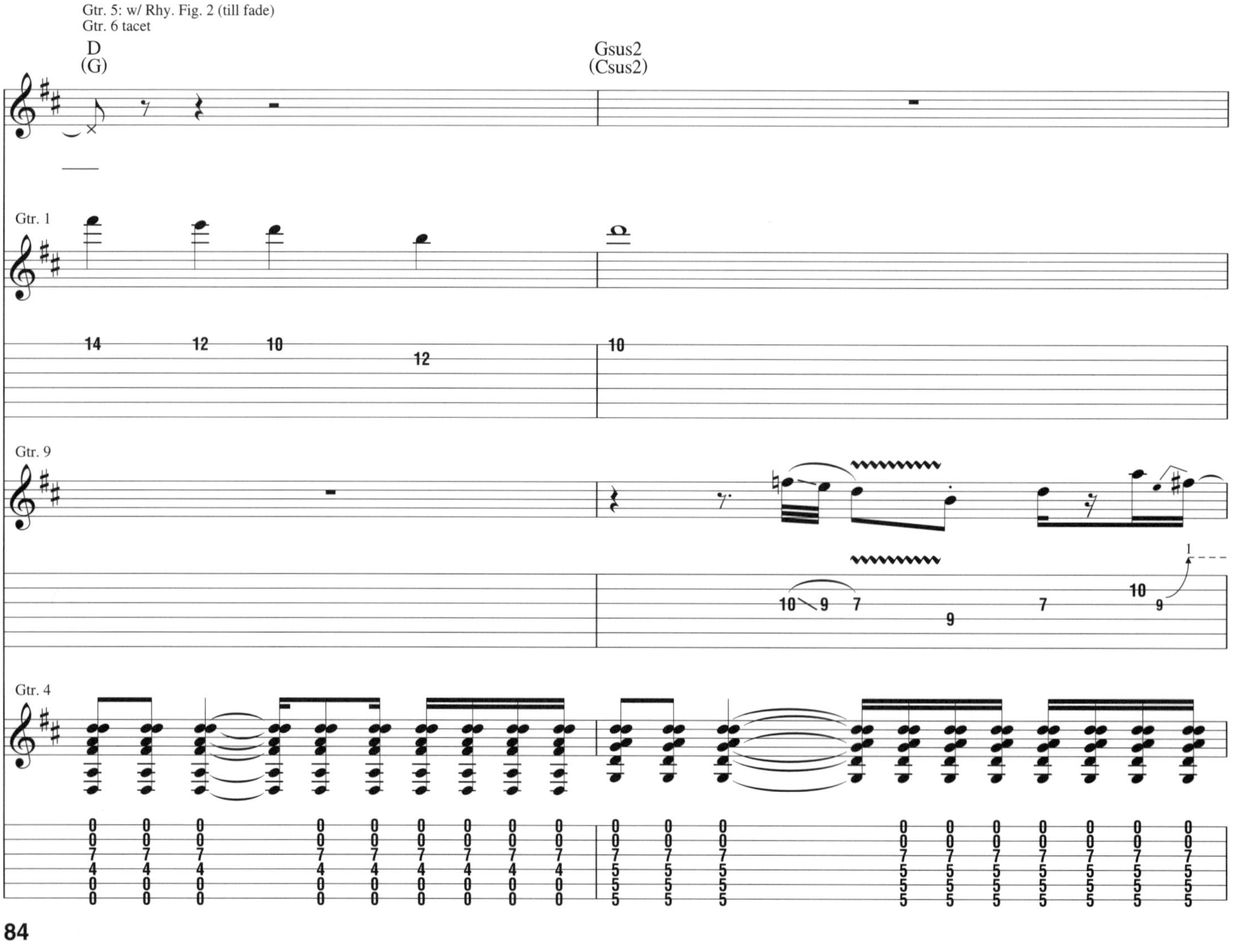

Gtr. 5: w/ Rhy. Fig. 2 (till fade)
Gtr. 6 tacet

D
(G)

Gsus2
(Csus2)

Gtr. 1

Gtr. 9

Gtr. 4

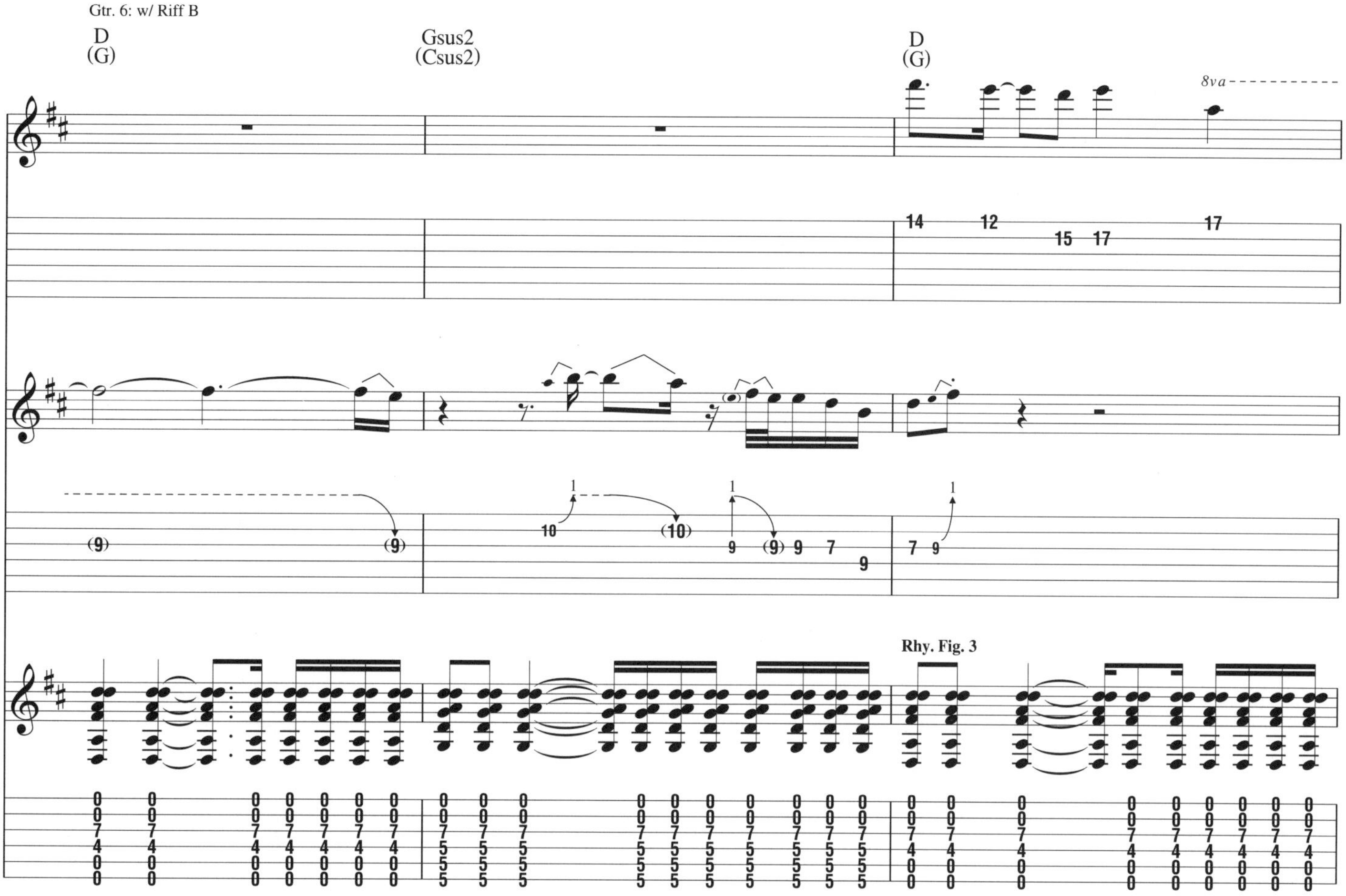

Gtr. 6: w/ Riff B

D
(G)

Gsus2
(Csus2)

D
(G)

8va

Rhy. Fig. 3

Gsus2
(Csus2)

8va

Gtr. 4: w/ Rhy. Fig. 3 (till fade)

D
(G)

Gsus2
(Csus2)

End Rhy. Fig. 3

Gtr. 6

D
(G)

loco

Begin fade

Gsus2
(Csus2)

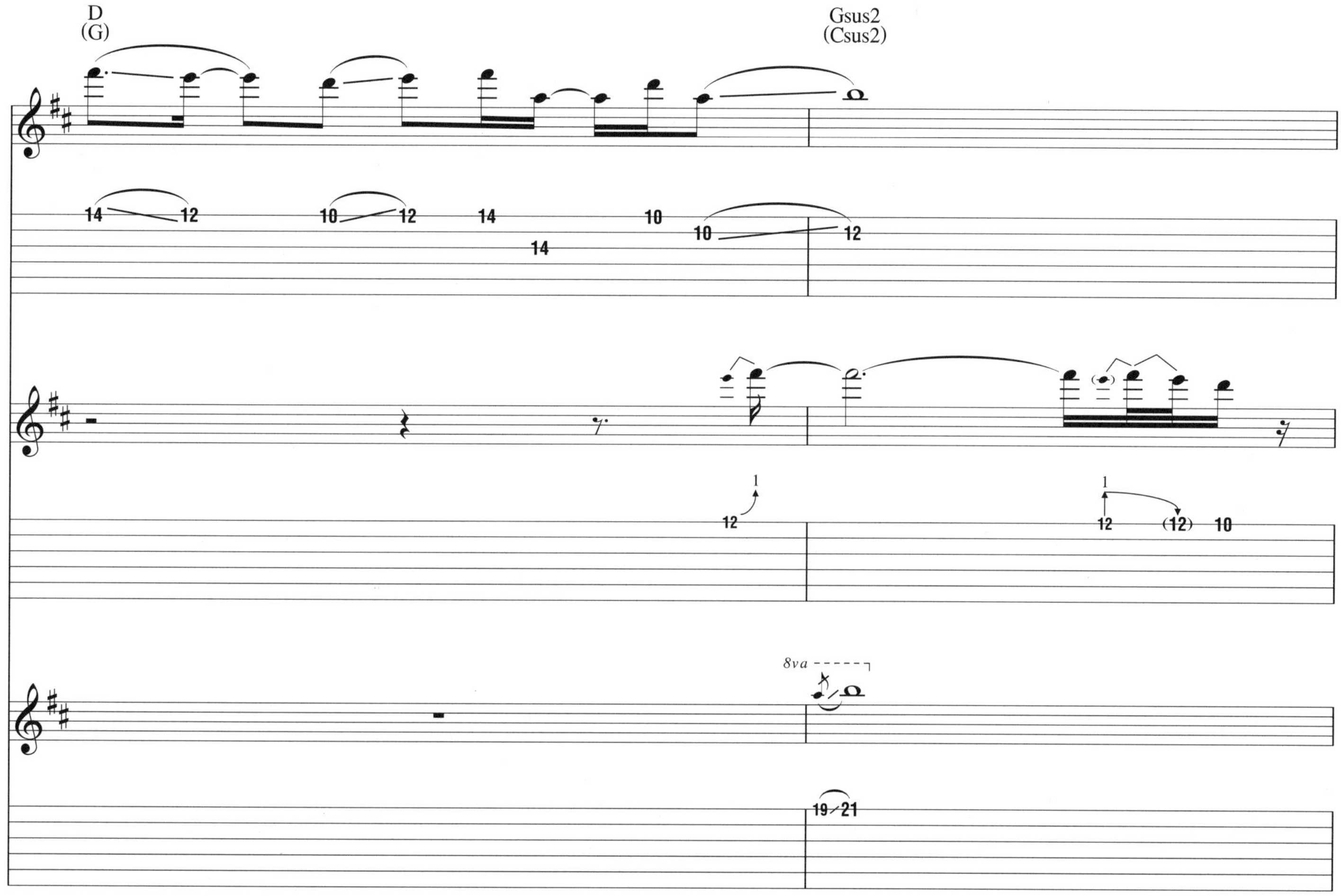

D
(G)

Gsus2
(Csus2)

8va

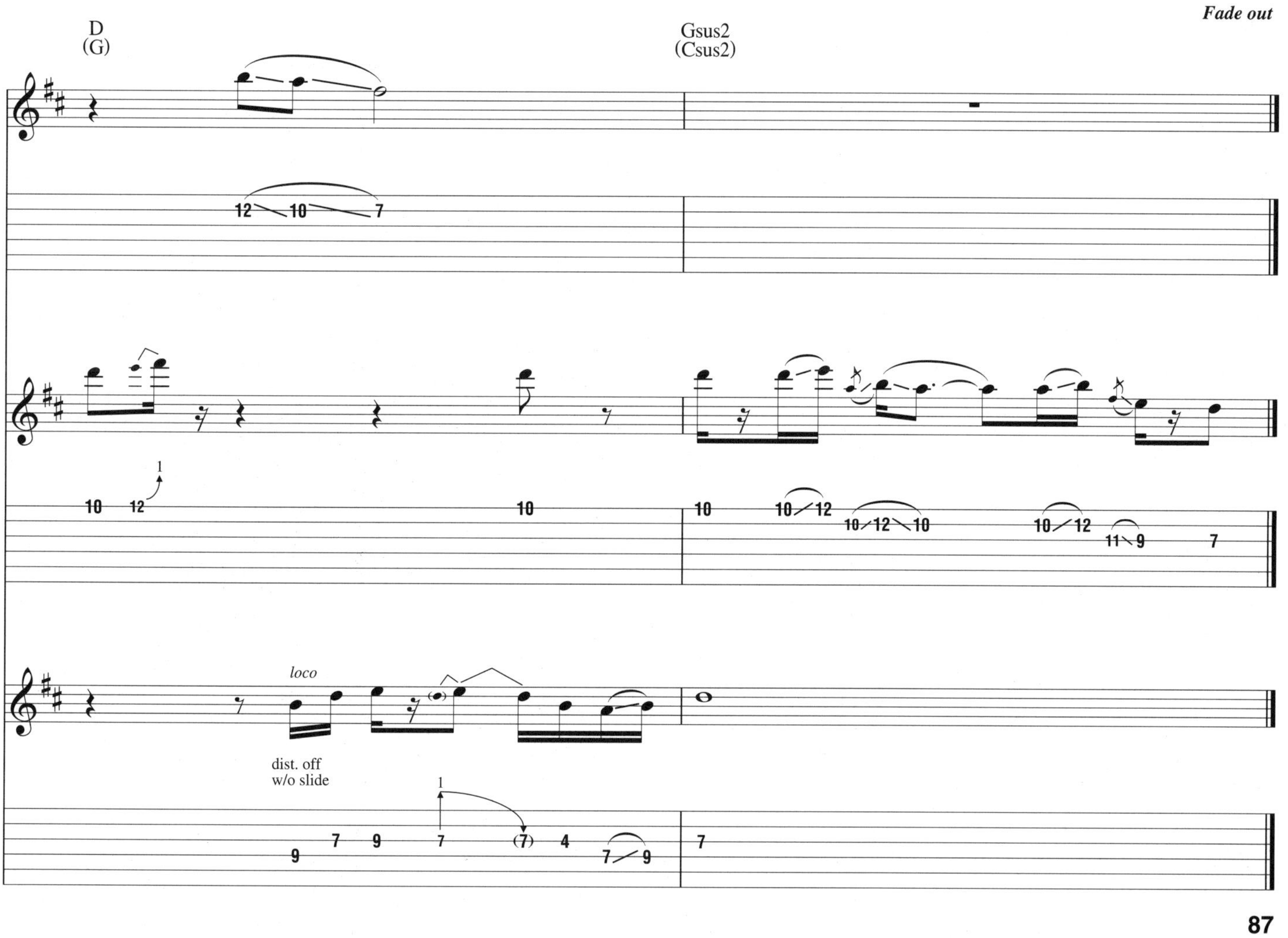

D
(G)

Gsus2
(Csus2)

Fade out

loco

dist. off
w/o slide

Could I Be You

Words and Music by Paul Doucette

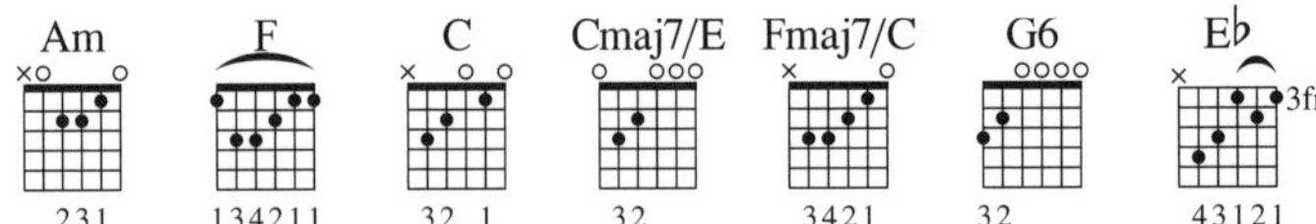

*Elec. piano arr. for gtr.

**Chord symbols reflect overall harmony.

***Set for eighth-note regeneration and 0% feedback.

C Cmaj7/E

to e - rase.

C Cmaj7/E Am

How can I be the on - ly one

F C

with - out a smile on my face?

Cmaj7/E

When, now you're laugh - in' out loud

(cont. in slashes)

Chorus
Gtr. 1 tacet
Fmaj7/C
G6
Rhy. Fig. 1
*Gtrs. 2 & 3
at just the thought of be - in' a - live
Gtr. 4 (elec.)
Rhy. Fig. 1A
f
w/ dist.
Gtr. 5 (elec.)
Rhy. Fig. 1B
mf
w/ clean tone
*Composite arrangement
Am
Gtr. 6 tacet
Fmaj7/C
Gtrs. 2 & 3
and I was won - der - in' could I just
Riff A
End Riff A
Gtr. 6 (elec.)
8va
H.H.
let ring
Gtr. 4
End Rhy. Fig. 1A
Gtr. 5

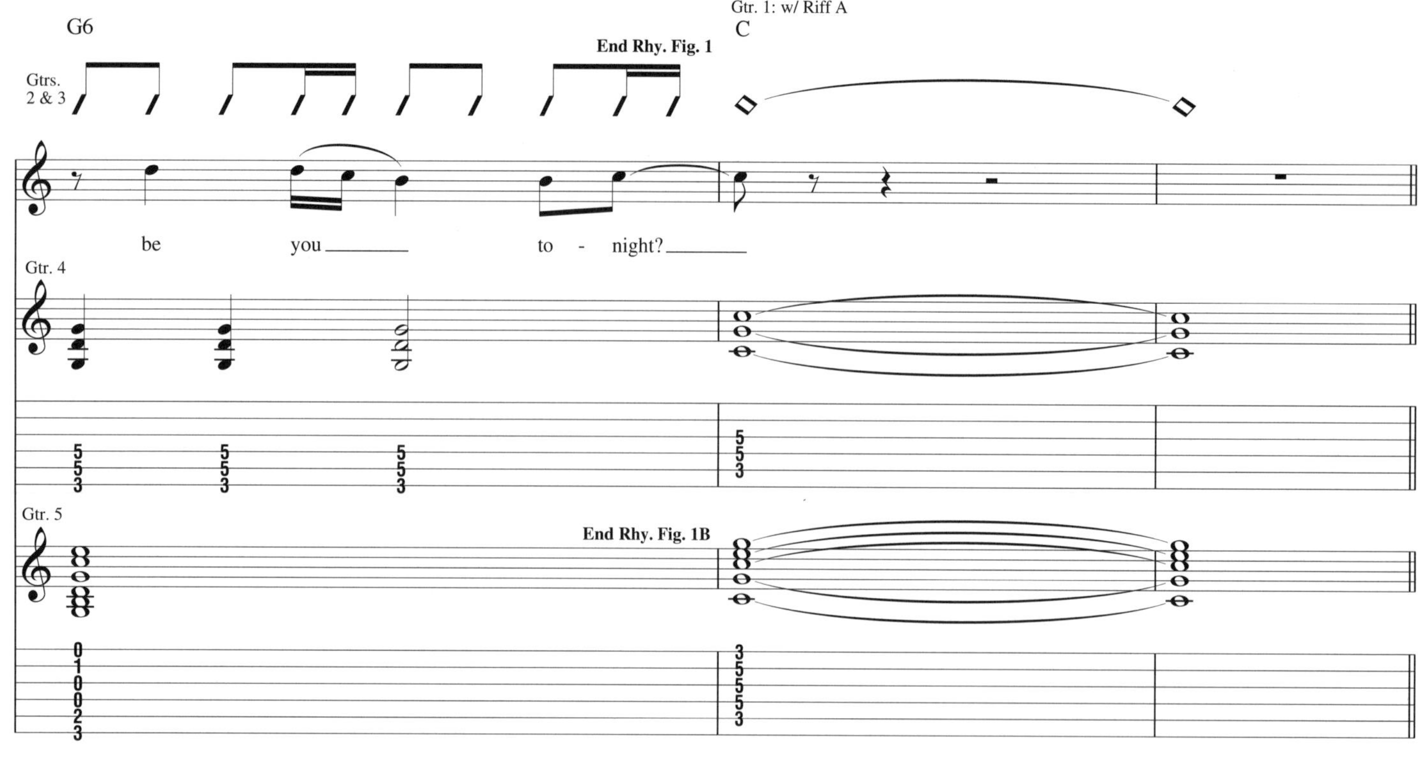
Gtr. 1: w/ Riff A
G6
C
End Rhy. Fig. 1
Gtrs. 2 & 3
be you to - night?
Gtr. 4
Gtr. 5
End Rhy. Fig. 1B

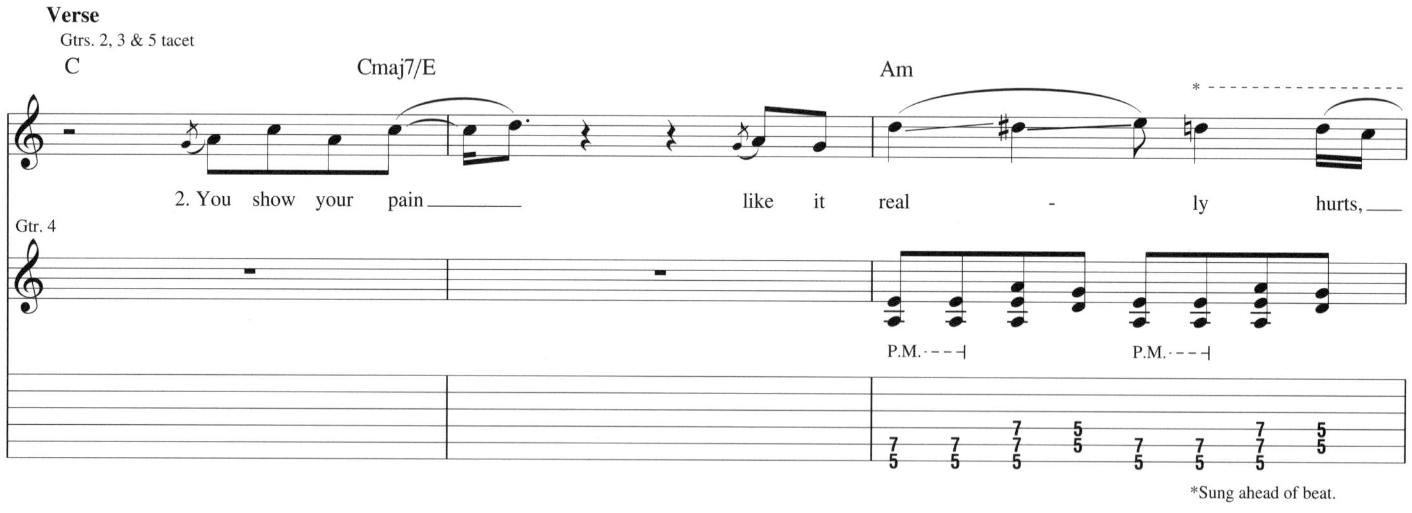
Verse
Gtrs. 2, 3 & 5 tacet
C
Cmaj7/E
Am
2. You show your pain like it real - ly hurts,
Gtr. 4
P.M.
P.M.
*Sung ahead of beat.

G5
F
and I can't e - ven start to feel mine.
Gtr. 7 (elec.)
f
steady gliss.
w/ dist. & slide
Gtr. 4
P.M.
P.M.

C
Cmaj7/E
C
And I'm stand - in' in place
Gtr. 7
steady gliss.
*Fret the second string with the second finger and avoid touching strings with slide.
**Bend 2nd string behind nut.
Gtr. 8 (elec.)
w/ dist.
Gtr. 4
Cmaj7/E
Gtr. 7 tacet
Am
with my head first, and I shake, I shake,
Gtr. 9 (elec.)
w/ dist. & phase shifter
P.M.

F

and I see your prog - ress stretched out for miles,

C Cmaj7/E

and miles. And you're laugh - in' out loud

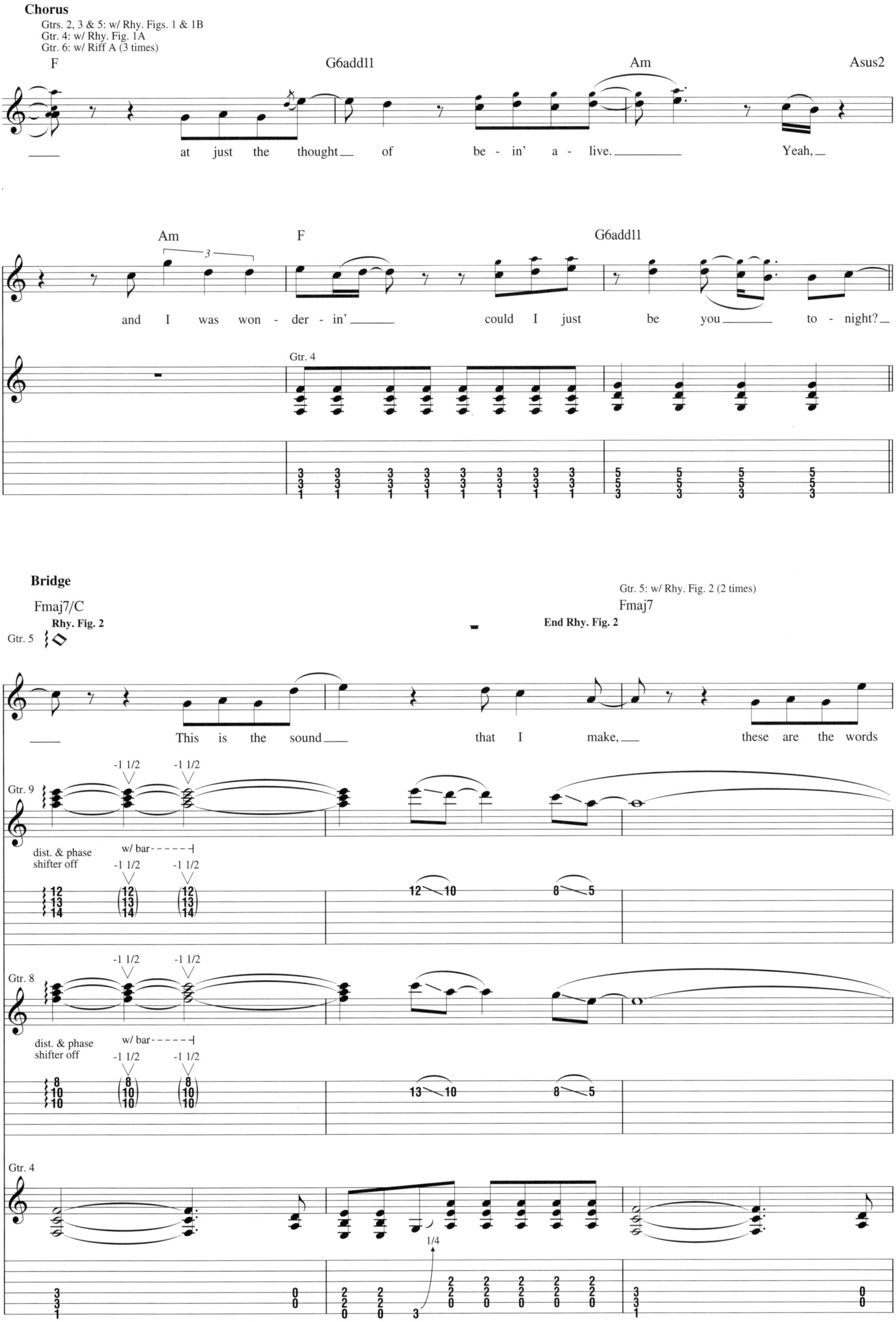

Chorus

Gtrs. 2, 3 & 5: w/ Rhy. Figs. 1 & 1B
Gtr. 4: w/ Rhy. Fig. 1A
Gtr. 6: w/ Riff A (3 times)

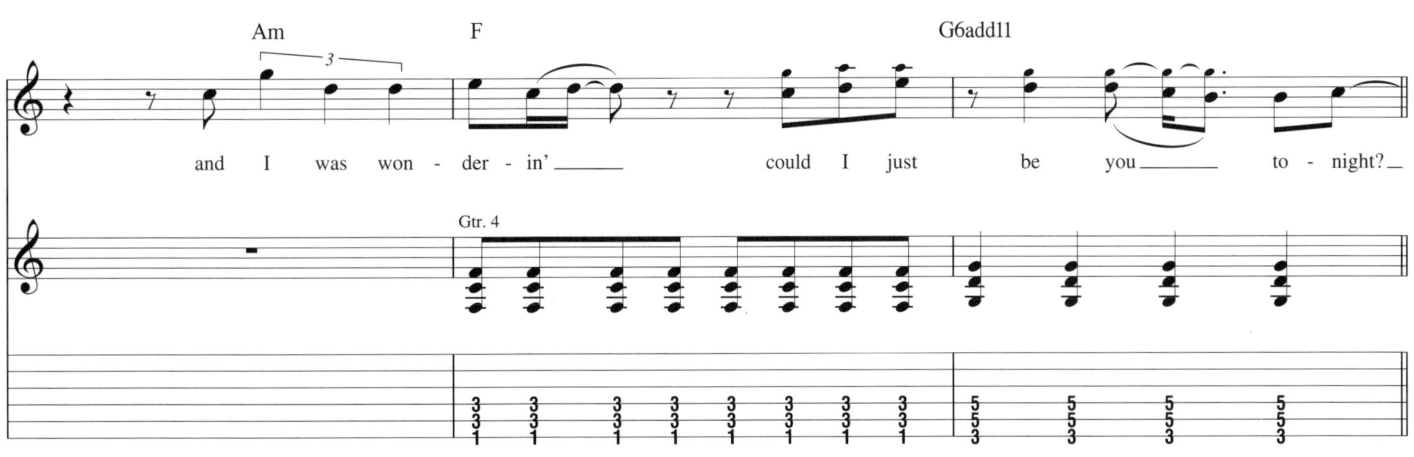

Bridge

Gtr. 5: w/ Rhy. Fig. 2 (2 times)

Fmaj7/C

Rhy. Fig. 2

Gtr. 5

End Rhy. Fig. 2

Fmaj7

This is the sound that I make, these are the words

Gtr. 9

-1 1/2 -1 1/2

dist. & phase shifter off

w/ bar

12 13 14 12 10 8 5

Gtr. 8

-1 1/2 -1 1/2

dist. & phase shifter off

w/ bar

8 10 10 13 10 8 5

Gtr. 4

1/4

3 3 1 0 0 2 2 0 3

E5 A5 Fmaj7 E5 A5

I chose. Some-how the right thing to say

-1 1/2 -1 1/2

w/ bar

(5) 12 13 14 (12 13 14) (12 13 14) 12 10 8 5

w/ bar

(5) 8 10 10 (8 10 10) (8 10 10) 13 10 8 5

1/4 1/4

Fmaj7/C

Gtr. 2

just won't come out,

Gtr. 9

Gtr. 8
divisi

Gtr. 3

Gtr. 4

Gtrs. 4, 8 & 9 tacet
(it) just won't come out.
And you're laugh - in' out loud
Gtr. 3
Chorus
Fmaj7/C
G6
Rhy. Fig. 3
at the thought of be - in' a - live.
Gtr. 4
Gtr. 3
Gtr. 6: w/ Riff A
Am
End Rhy. Fig. 3
And I was won -

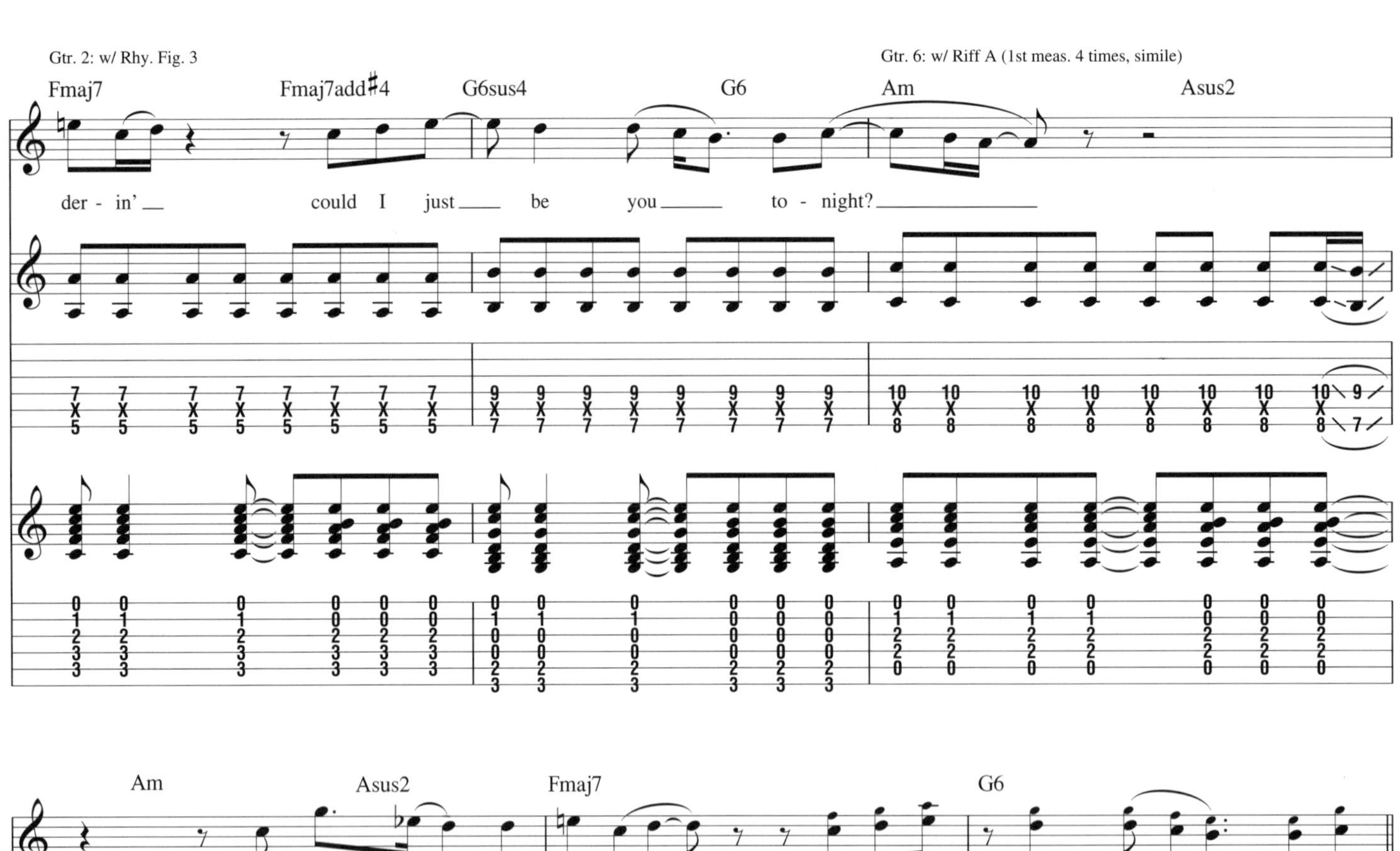

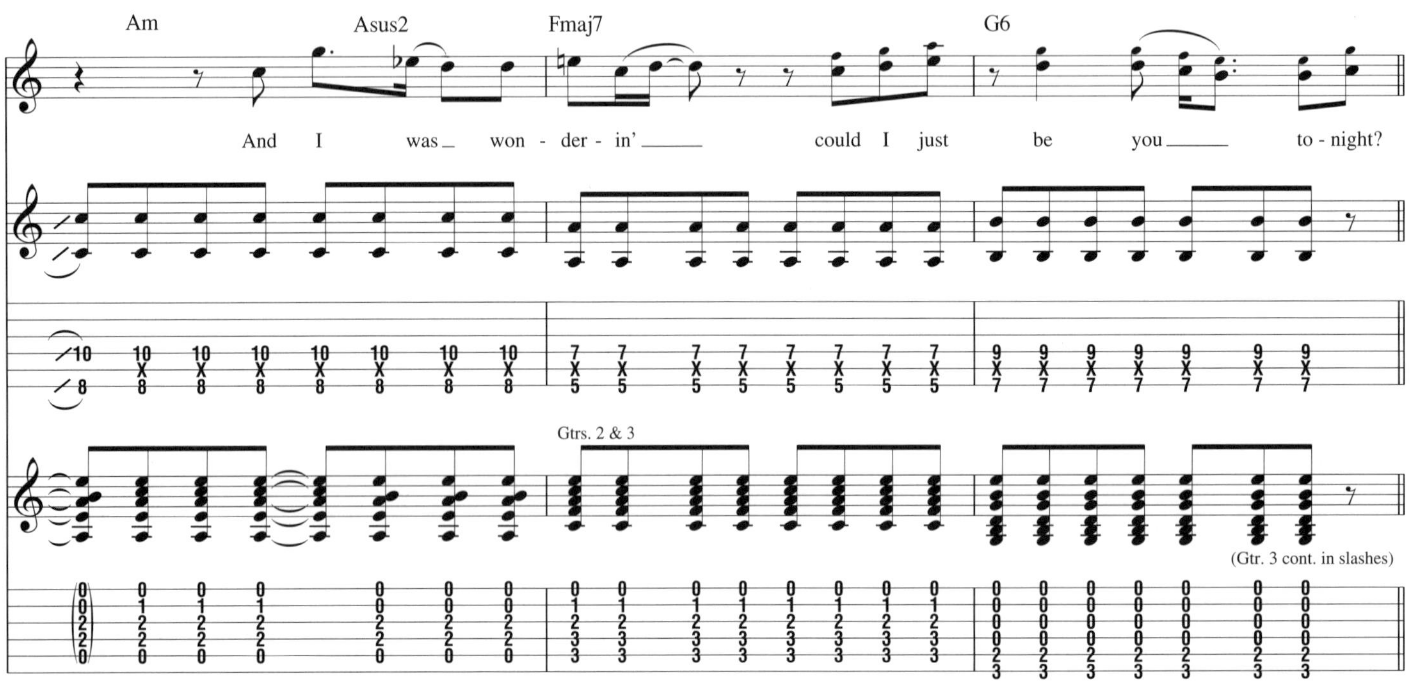

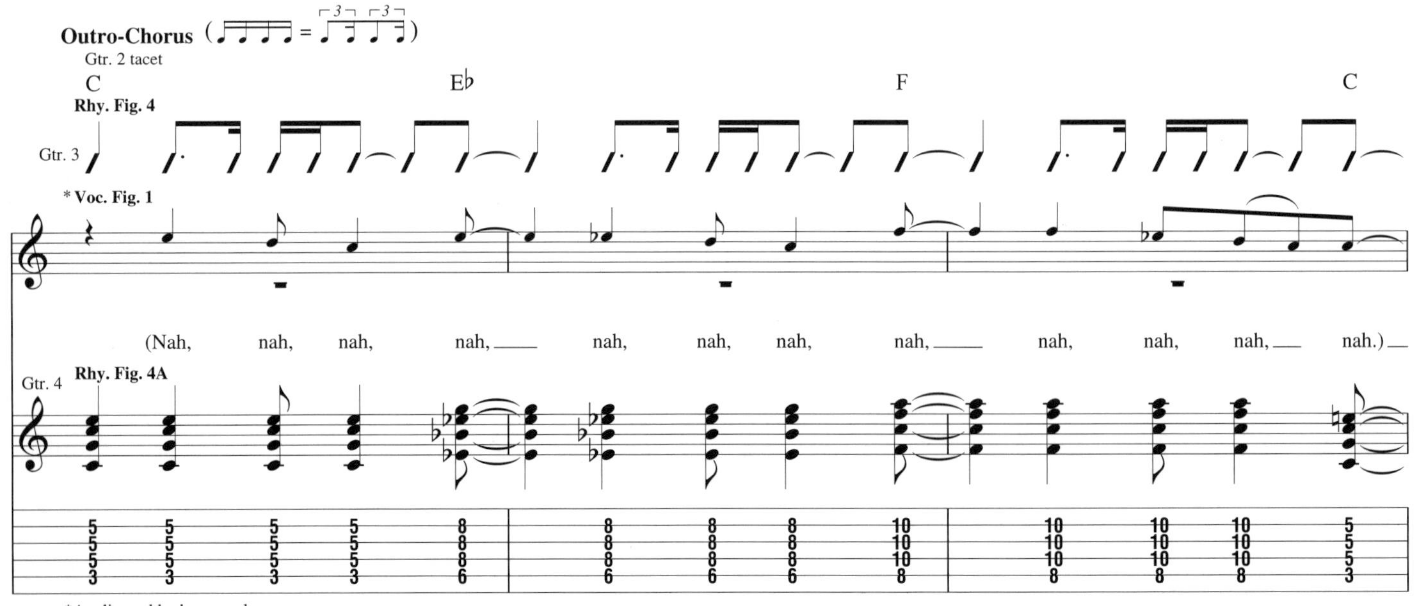

*Applies to bkgd. voc. only.

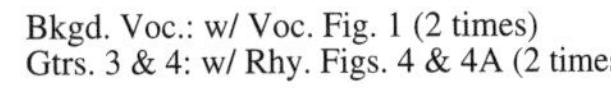
Bkgd. Voc.: w/ Voc. Fig. 1 (2 times)
Gtrs. 3 & 4: w/ Rhy. Figs. 4 & 4A (2 times)

C
E♭
F
End Rhy. Fig. 4
End Voc. Fig. 1
And I was won - der - in'.
End Rhy. Fig. 4A

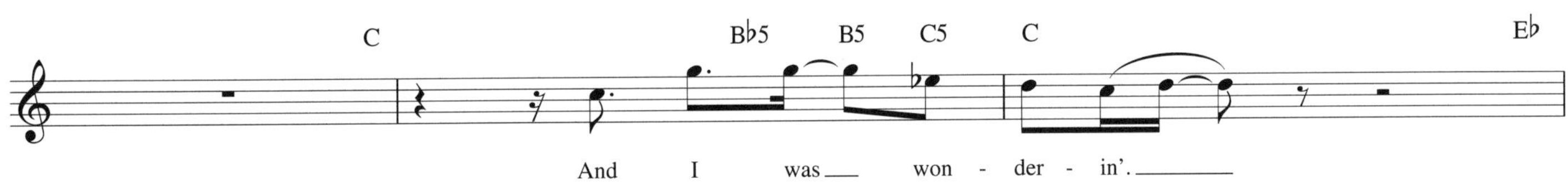
C
B♭5
B5
C5
C
E♭
And I was won - der - in'.

F
C
B♭5
B5
C5
Yeah, I, and I was won -

C
A♭
F
Gtrs. 3 & 4 tacet
C
Gtr. 3
rit.
der - in', I was won - der - in', ah, yeah.
(Nah, nah, nah, nah, nah, nah, nah.)
Gtr. 4

Downfall

Words and Music by Rob Thomas and Matt Serletic

*Piano arr. for gtr.

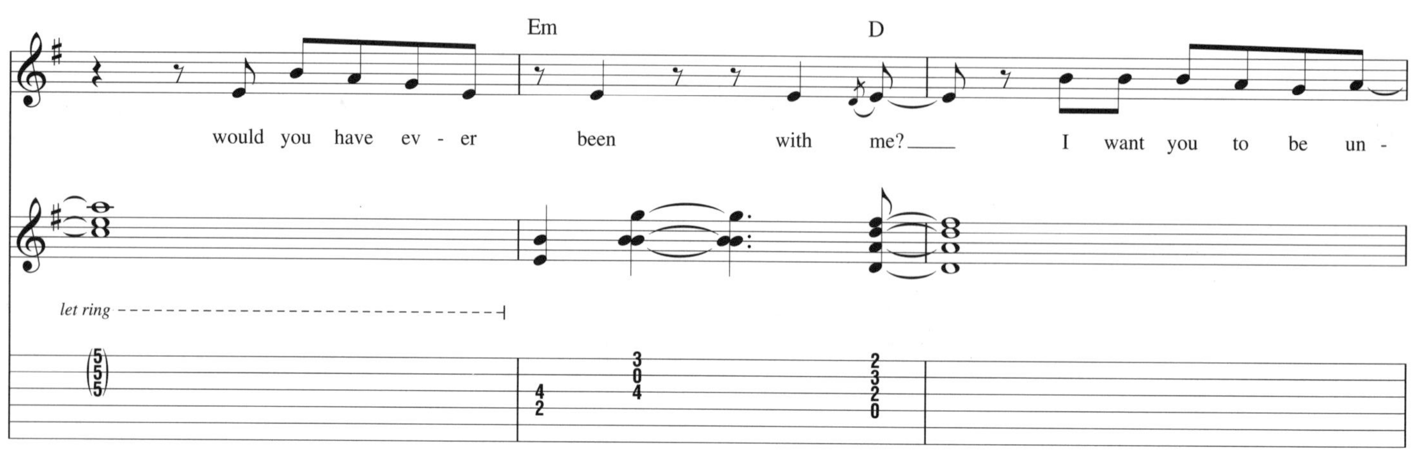

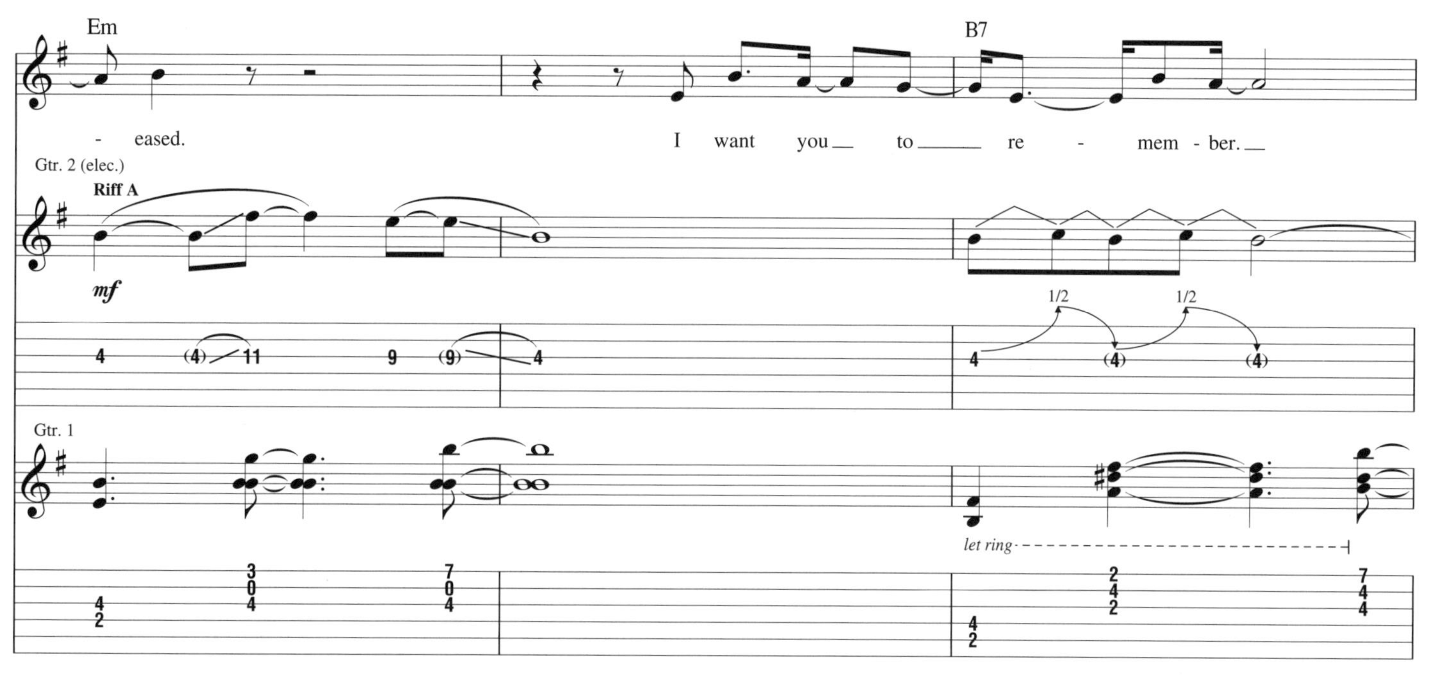
Em
B7
- eased.
I want you to re - mem - ber.
Gtr. 2 (elec.)
Riff A
mf
1/2
1/2
Gtr. 1
let ring

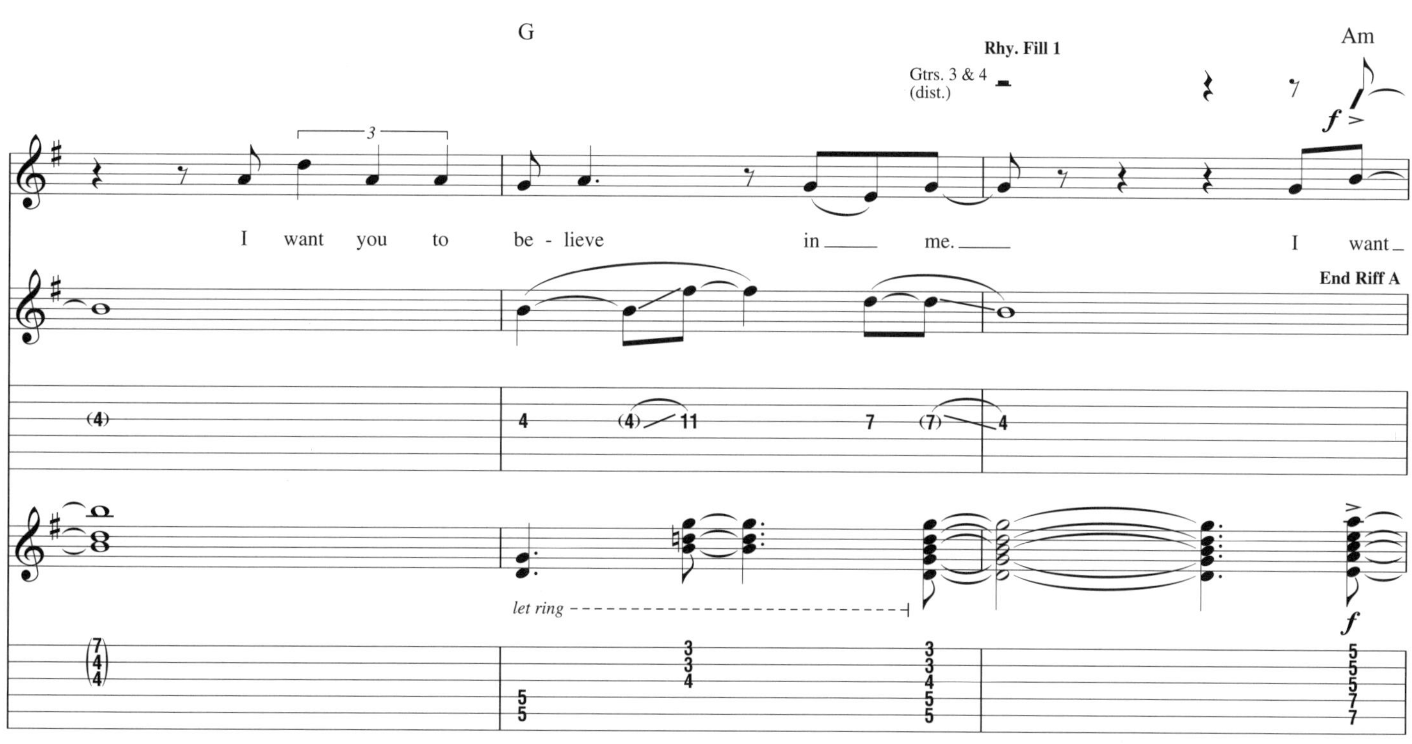
G
Rhy. Fill 1
Gtrs. 3 & 4
(dist.)
Am
f
I want you to be - lieve in me. I want
End Riff A
let ring
f

Gtr. 2 tacet
Chorus
Gtr. 1 tacet
E5 D5/E E5
C
End Rhy. Fill 1
(cont. in notation)
you on my side. Come on and lay it down,
Gtr. 1
Rhy. Fig. 2
*Gtrs. 3 & 4
End Rhy. Fig. 1
*Composite arrangement

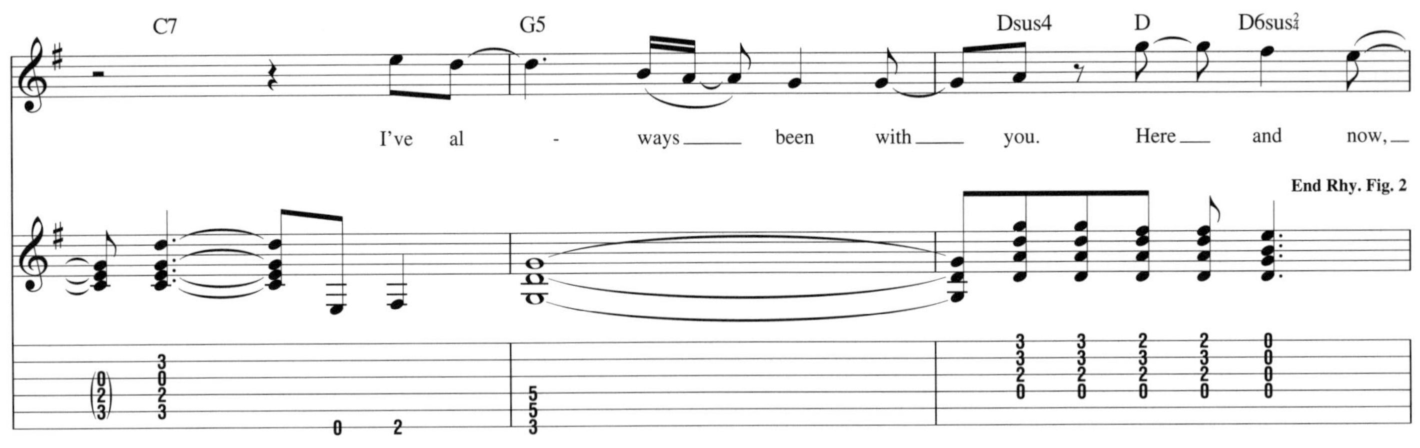
C7
G5
Dsus4
D
D6sus2/4
I've al - ways been with you. Here and now,
End Rhy. Fig. 2

Gtrs. 3 & 4: w/ Rhy. Fig. 2 (2 times)
E5 D5/E E5
C
C7
G5
give all that's with - in

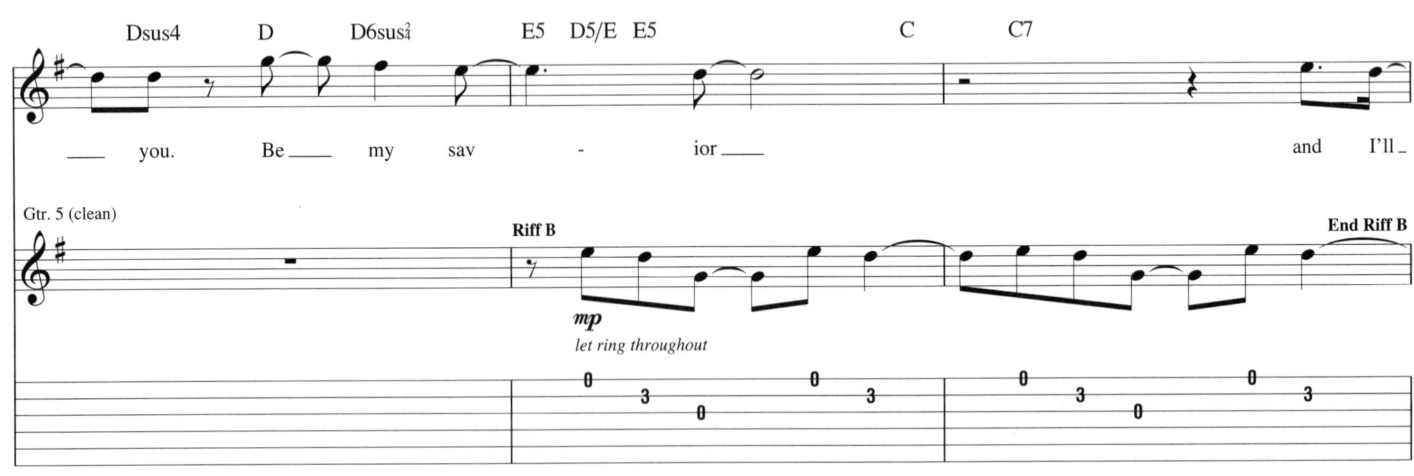
Dsus4
D
D6sus2/4
E5 D5/E E5
C
C7
you. Be my sav - ior and I'll
Gtr. 5 (clean)
Riff B
mp
let ring throughout
End Riff B

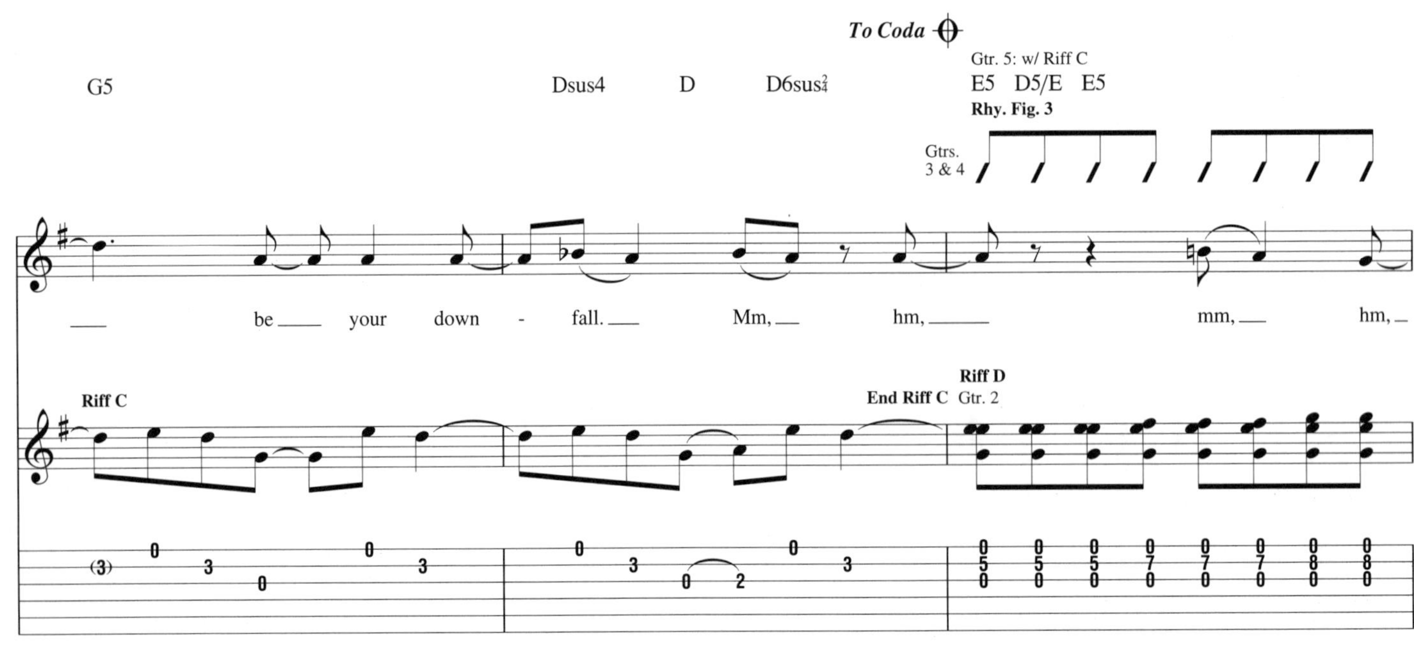
To Coda
Gtr. 5: w/ Riff C
G5
Dsus4
D
D6sus2/4
E5 D5/E E5
Rhy. Fig. 3
Gtrs. 3 & 4
be your down - fall. Mm, hm, mm, hm,
Riff C
End Riff C
Riff D
Gtr. 2

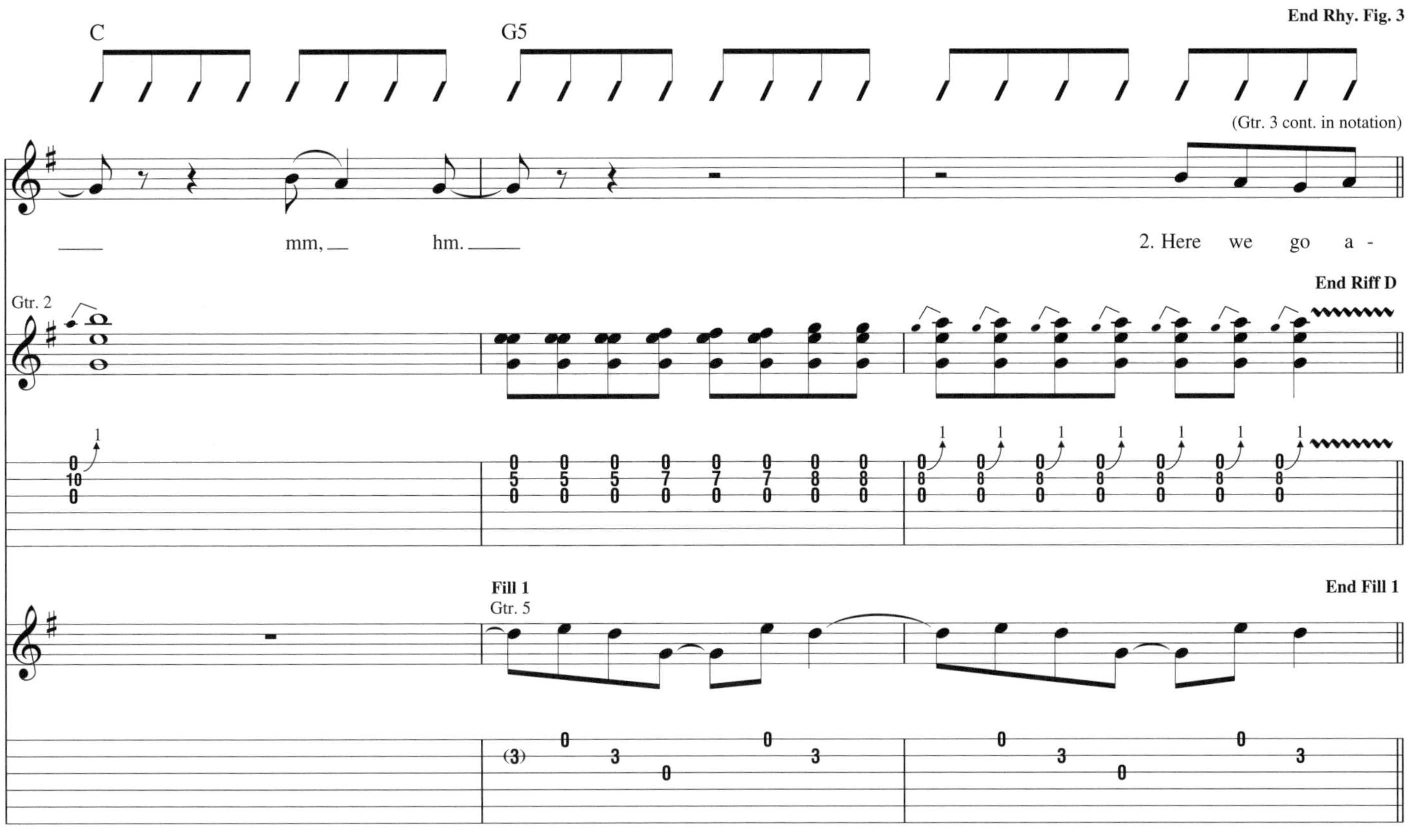
C
G5
End Rhy. Fig. 3
(Gtr. 3 cont. in notation)
mm, hm.
2. Here we go a -
Gtr. 2
End Riff D
Fill 1
Gtr. 5
End Fill 1

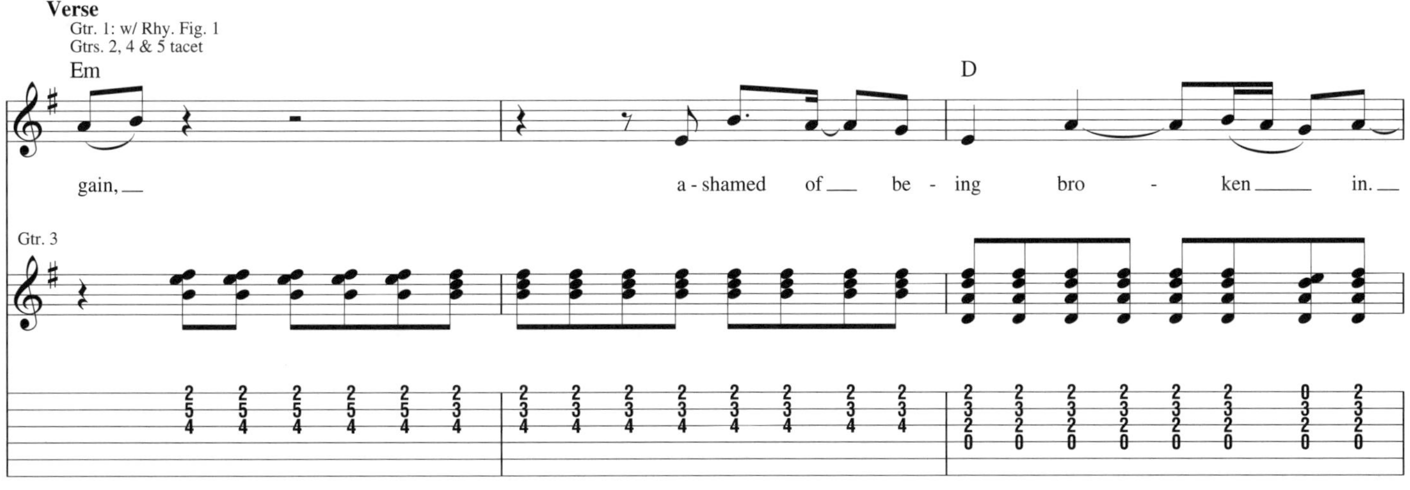
Verse
Gtr. 1: w/ Rhy. Fig. 1
Gtrs. 2, 4 & 5 tacet
Em
D
gain,
a - shamed of be - ing bro - ken in.
Gtr. 3

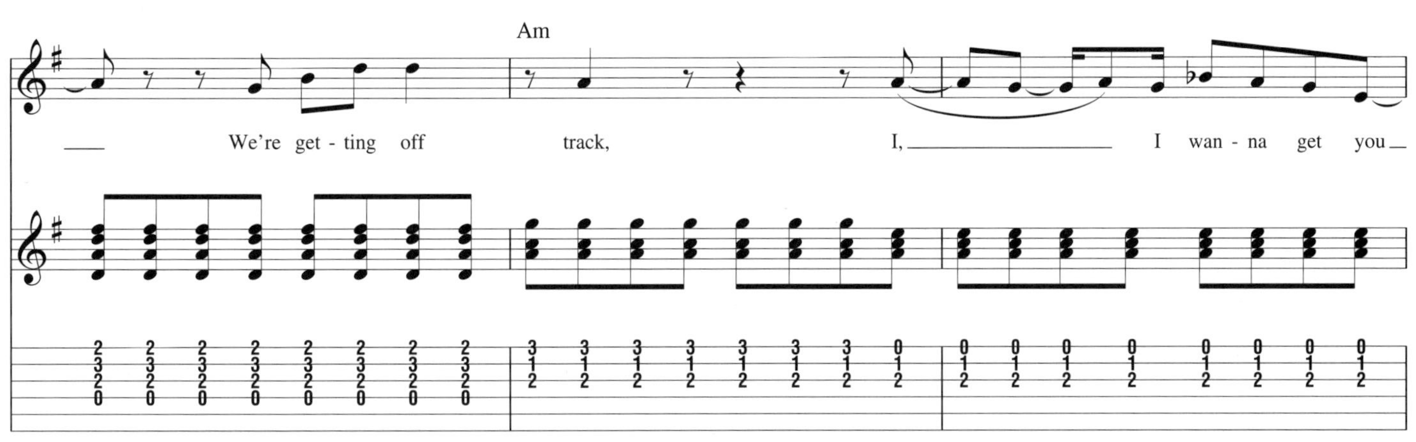
Am
We're get - ting off track,
I,
I wan - na get you

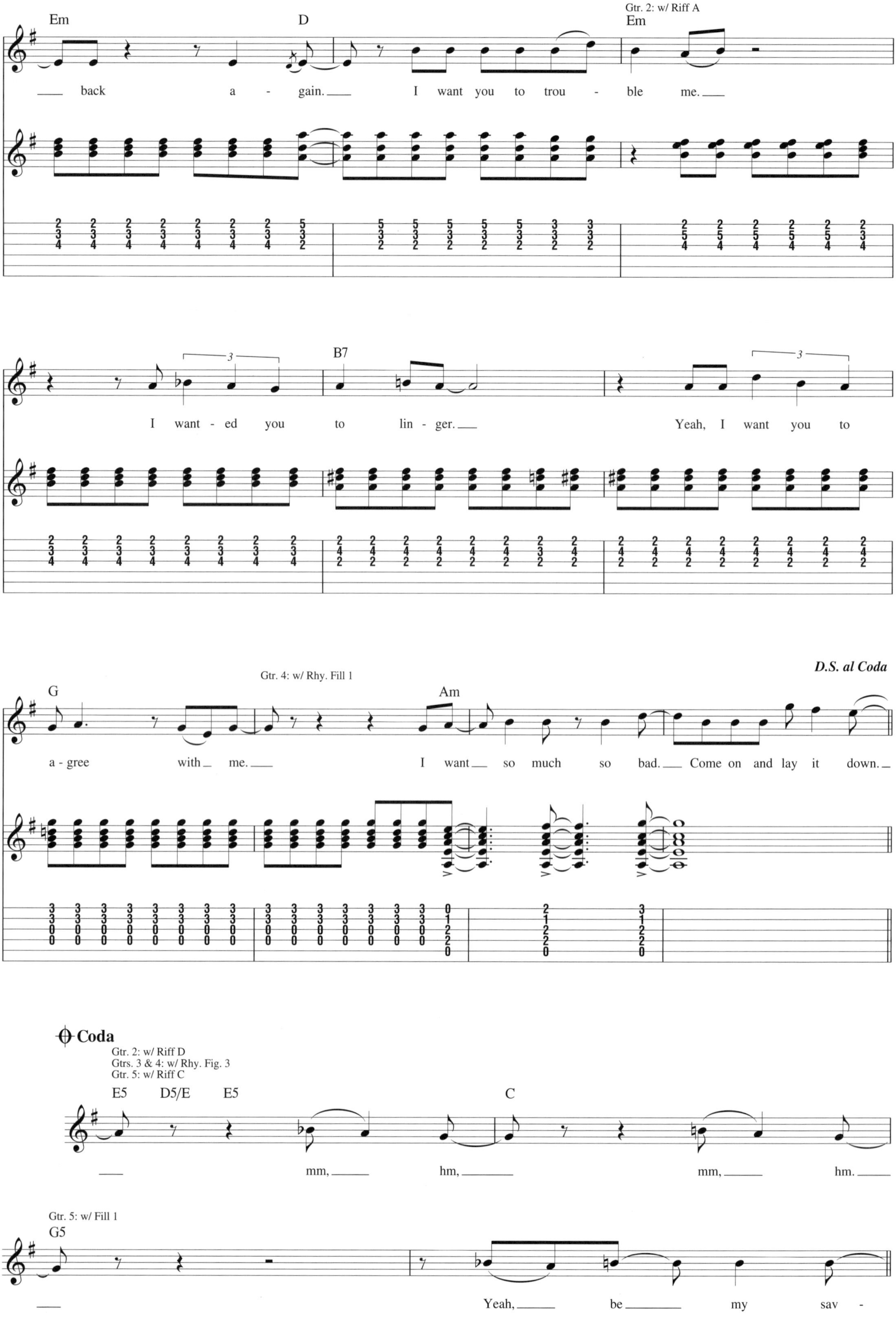

Gtr. 2: w/ Riff A
Em D Em
back a - gain. I want you to trou - ble me.
B7
I want - ed you to lin - ger. Yeah, I want you to
D.S. al Coda
Gtr. 4: w/ Rhy. Fill 1
G Am
a - gree with me. I want so much so bad. Come on and lay it down.
Coda
Gtr. 2: w/ Riff D
Gtrs. 3 & 4: w/ Rhy. Fig. 3
Gtr. 5: w/ Riff C
E5 D5/E E5 C
mm, hm, mm, hm.
Gtr. 5: w/ Fill 1
G5
Yeah, be my sav -

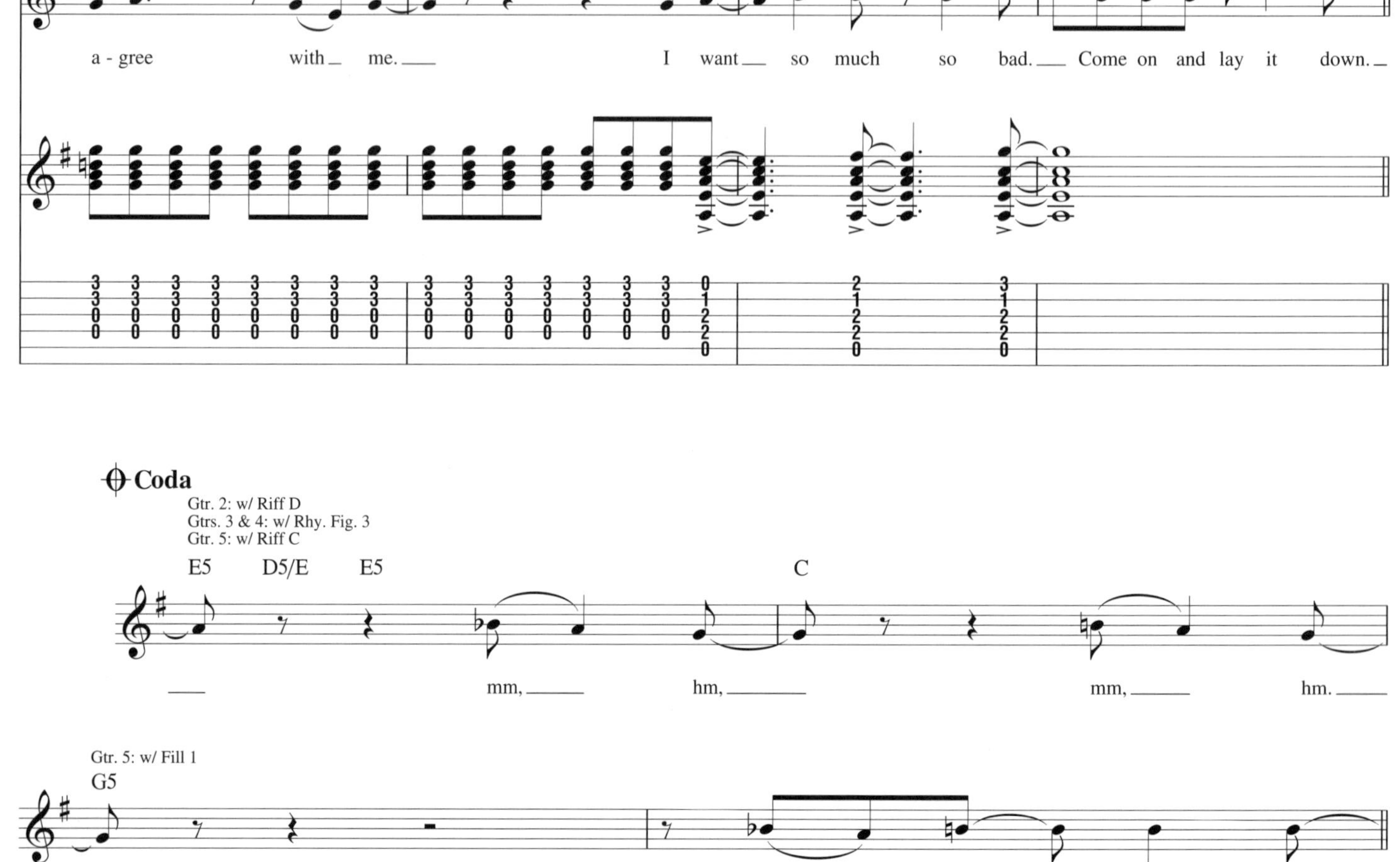

Bridge

Half-time feel

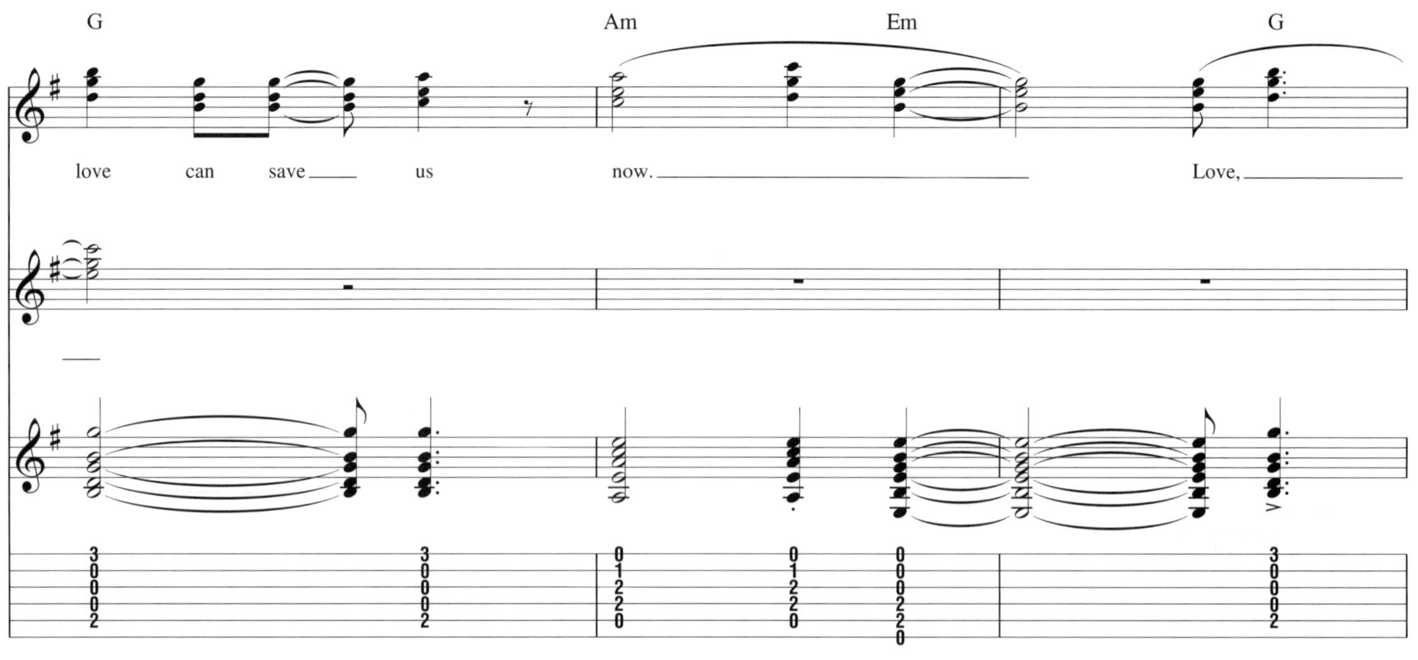
G
Am
Em
G
love can save us now.
Love,
3
0
0
0
2
3
0
0
0
2
0
1
2
2
0
0
1
2
2
0
0
0
0
2
2
0
3
0
0
0
2

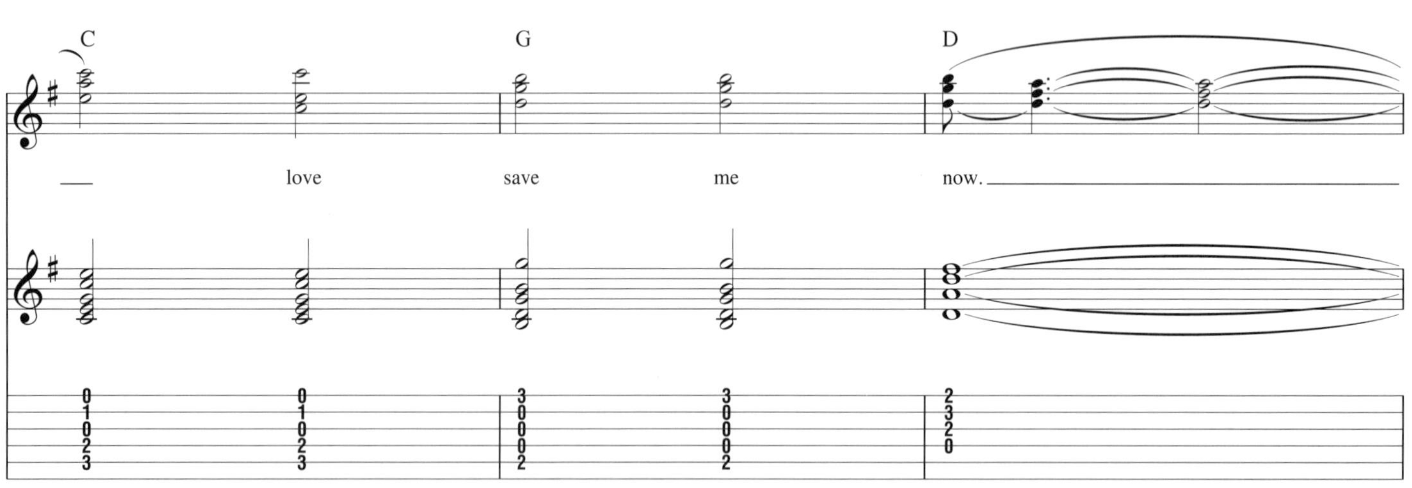
C
G
D
love save me now.
0
1
0
2
3
0
1
0
2
3
3
0
0
0
2
3
0
0
0
2
2
3
2
0

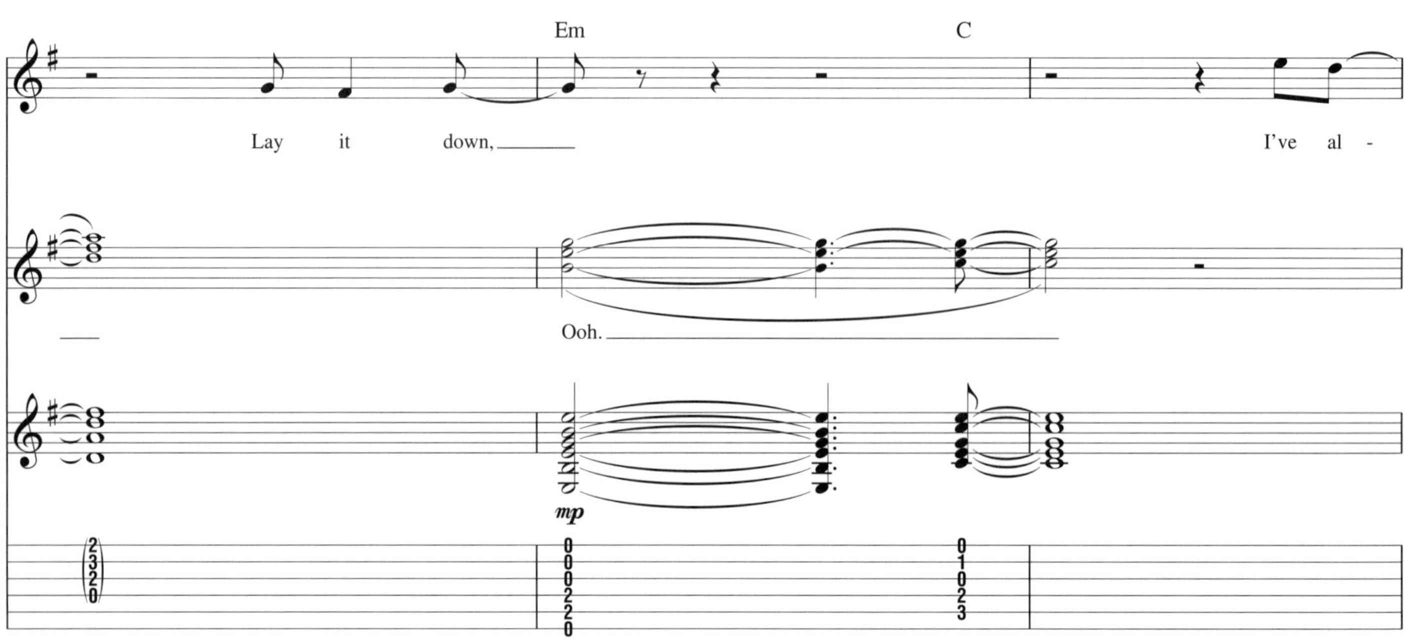
Em
C
Lay it down,
I've al -
Ooh.
mp
2
3
2
0
0
0
0
0
2
2
0
0
1
0
2
3

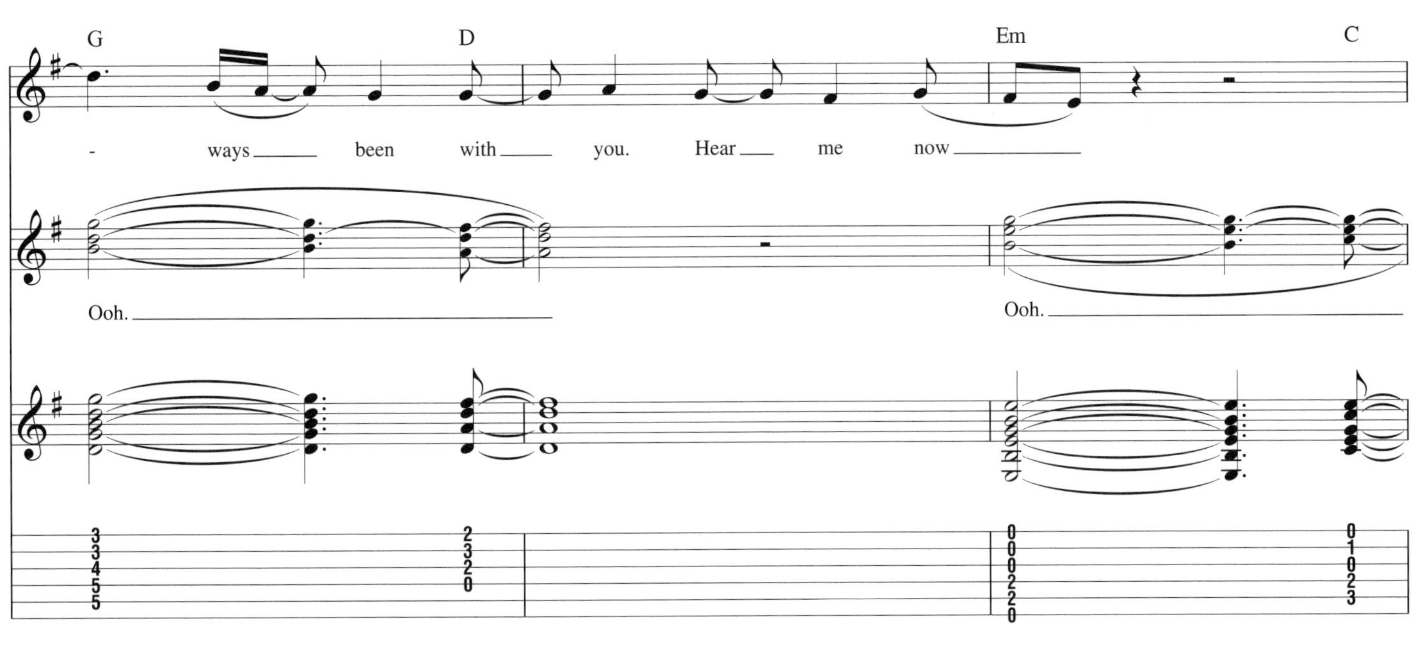
G
D
Em
C
- ways been with you. Hear me now
Ooh.
Ooh.

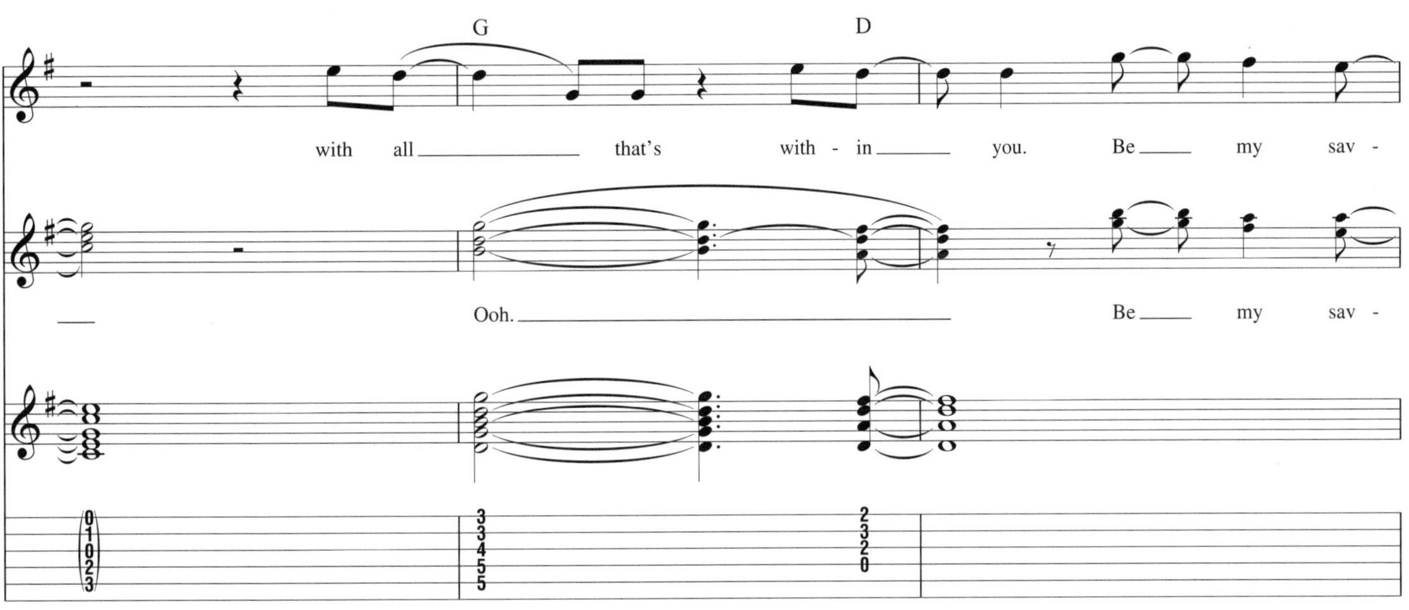
G
D
with all that's with - in you. Be my sav -
Ooh.
Be my sav -

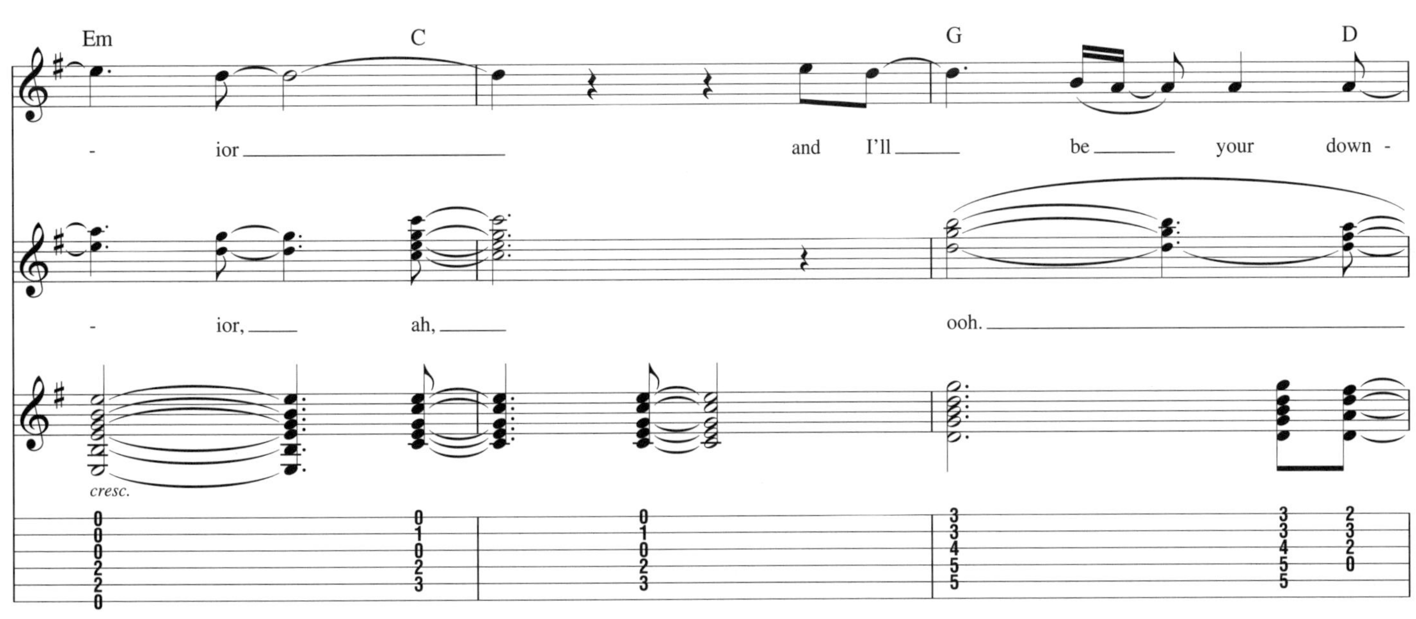
Em
C
G
D
- ior and I'll be your down -
- ior, ah,
ooh.
cresc.

Outro
End half-time feel
Gtr. 1 tacet
Dsus4
D
Em
C
C7
N.C.
- fall. Mm, hm, mm, hm, mm, hm.
Voc. Fig. 1
Ah.
Gtrs. 3 & 4
G
D
Bkgd. Voc.: w/ Voc. Fig. 1 (till fade)
Em
C
End Voc. Fig. 1
Ah.
C7
N.C.
G
D
Dsus4
D
Dsus2
Now I'm back
Gtrs. 3 & 4
Gtr. 5

Gtr. 5: w/ Riff B
Em C C7 N.C.
Gtr. 5: w/ Riff C (till fade)
G D
on my own. Lift my feet. Feel like they're made of stone.
Gtrs. 3 & 4
Dsus4 D Dsus2 Em C C7
Man, I make you go where I go. It's kill - ing me.
Rhy. Fig. 4
G D Dsus4 D Dsus2
Gtrs. 3 & 4: w/ Rhy. Fig. 4 (till fade)
Em C
Can I take you home? Yeah, I'm com - ing home on my back.
End Rhy. Fig. 4
C7 G D Dsus4 D Dsus2
Is it me, or did she paint it black? She sings, oh, oh, oh,
Em C C7 G D
oh, oh, oh, oh, oh, oh, let me be your down -

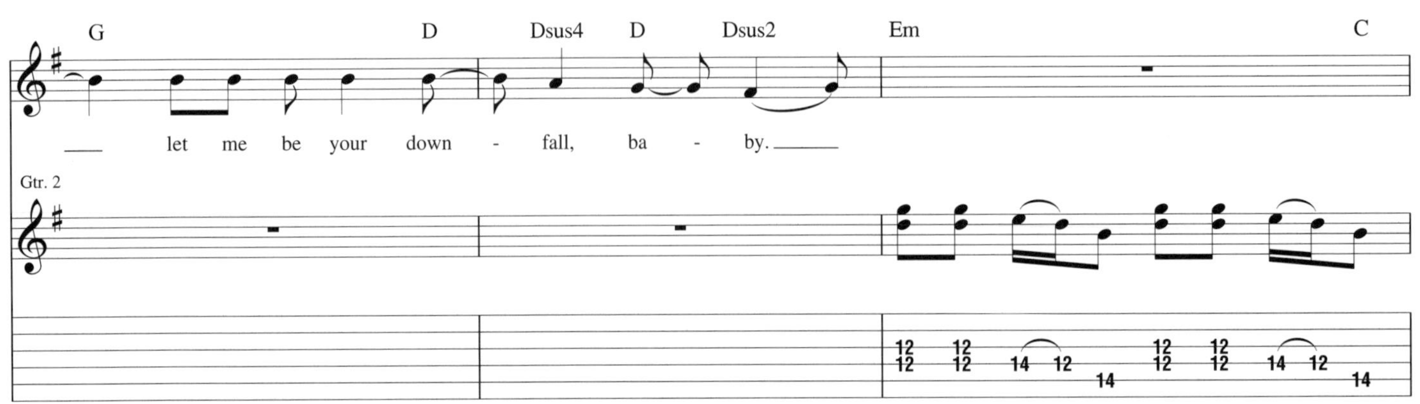

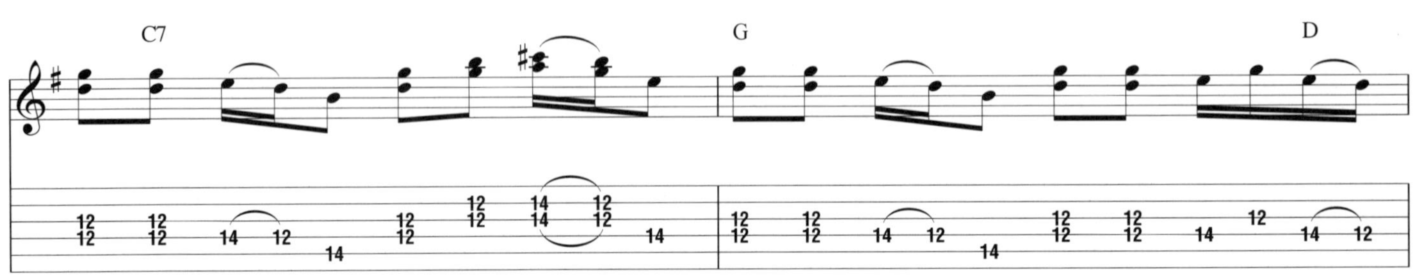

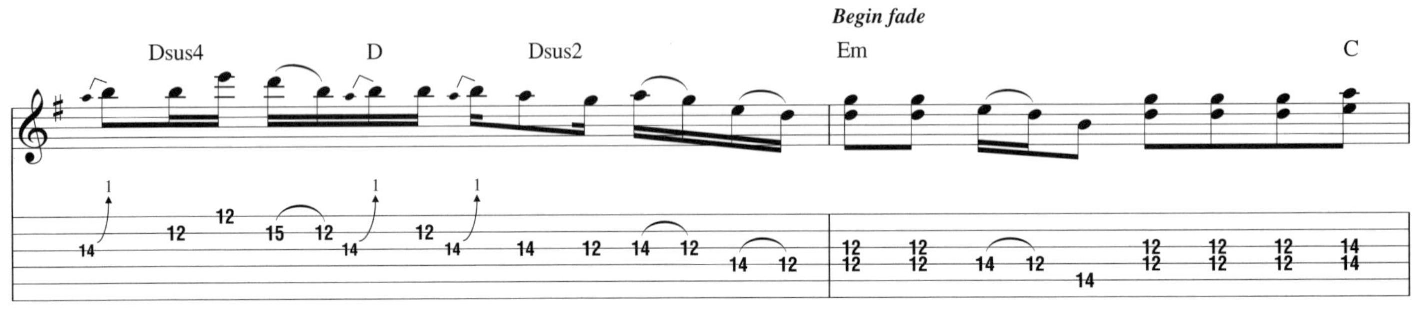

Fade out

Gtr. 2: w/ Riff D

Em C C7 G D Dsus4 D Dsus2

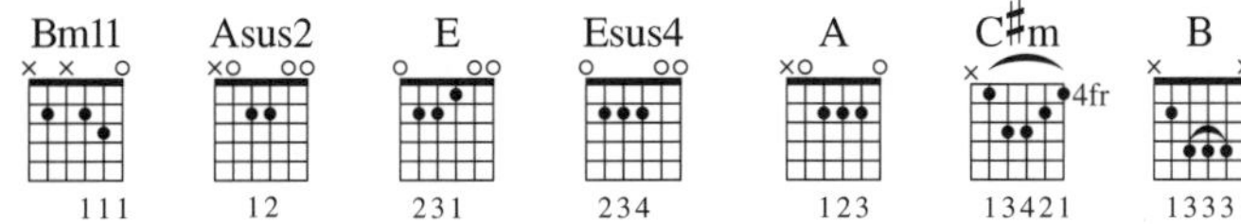

Soul

Words and Music by Rob Thomas, Paul Doucette and Kyle Cook

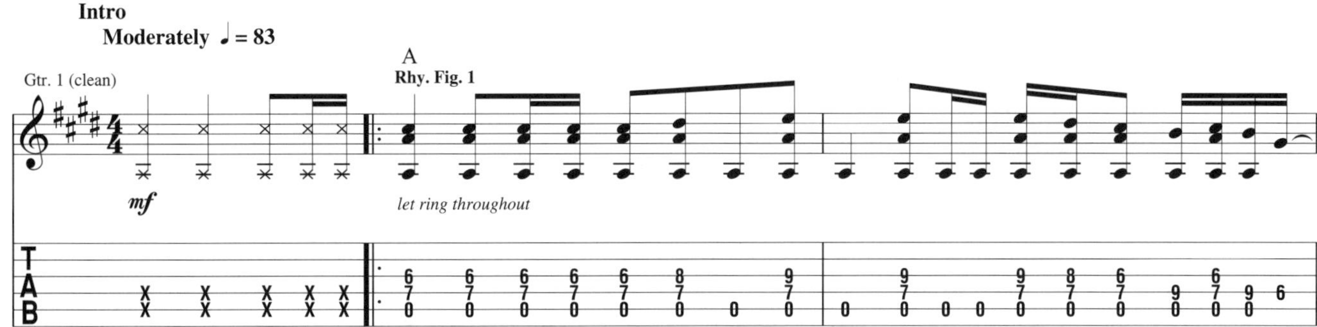

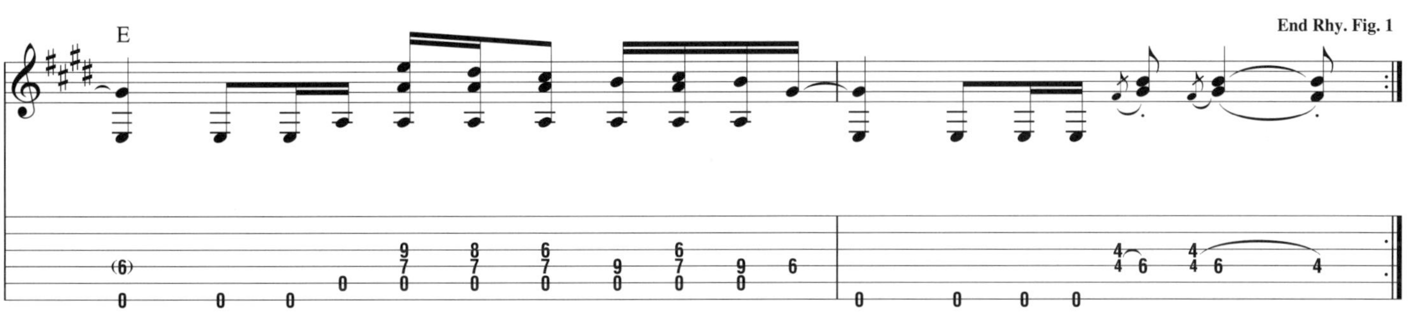

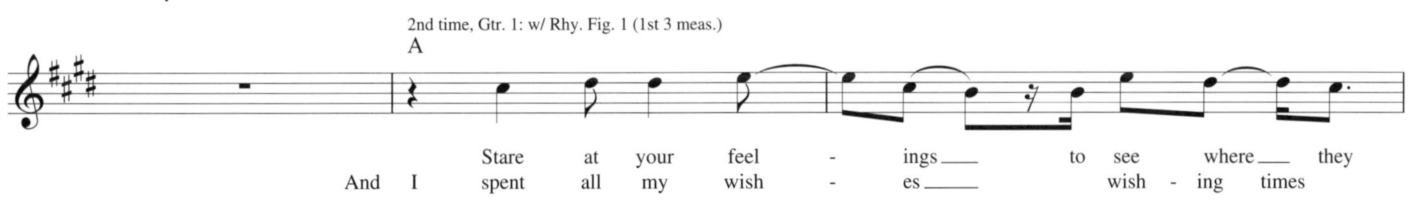

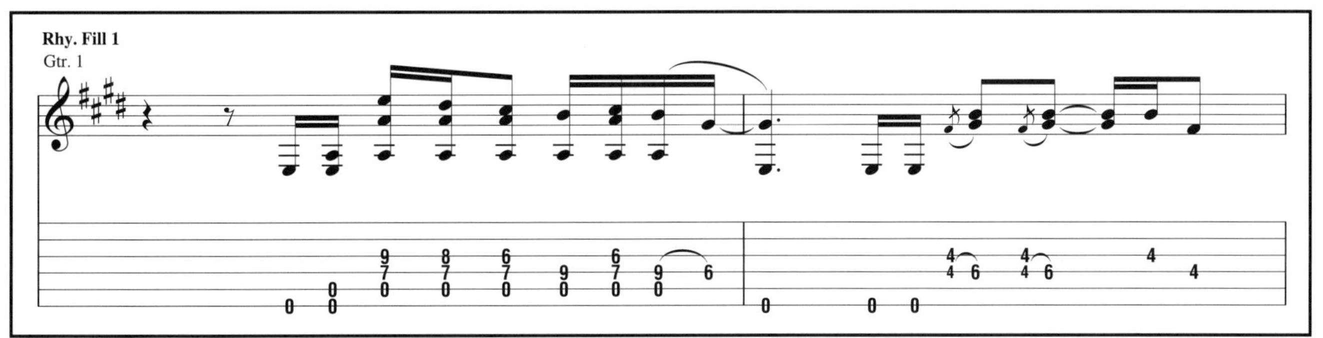

E
2nd time, Gtr. 1: w/ Rhy. Fill 2
Pre-Chorus
Bm11
*Gtr. 2 (acous.)
mf
end.
were good, when I still could.
You're wait - ing here for some - one else to break
Wait a-round here for some - one else to take
Gtr. 1
w/ tremolo
*Two gtrs. arr. for one.
Asus2
E
Esus4 E
you from the in - side.
me past the good side.
let ring
tremolo off
Bm11
Asus2
You've been so com - posed.
You've been here so long now.
We all know there's
w/ tremolo
tremolo off
let ring
Rhy. Fill 2
Gtr. 1

Chorus
E
A
Rhy. Fig. 2A
Gtr. 2
al - ways some - thing tear - ing you a - part.
Gtr. 1
Rhy. Fig. 2
Gtr. 3
(elec.)
Rhy. Fig. 2B
E
A E
End Rhy. Fig. 2A
It's
End Rhy. Fig. 2
End Rhy. Fig. 2B

Gtrs. 1 & 2: w/ Rhy. Figs. 2A & 2B

E A

al - ways so much long - er than you count -

Gtr. 1

E A E

- ed on.

And it

C#m A E A E

Rhy. Fig. 3A

Gtr. 2

hits you so much hard - er than you thought.

Gtr. 1

Rhy. Fig. 3

sim.

Gtr. 3

Rhy. Fig. 3B

1.

B A E

End Rhy. Fig. 3A

But you don't wor - ry, you don't wor - ry__ 'cause you've got soul.__

End Rhy. Fig. 3

9 9 9 9 9 9 9 9
X X X X X X X X
7 7 7 7 7 7 7 7

16 14
X X
14 12

(14)
(12)

End Rhy. Fig. 3B

(2)
(0)

4 2
2 0

2 2 4
0 0 2
2
0

2.

ry__ 'cause dar - lin', you've__ got

(14) (14)
(12) (12)

(4)
(2)
(2)
(0)

(2)
(0)

2 0
4 3

Guitar Solo

Gtrs. 1 & 2 tacet

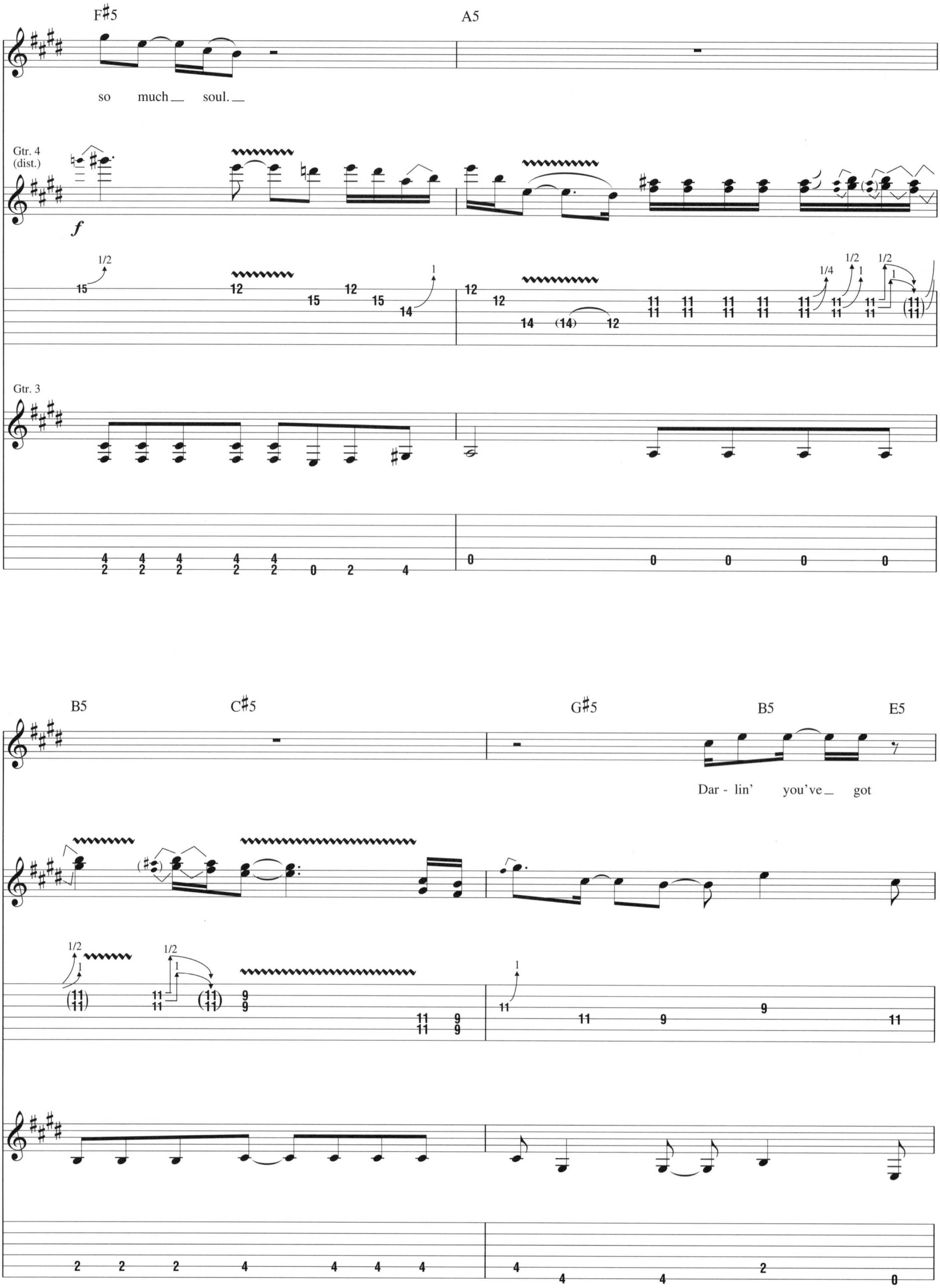

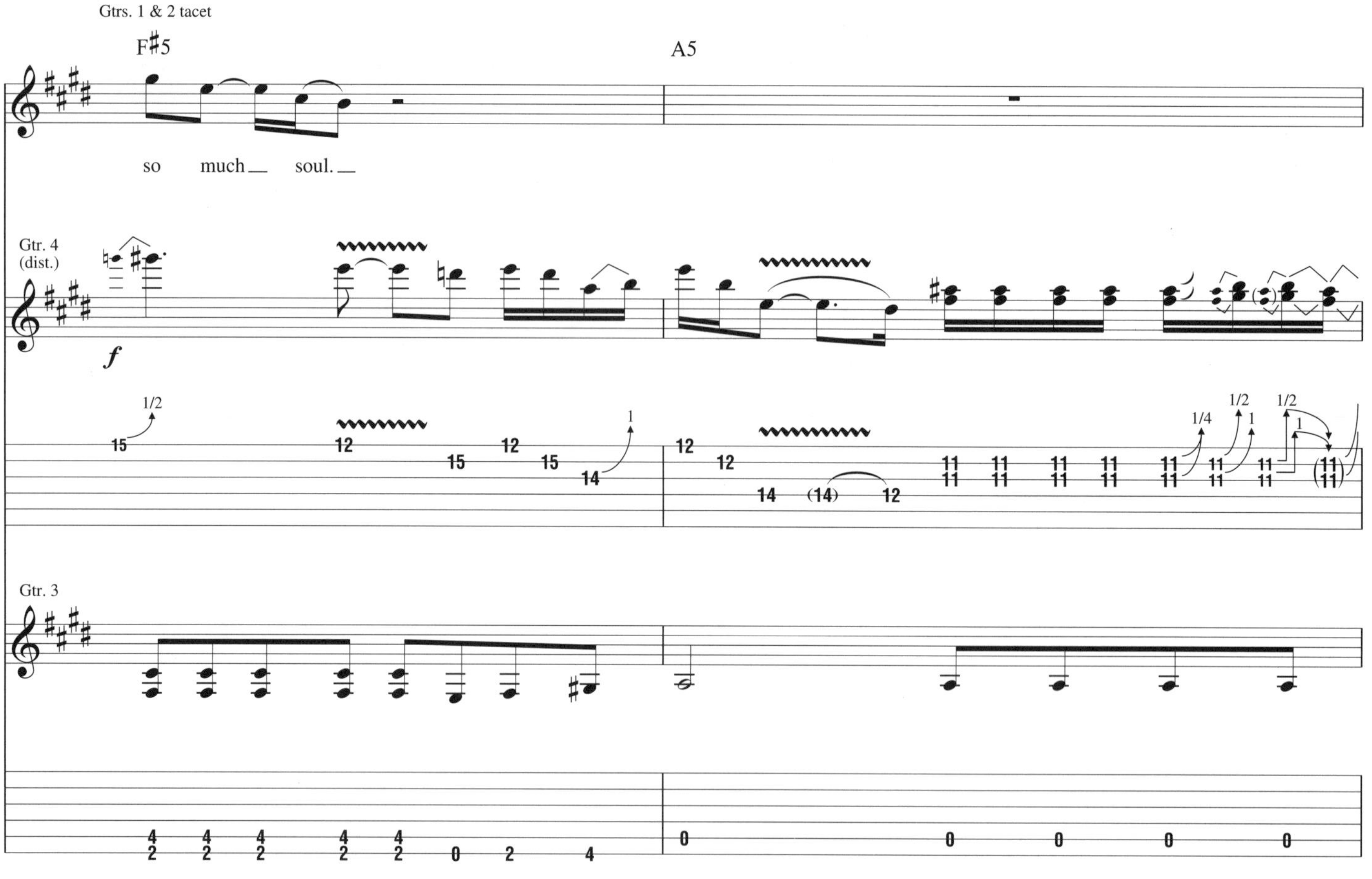

B5 C♯5 G♯5 B5 E5

Dar - lin' you've__ got

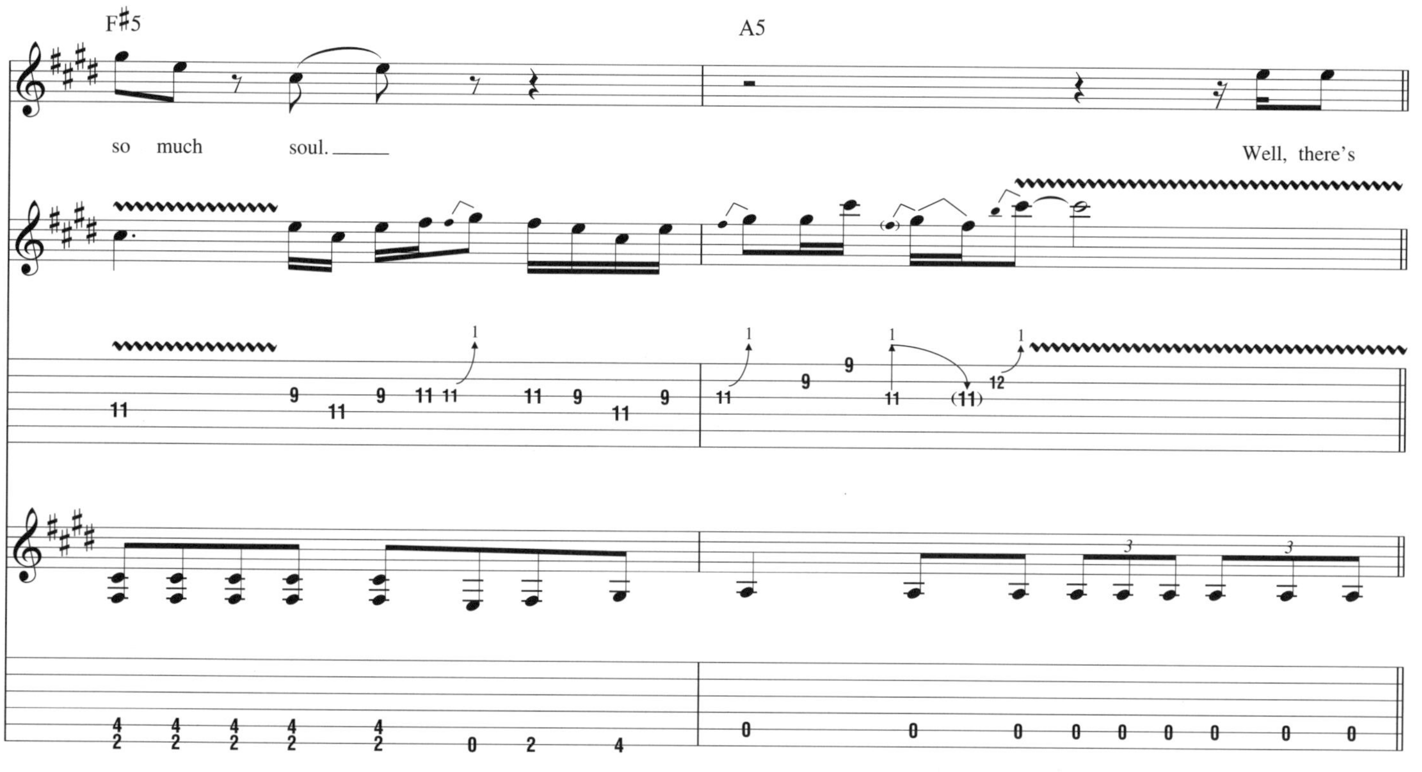
F♯5
A5
so much soul.
Well, there's

Outro-Chorus

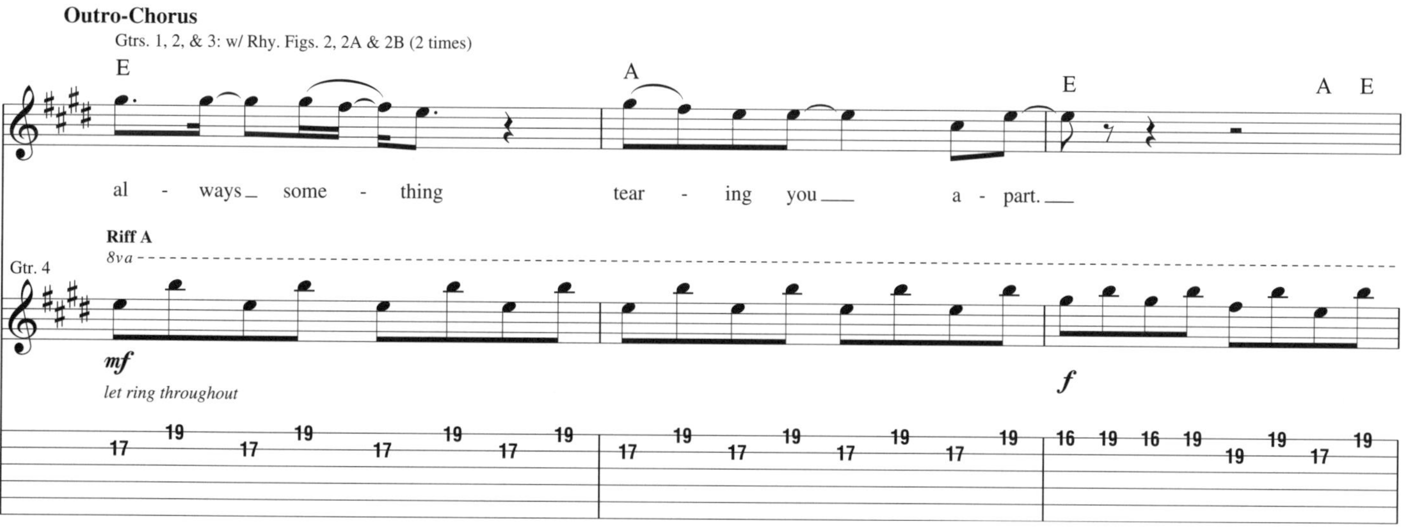
Gtrs. 1, 2, & 3: w/ Rhy. Figs. 2, 2A & 2B (2 times)
E
A
E
A E
al - ways some - thing tear - ing you a - part.
Riff A
8va
Gtr. 4
mf
let ring throughout
f

Gtr. 4: w/ Riff A
E
A
It's al - ways so much long - er than you count -
8va
End Riff A

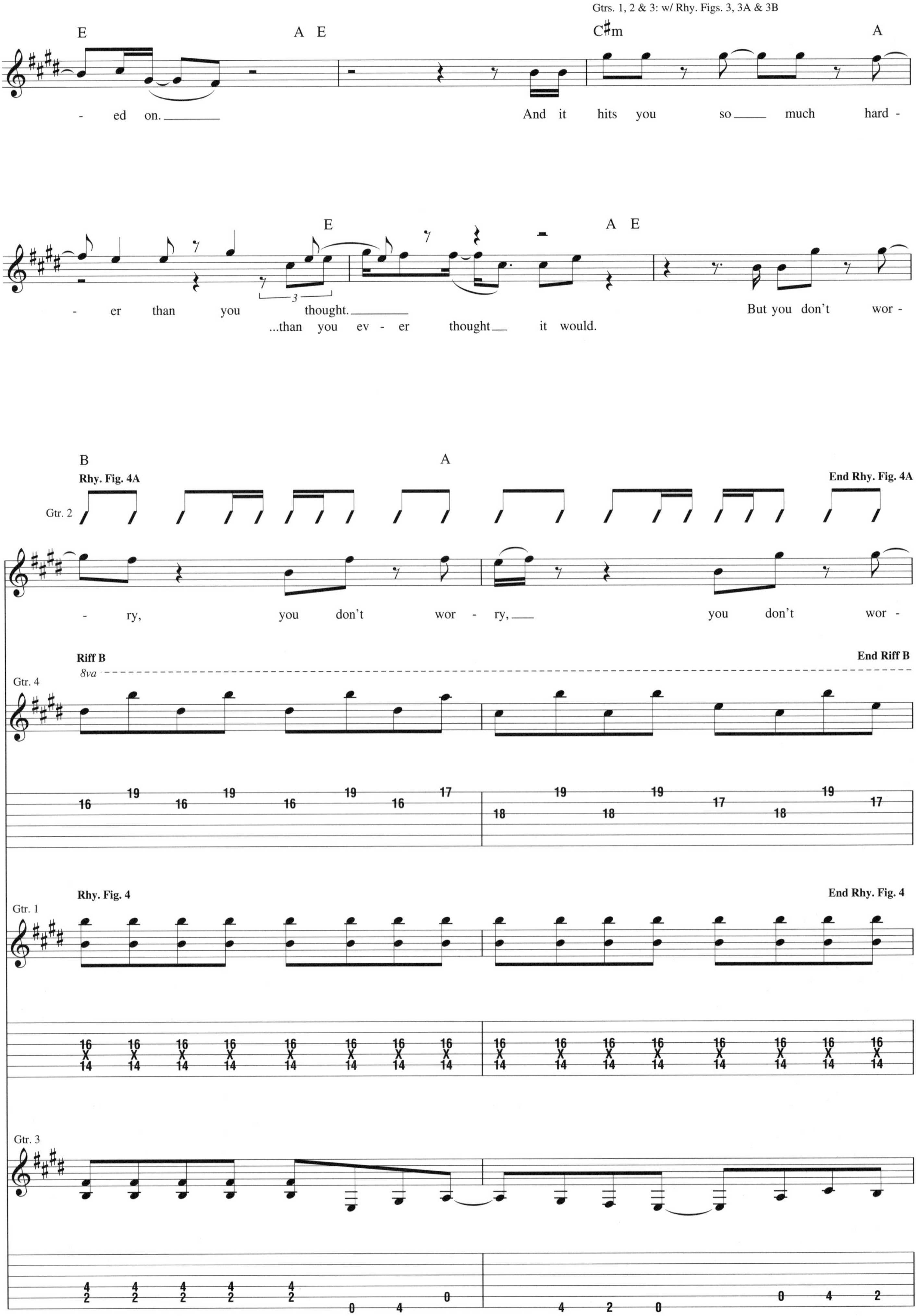

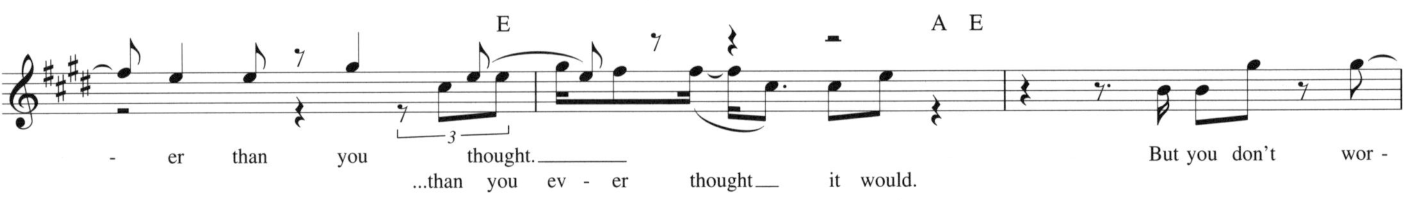

B A

Rhy. Fig. 4A

End Rhy. Fig. 4A

Gtr. 2

- ry, you don't wor - ry, you don't wor -

Riff B

End Riff B

8va

Gtr. 4

Rhy. Fig. 4

End Rhy. Fig. 4

Gtr. 1

Gtr. 3

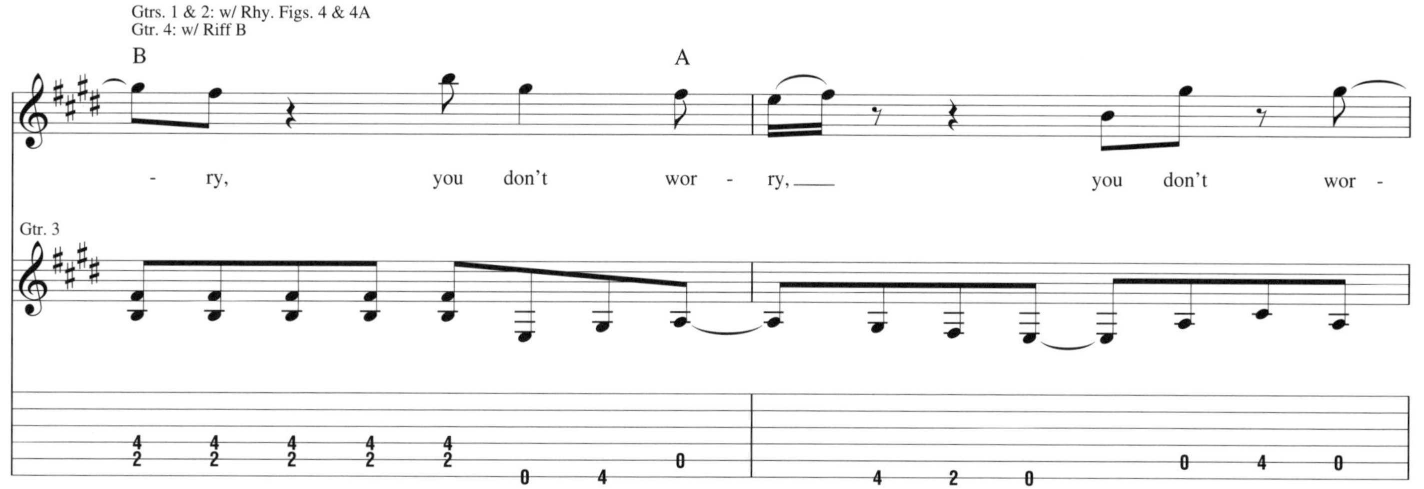

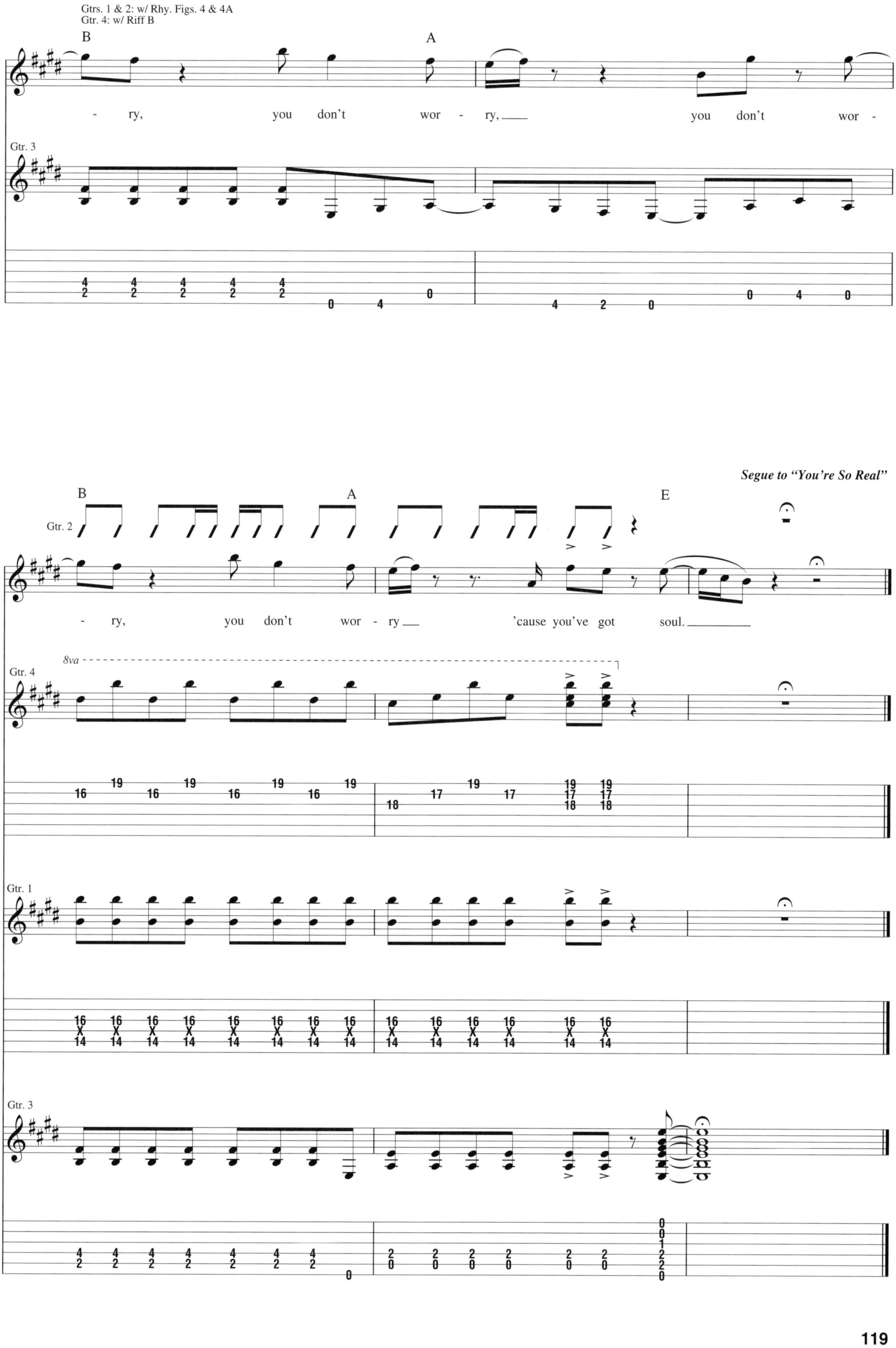

Segue to "You're So Real"

B A E

Gtr. 2

- ry, you don't wor - ry 'cause you've got soul.

8va

Gtr. 4

Gtr. 1

Gtr. 3

You're So Real

Words and Music by Rob Thomas

Intro
Moderately ♩ = 132
* F♯7
**Gtr. 1
Riff A
mf
T
A
B
2 4 2 4
2 4 2 4
2 4 2 4

*Chord symbols reflect implied harmony.

**Bass arr. for gtr.

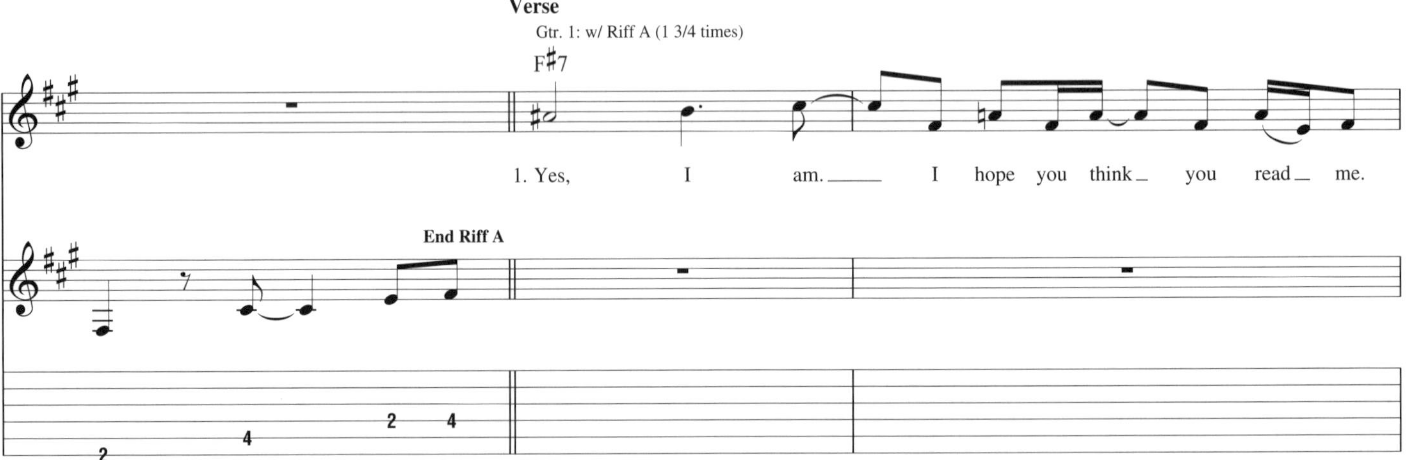
Verse
Gtr. 1: w/ Riff A (1 3/4 times)
F♯7
1. Yes, I am. I hope you think you read me.
End Riff A
2 4 2 4

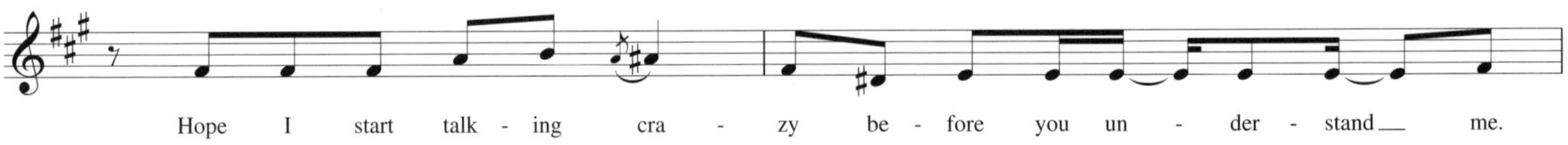
Hope I start talk - ing cra - zy be - fore you un - der - stand me.

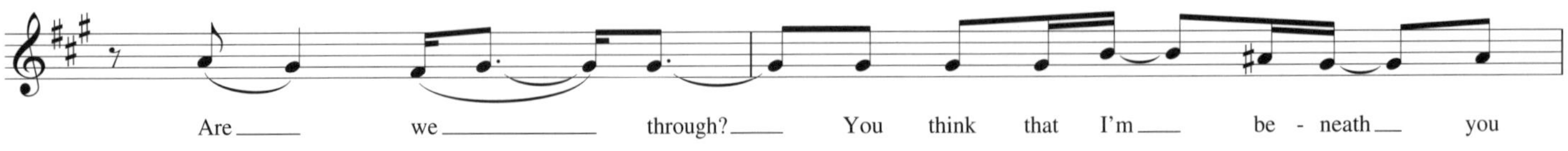
Are we through? You think that I'm be - neath you

but you like the things that I do. Wrap them up and take them with you.

Interlude
F♯7
*Gtr. 2 (elec.)
f
w/ slight dist.
*Two gtrs. arr. for one.

Verse
F♯7
2. I'm al - right, hope I can sleep for one night.
Riff B
mf
P.M.
P.M.

If not to cool my in - sides, may - be to calm my back side.
End Riff B
P.M.
P.M.

Gtr. 2: w/ Riff B
Rain on me. I got a weak - ness in me

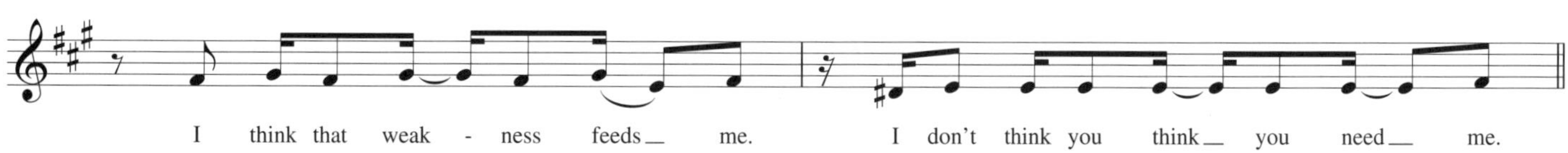

I think that weak - ness feeds me. I don't think you think you need me.

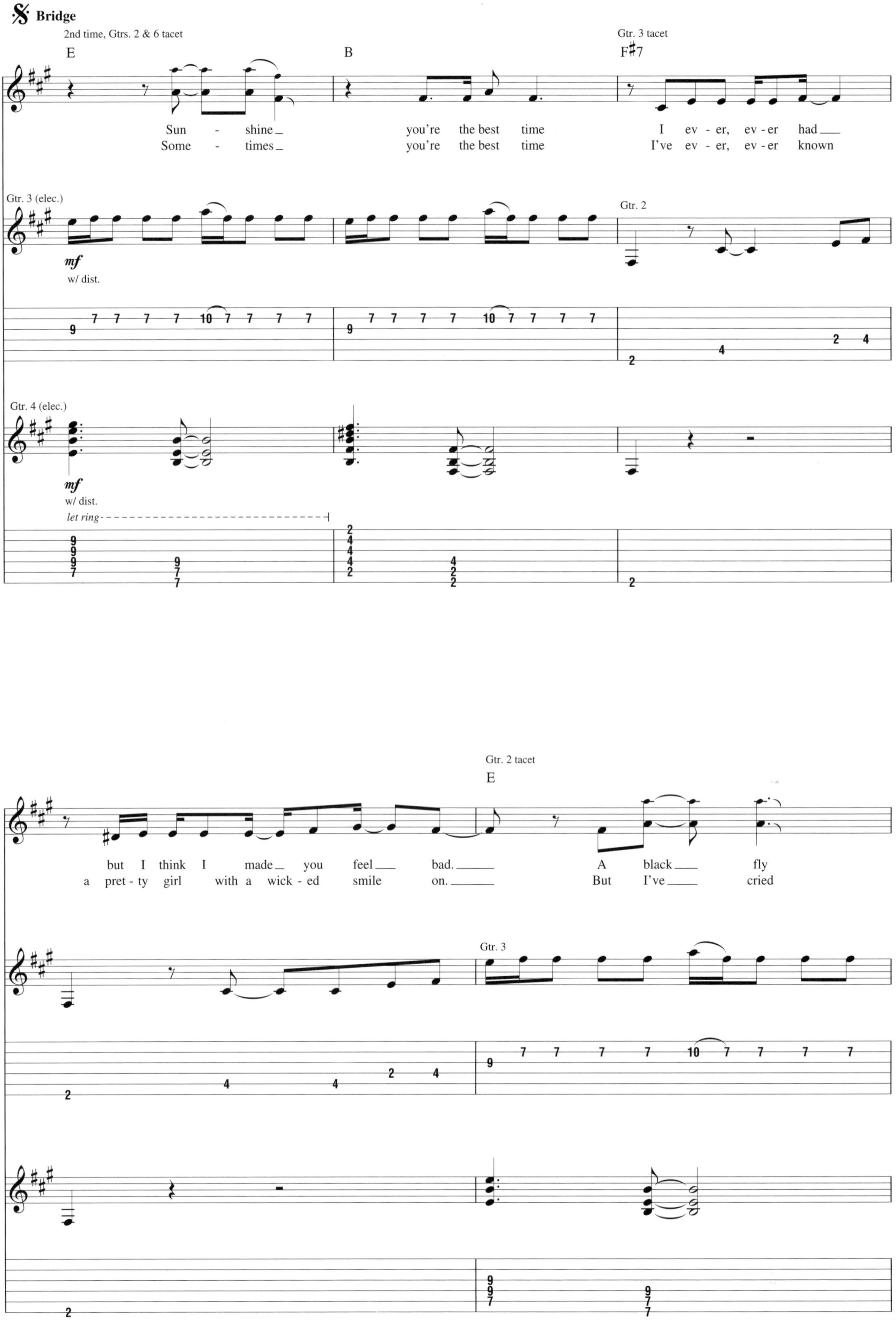

𝄋 Bridge

2nd time, Gtrs. 2 & 6 tacet

Gtr. 3 tacet

E B F♯7

Sun - shine you're the best time I ev - er, ev - er had
Some - times you're the best time I've ev - er, ev - er known

Gtr. 3 (elec.)

mf

w/ dist.

Gtr. 2

Gtr. 4 (elec.)

mf

w/ dist.

let ring

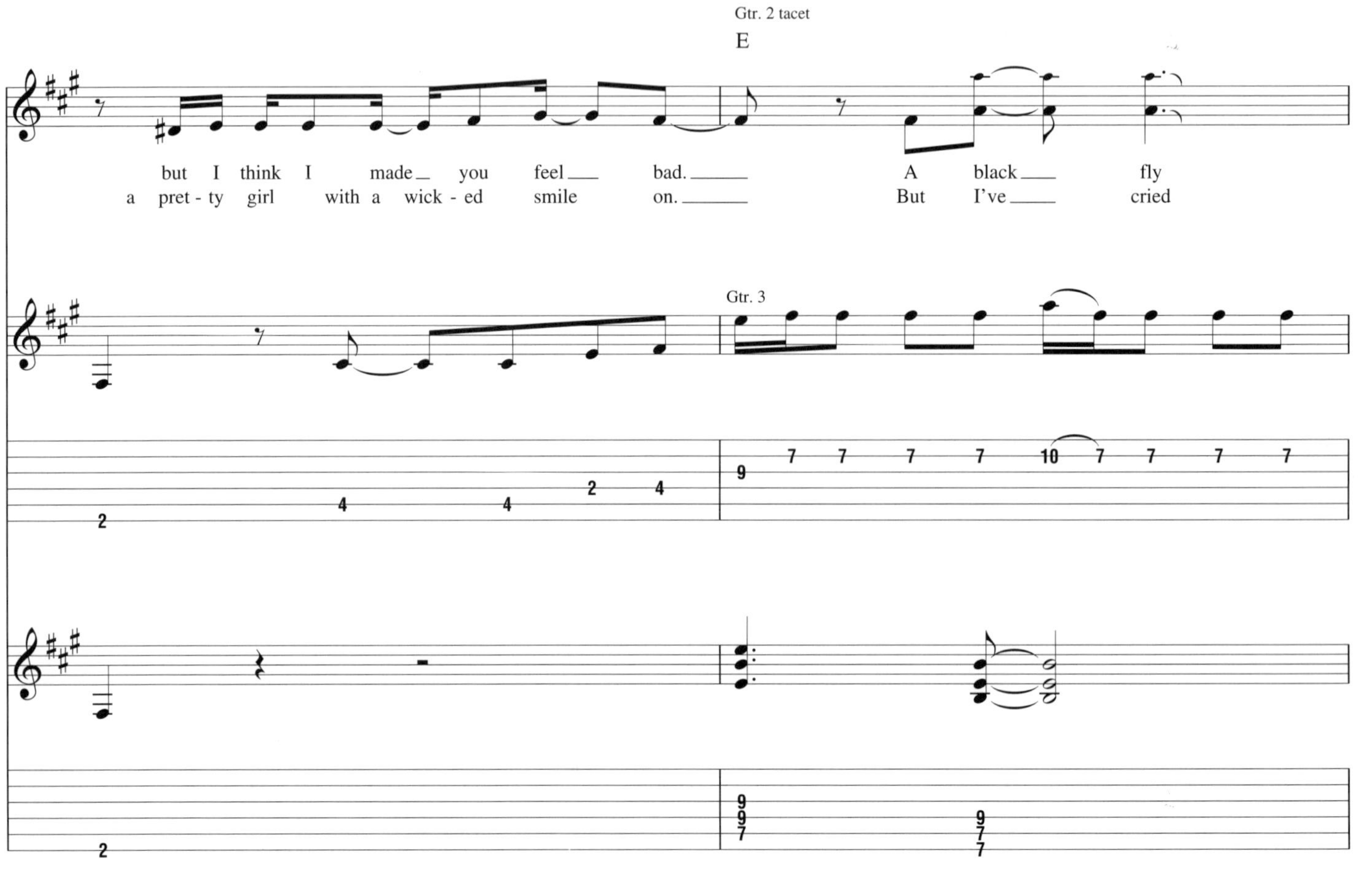

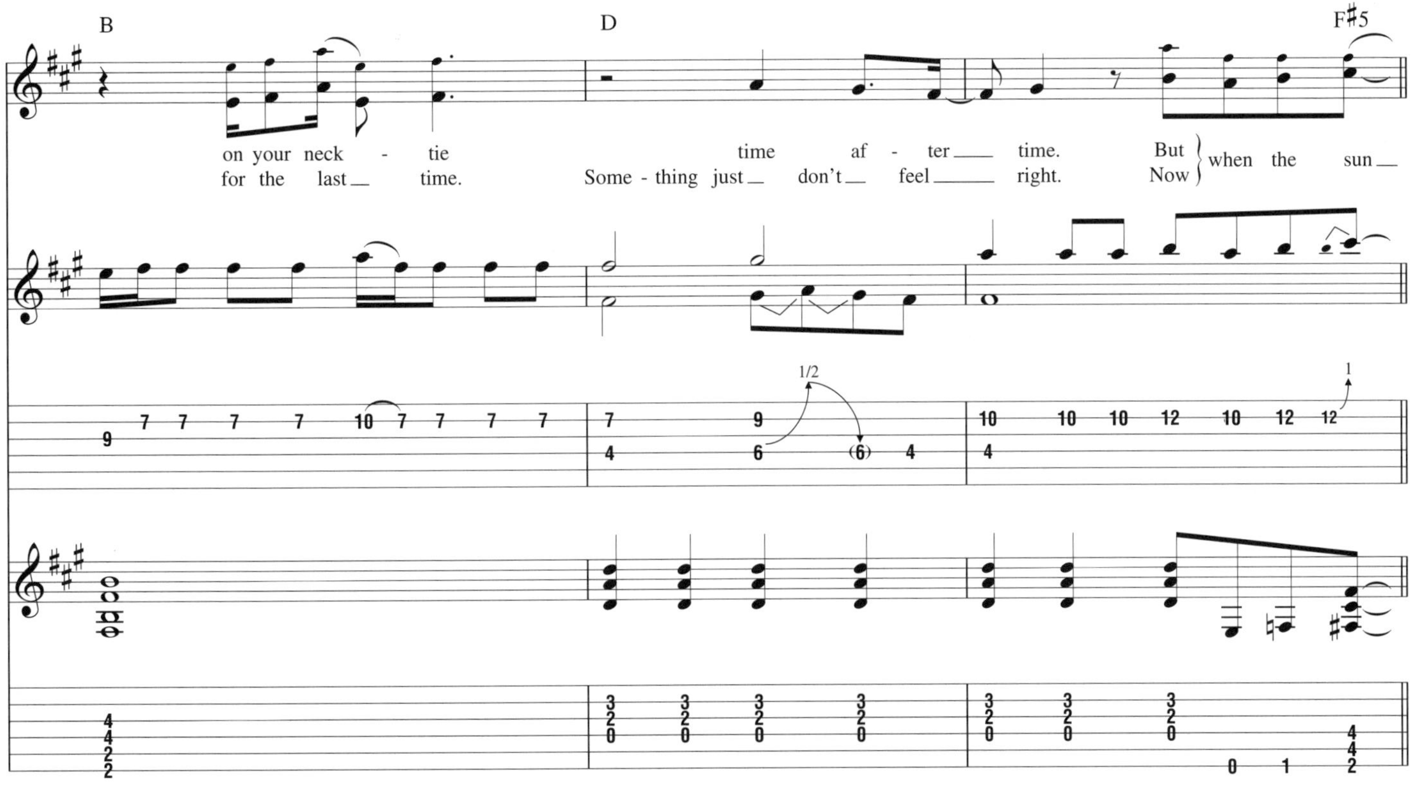

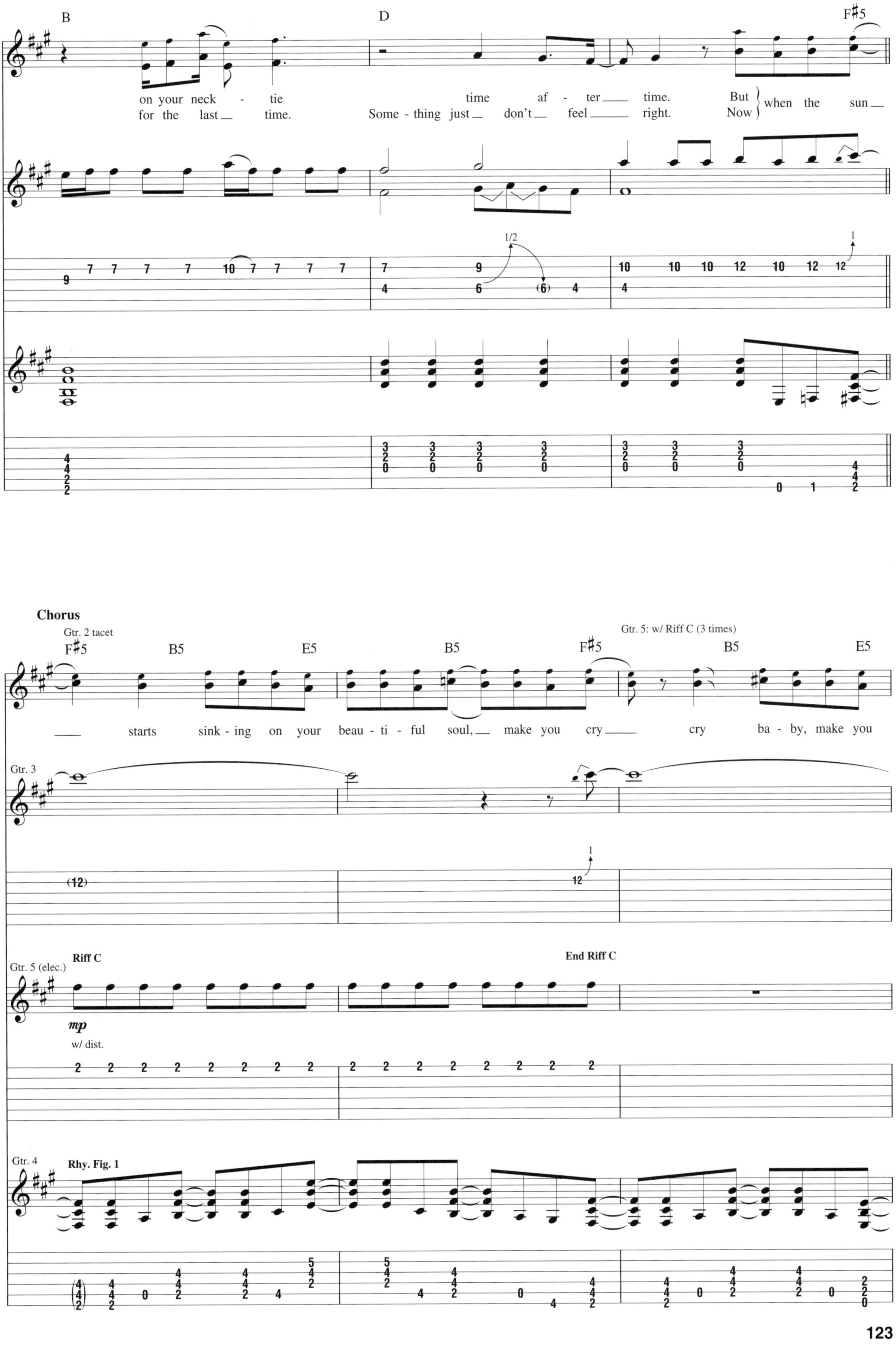

Chorus

Gtr. 2 tacet

Gtr. 5: w/ Riff C (3 times)

F♯5 B5 E5 B5 F♯5 B5 E5

starts sink - ing on your beau - ti - ful soul, make you cry cry ba - by, make you

Gtr. 3

Gtr. 5 (elec.)

Riff C

End Riff C

mp

w/ dist.

Gtr. 4

Rhy. Fig. 1

B5 F♯5 B5 E5 B5 E5

feel so cold. Don't you know it's al - right? Some - times you just got to show how you feel

Gtr. 3

Gtr. 4

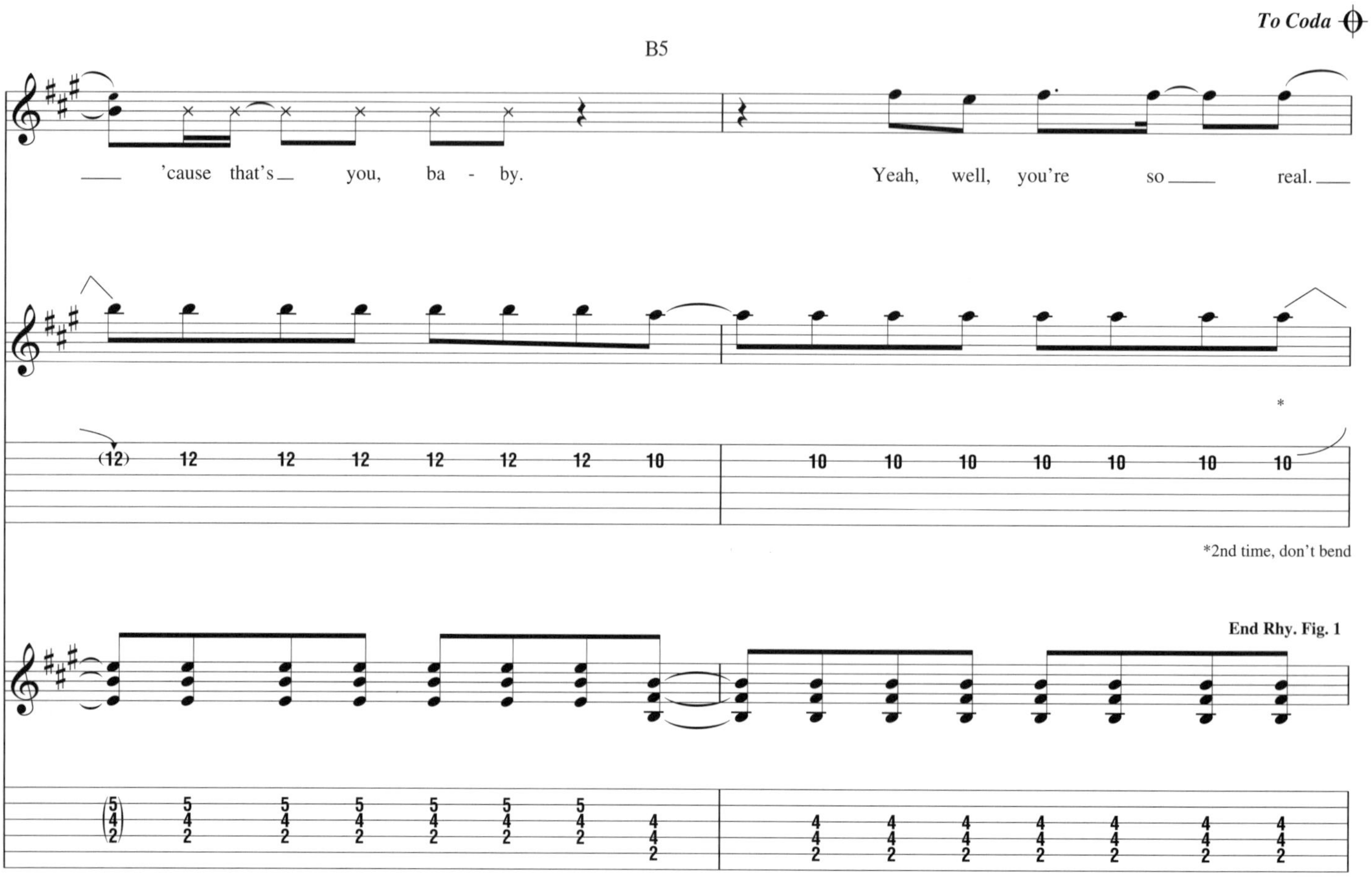

To Coda

B5

'cause that's you, ba - by. Yeah, well, you're so real.

*2nd time, don't bend

End Rhy. Fig. 1

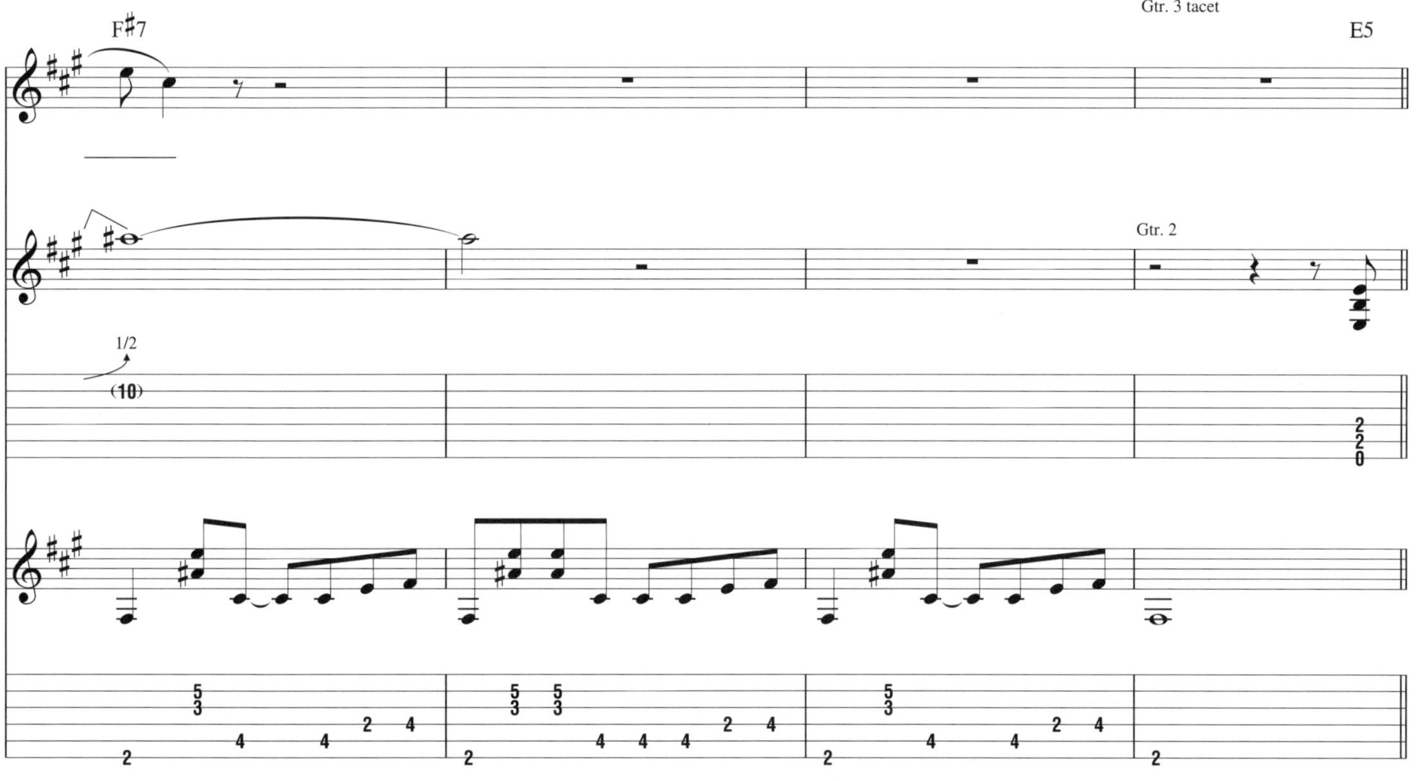
Gtr. 3 tacet
F#7
E5
Gtr. 2
1/2
(10)

Verse

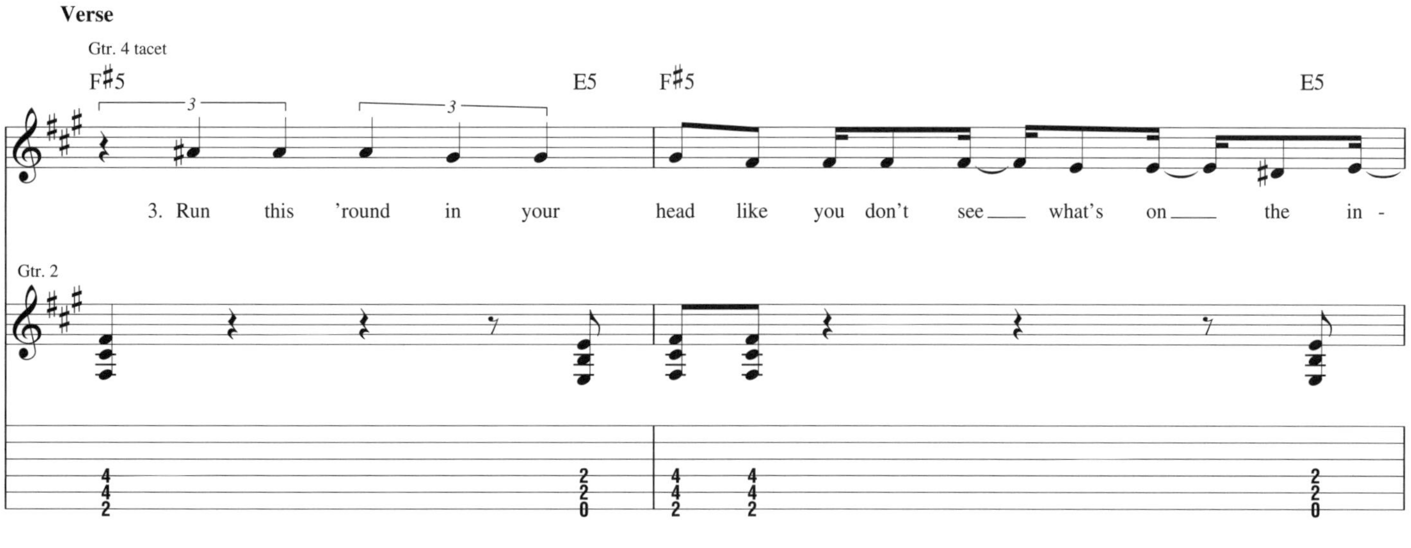
Gtr. 4 tacet
F#5
E5
F#5
E5
3. Run this 'round in your head like you don't see what's on the in -
Gtr. 2

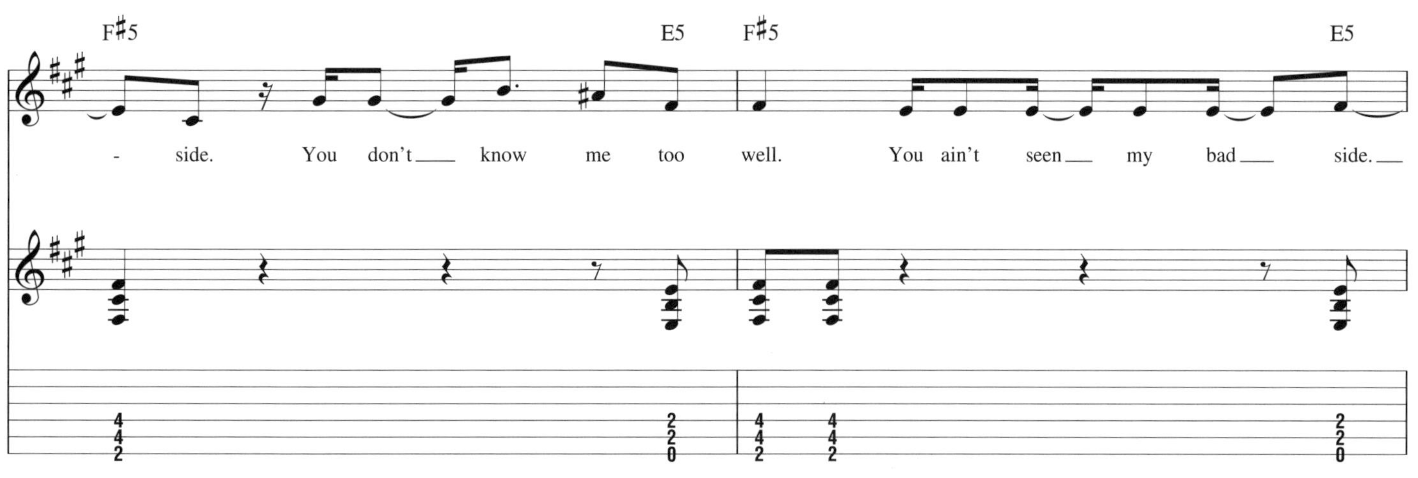
F#5
E5
F#5
E5
- side. You don't know me too well. You ain't seen my bad side.

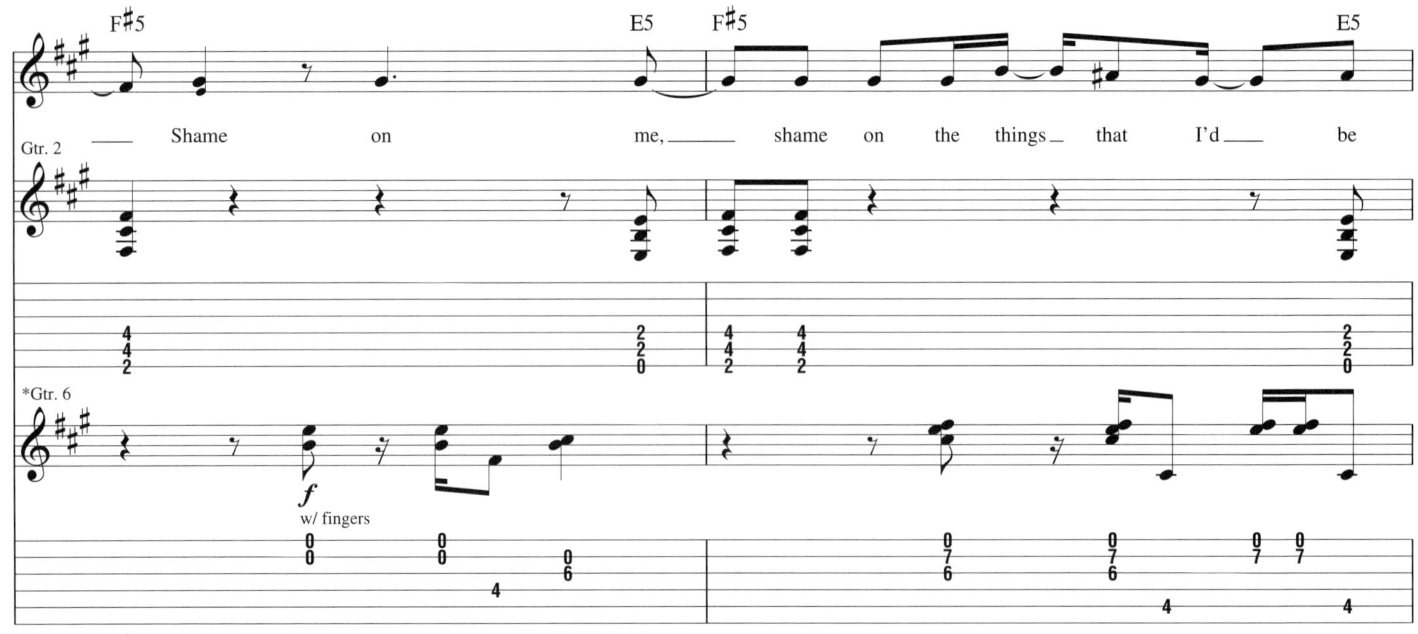

*Clavinet arr. for gtr.

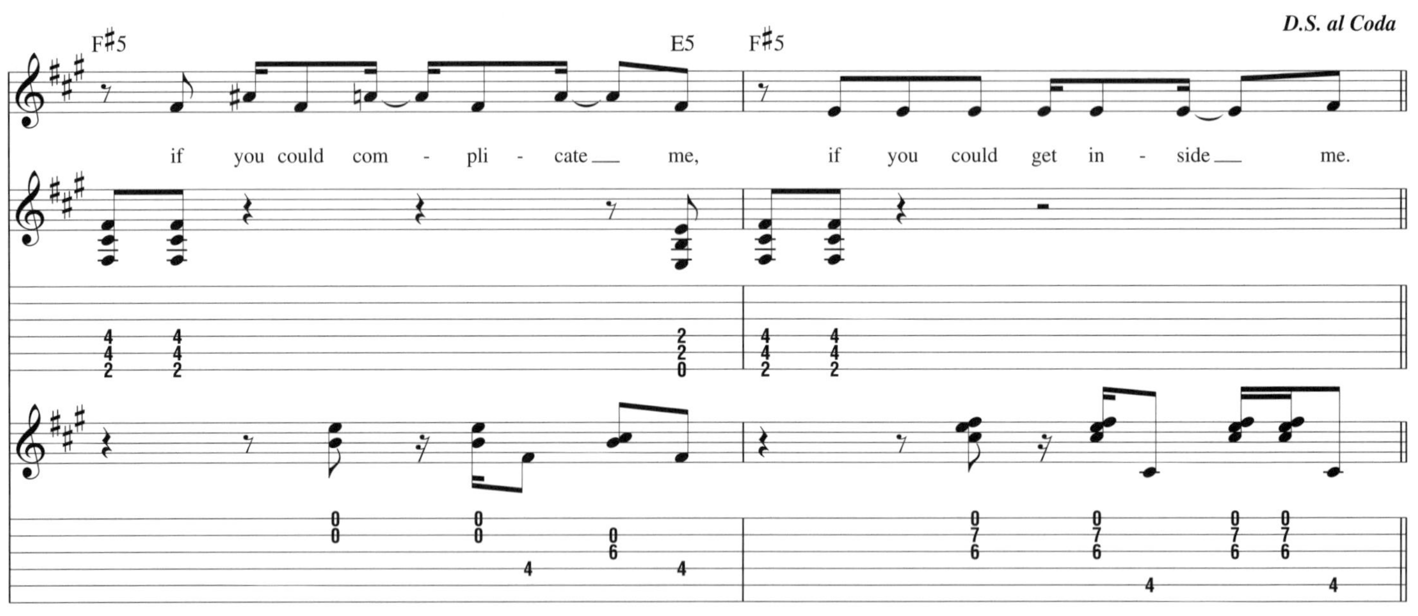

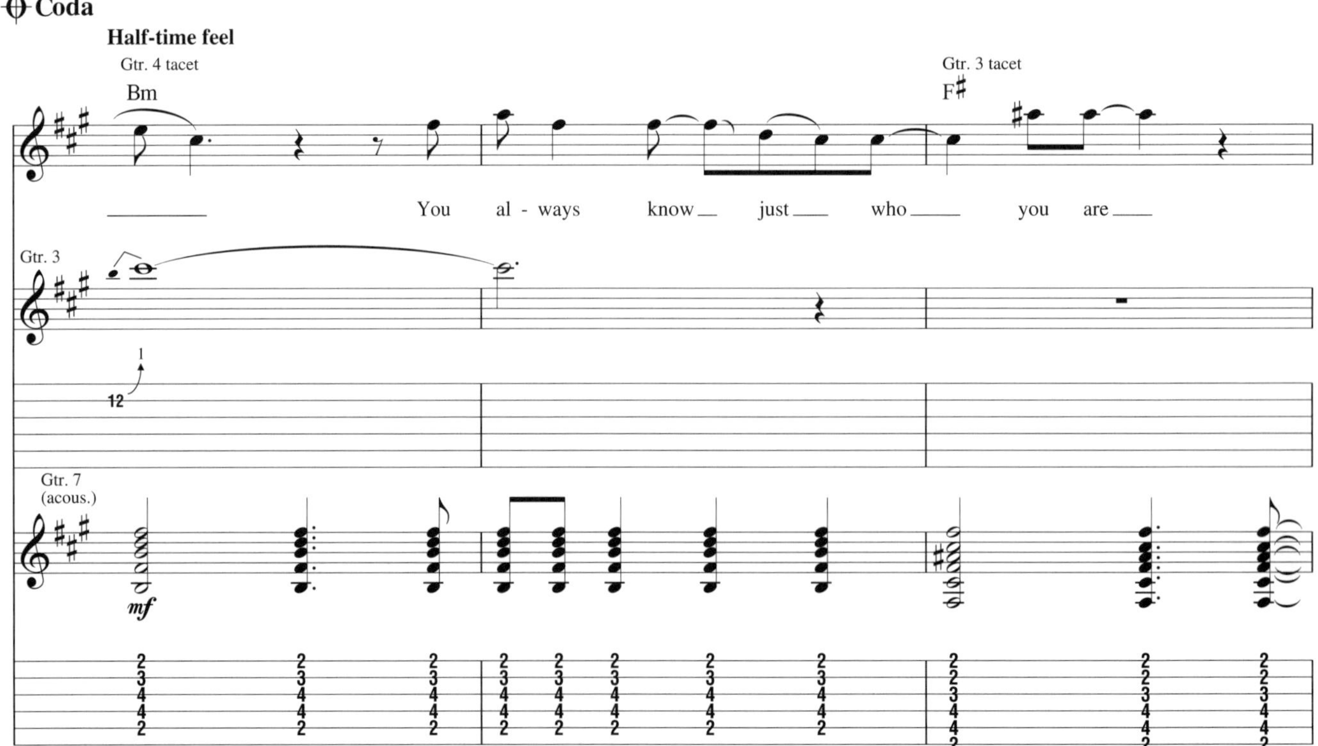

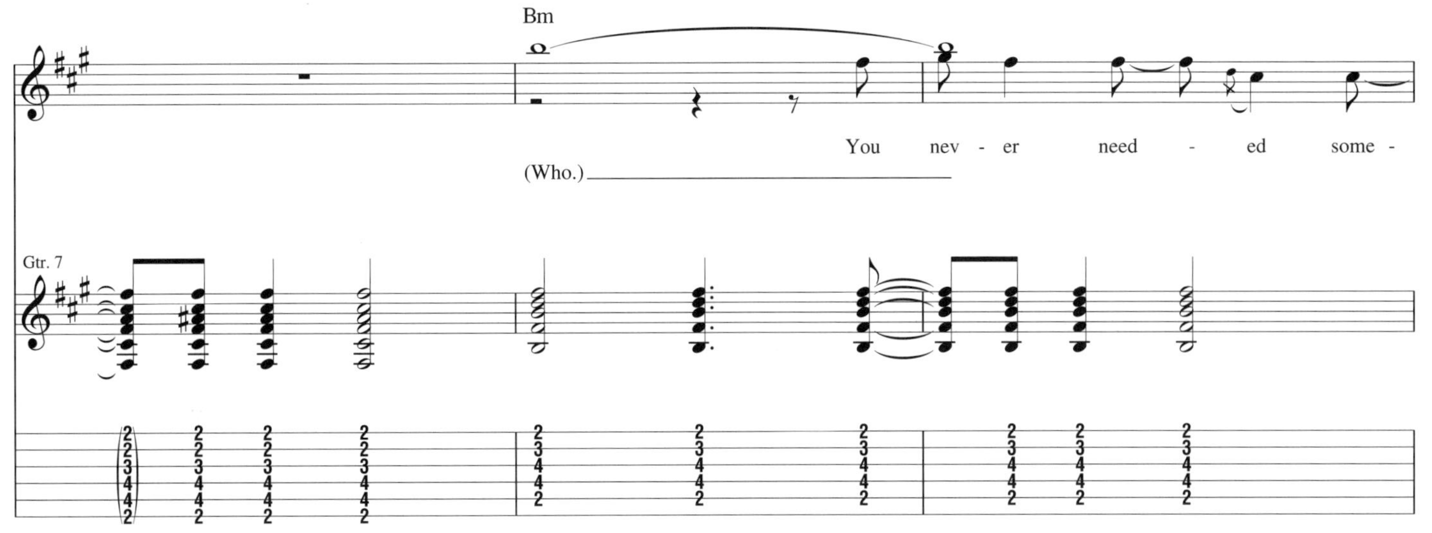
Bm
You nev - er need - ed some -
(Who.)
Gtr. 7

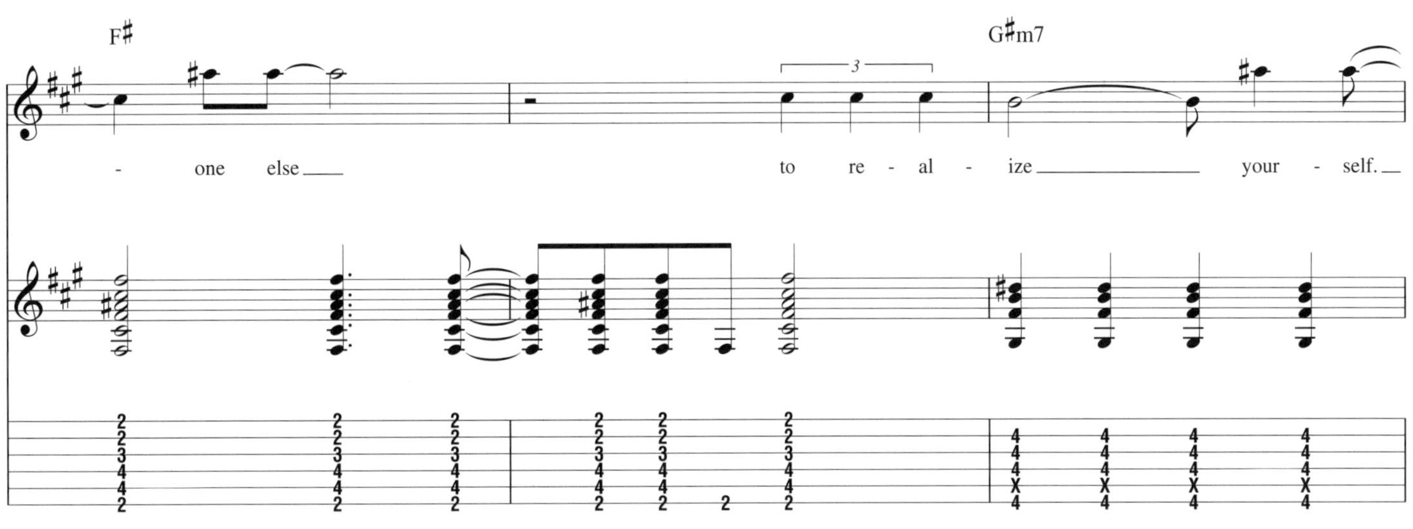
F♯
G♯m7
- one else
to re - al - ize
your - self.

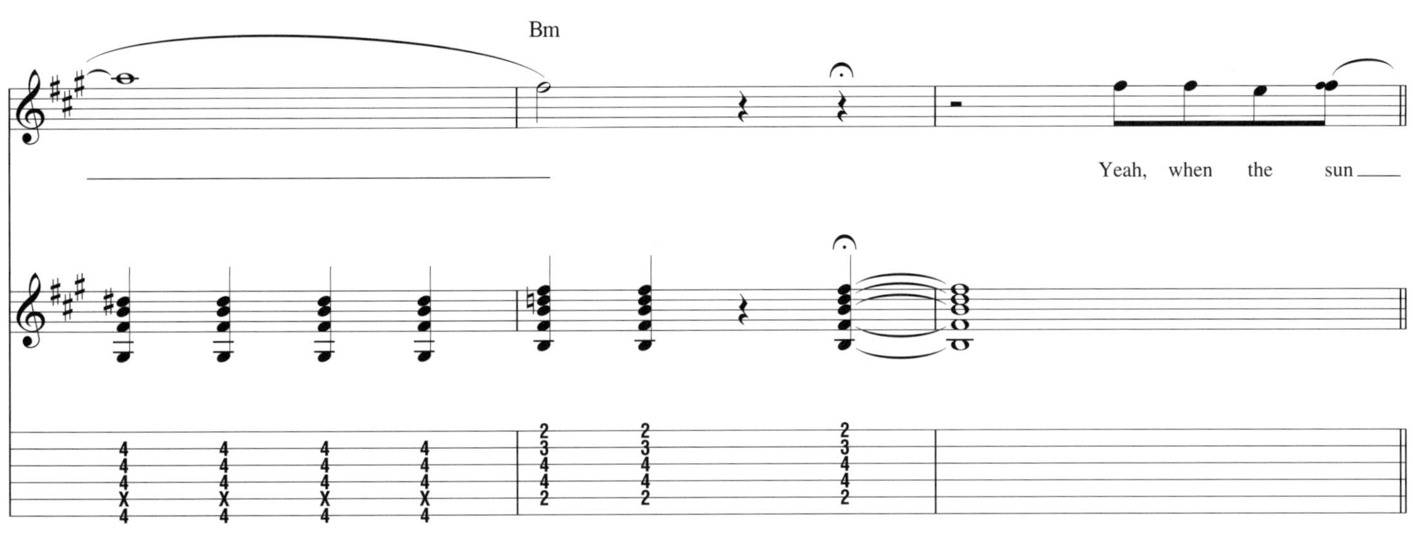
Bm
Yeah, when the sun

Chorus
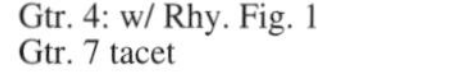
Gtr. 4: w/ Rhy. Fig. 1
Gtr. 7 tacet
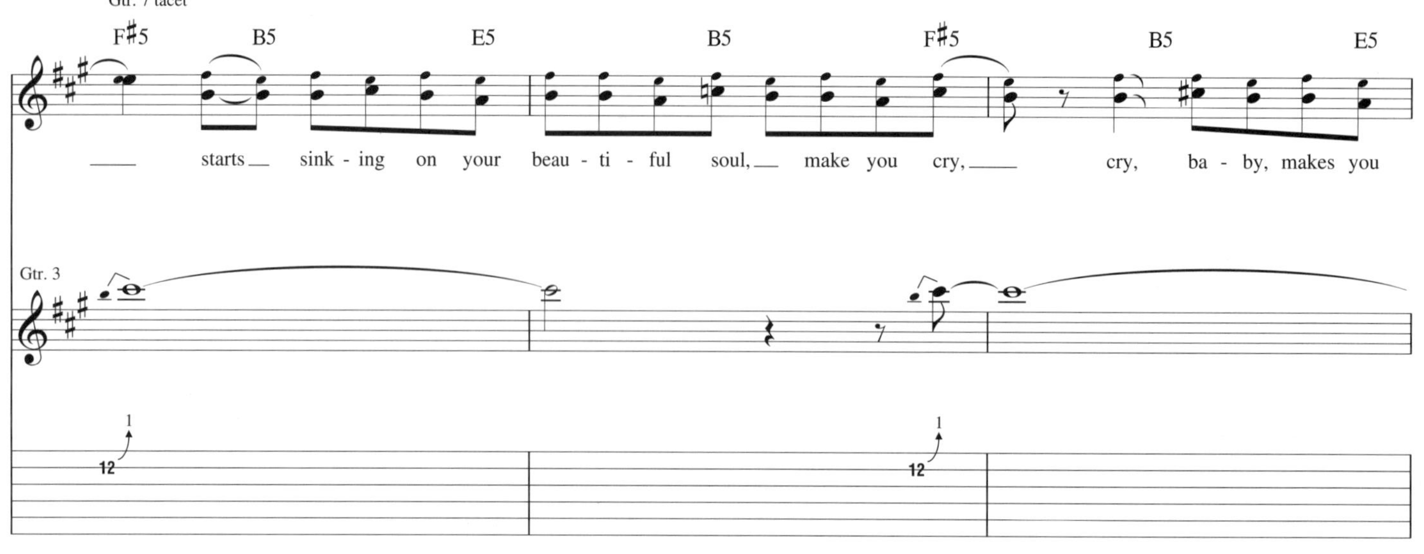
F#5
B5
E5
B5
F#5
B5
E5
starts sink - ing on your beau - ti - ful soul, make you cry, cry, ba - by, makes you
Gtr. 3
1
12
1
12
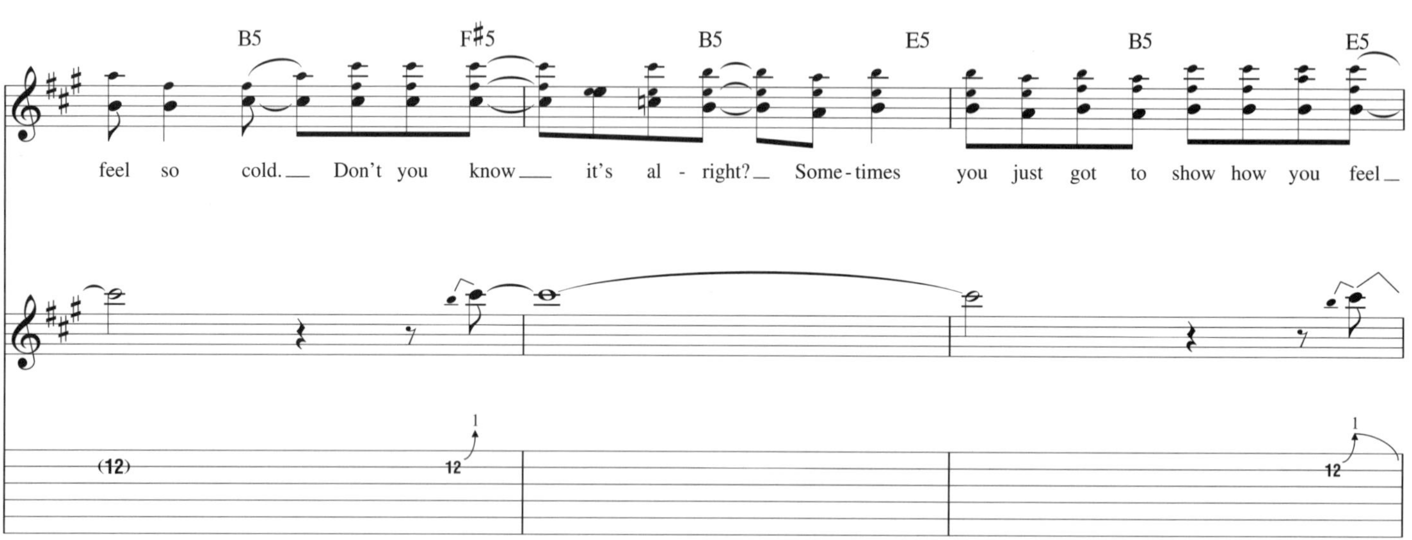
B5
F#5
B5
E5
B5
E5
feel so cold. Don't you know it's al - right? Some - times you just got to show how you feel
(12)
1
12
1
12
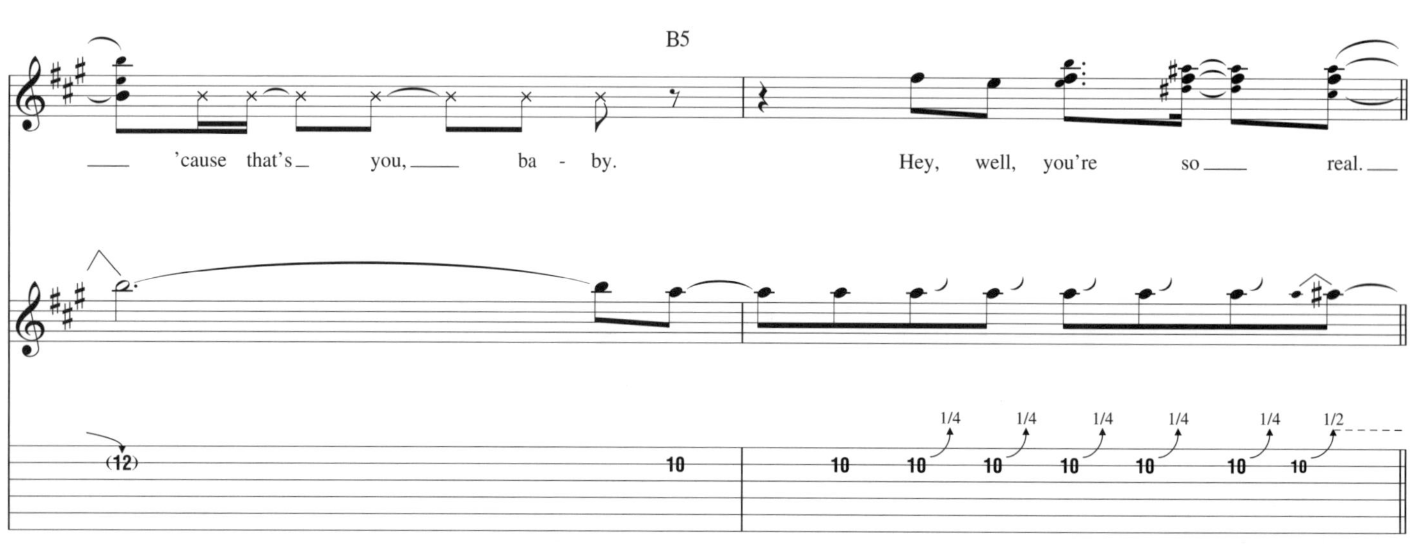
B5
'cause that's you, ba - by. Hey, well, you're so real.
(12)
10
10
10
10
10
10
10
10
1/4
1/4
1/4
1/4
1/4
1/2

Outro

Gtrs. 3 & 4: w/ Riff D & Rhy. Fig. 2 (2 times)

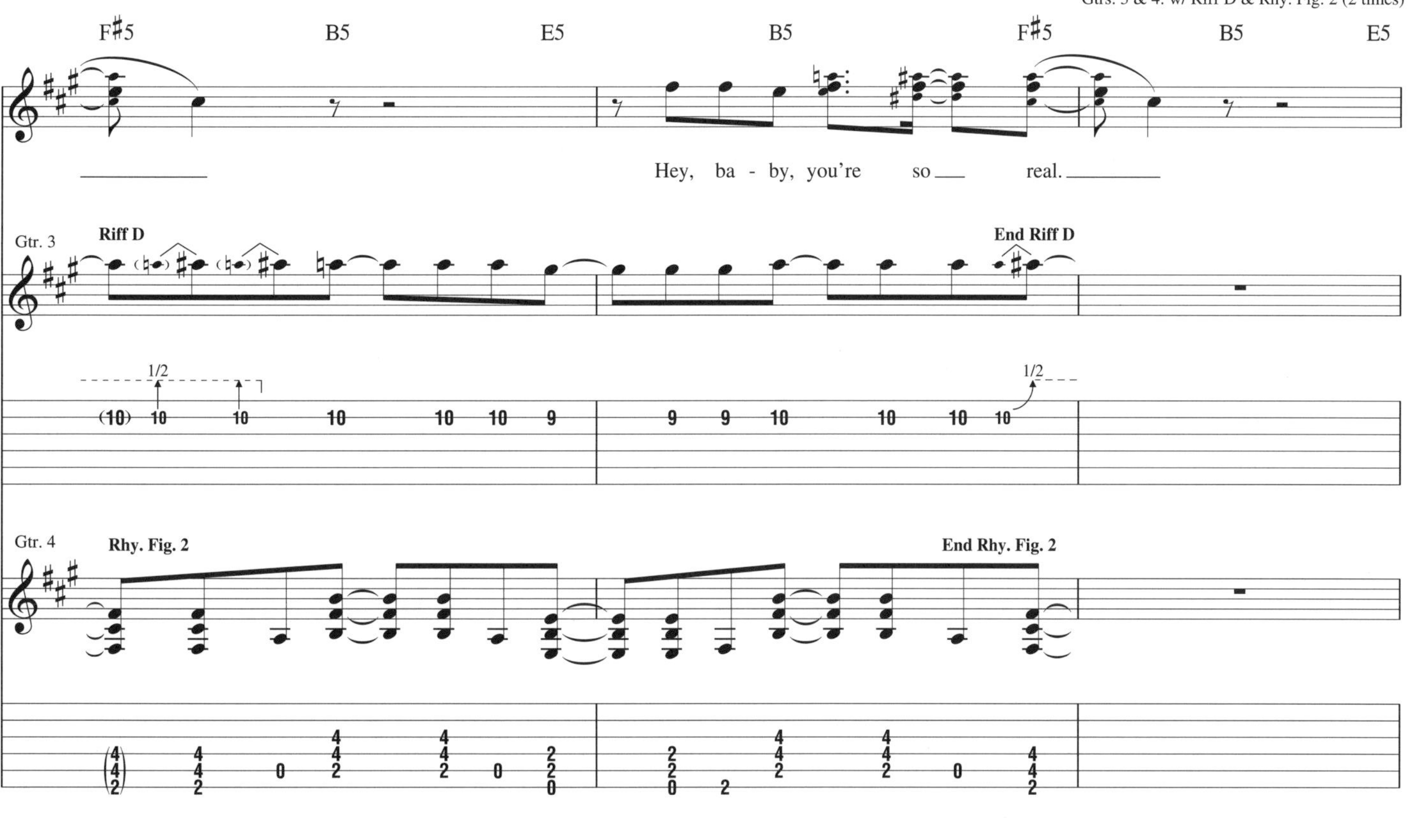
F#5
B5
E5
B5
F#5
B5
E5
Hey, ba - by, you're so real.
Gtr. 3
Riff D
End Riff D
1/2
1/2
Gtr. 4
Rhy. Fig. 2
End Rhy. Fig. 2

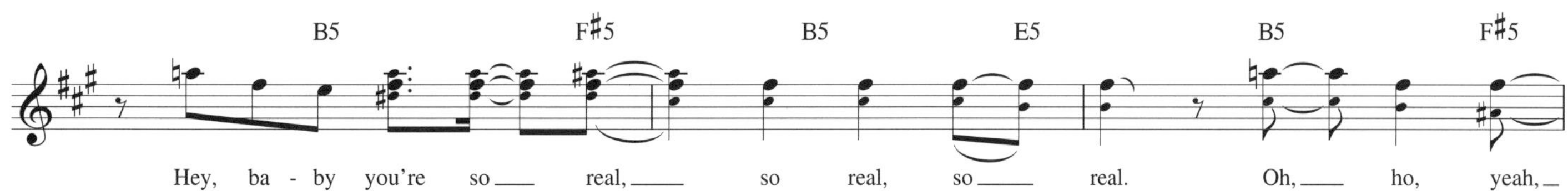
B5
F#5
B5
E5
B5
F#5
Hey, ba - by you're so real, so real, so real. Oh, ho, yeah,

B5
E5
B5
F#5
rit.
yeah, yeah, ho.
Gtr. 3
rit.
1/2
1/2
Gtr. 4
rit.

The Difference

Words and Music by Rob Thomas

C G D/A D9 Cadd9 G5 Am Am type2 Csus2

32 1 | 21 34 | 132 | 21 | 1 34 | 1 34 | 1444 | 231 | 3 1

Intro

Moderately ♩ = 100

Csus2/G Cadd9/G | Gtr. 1 tacet | C G | C G | D5/A G

*Gtr. 2 | mp — mf | Rhy. Fig. 1 | Gtr. 2 | End Rhy. Fig. 1

Gtr. 1 (elec.) | mp — mf | w/ clean tone

*Kybd. and piano arr. for gtr.

Gtr. 1 | Gtr. 2: w/ Rhy. Fig. 1 | C G | C G

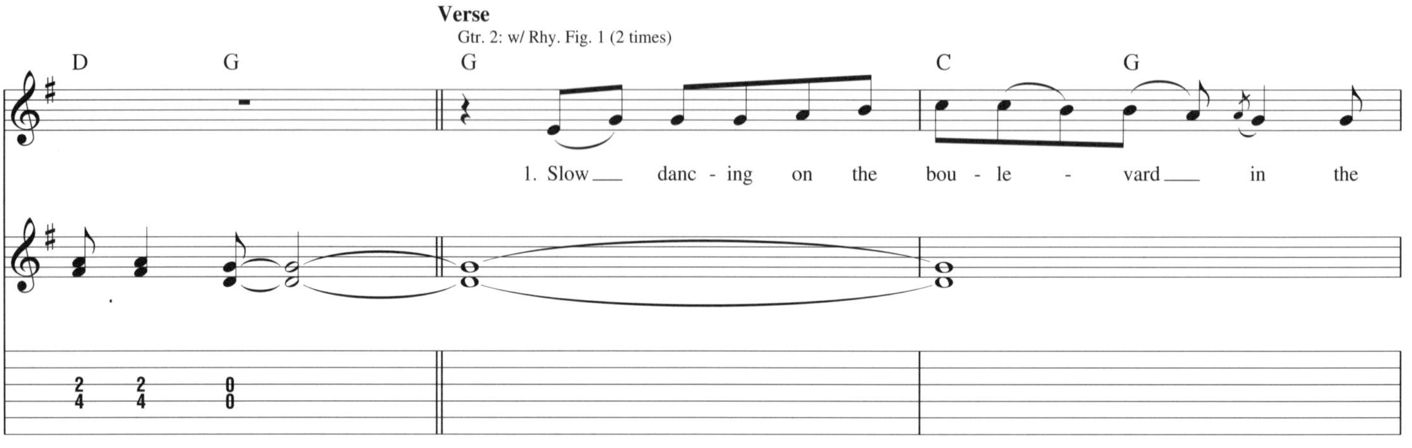

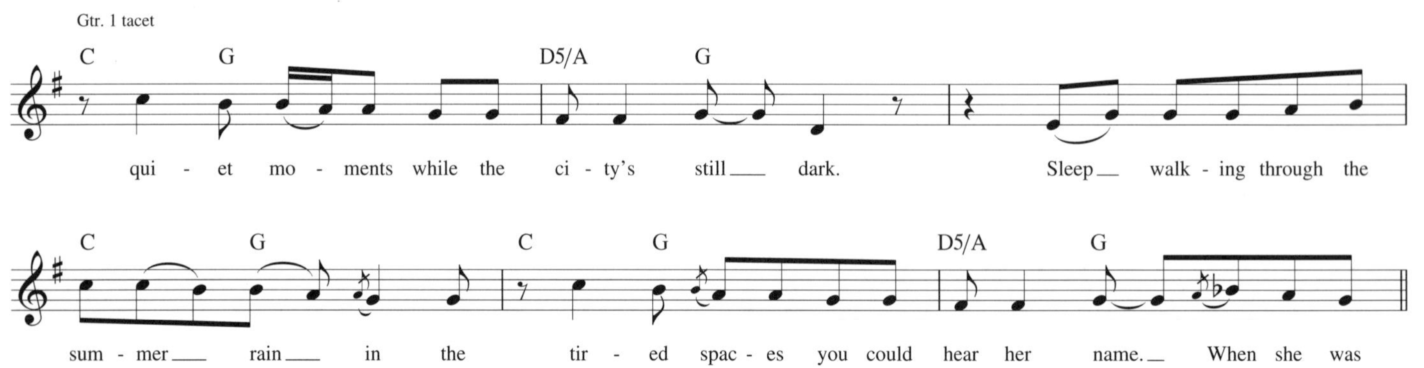

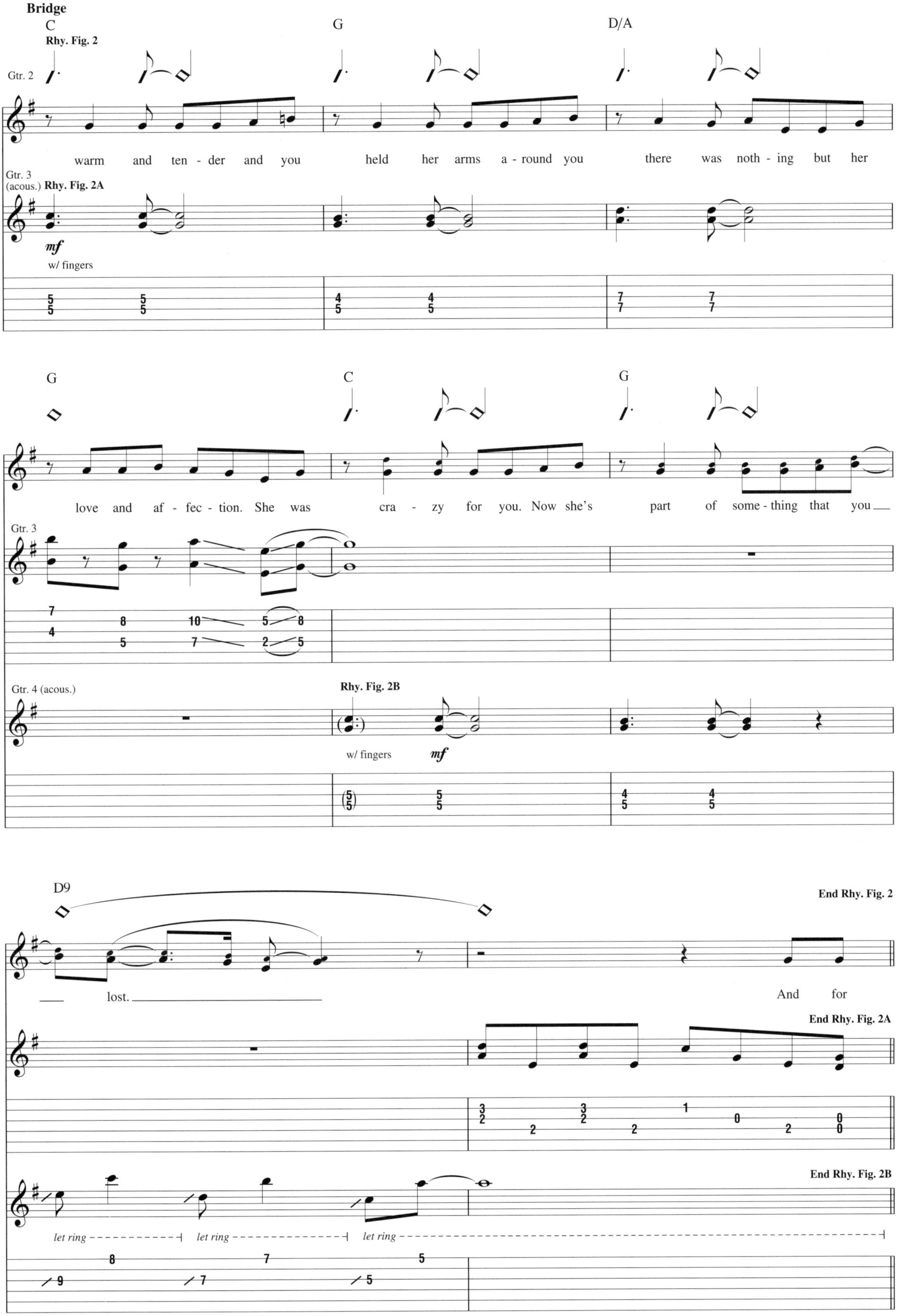

Bridge
C
Rhy. Fig. 2
G
D/A
Gtr. 2
warm and ten - der and you held her arms a - round you there was noth - ing but her
Gtr. 3 (acous.) Rhy. Fig. 2A
mf
w/ fingers
G
C
G
love and af - fec - tion. She was cra - zy for you. Now she's part of some - thing that you
Gtr. 3
Gtr. 4 (acous.)
Rhy. Fig. 2B
w/ fingers
mf
D9
End Rhy. Fig. 2
lost.
And for
End Rhy. Fig. 2A
End Rhy. Fig. 2B
let ring
let ring
let ring

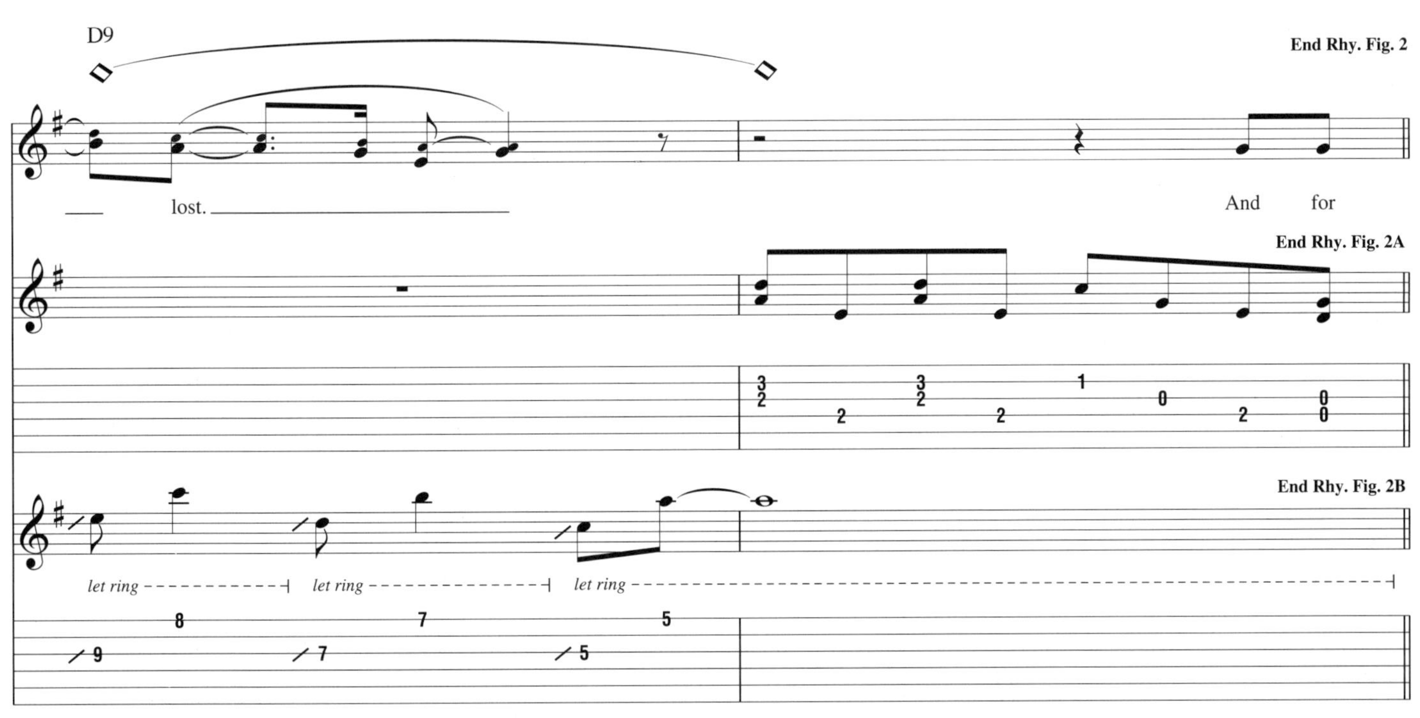

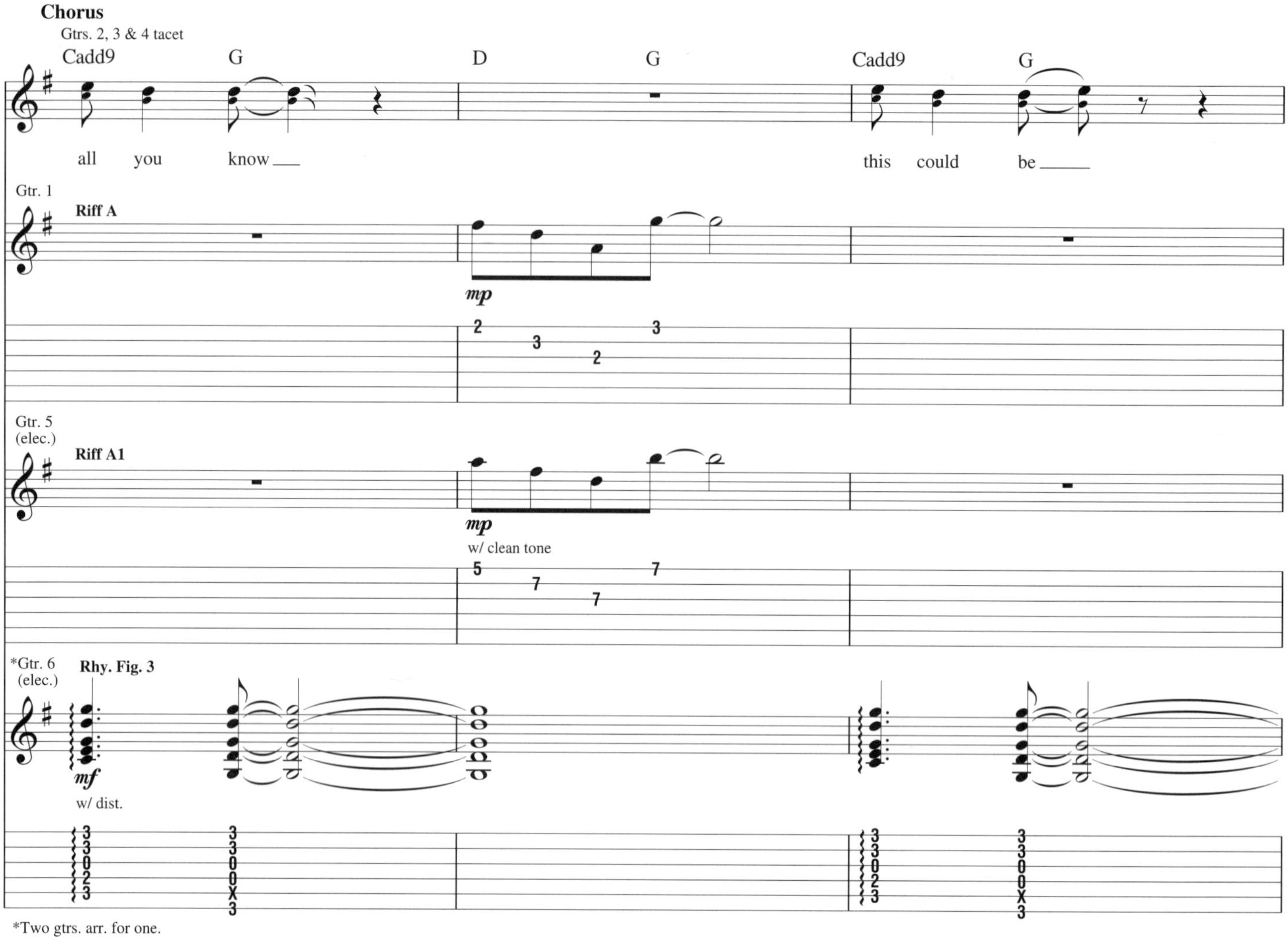

Chorus

Gtrs. 2, 3 & 4 tacet

Cadd9 G D G Cadd9 G

all you know___ this could be___

Gtr. 1

Riff A

mp

Gtr. 5 (elec.)

Riff A1

mp

w/ clean tone

*Gtr. 6 (elec.)

Rhy. Fig. 3

mf

w/ dist.

*Two gtrs. arr. for one.

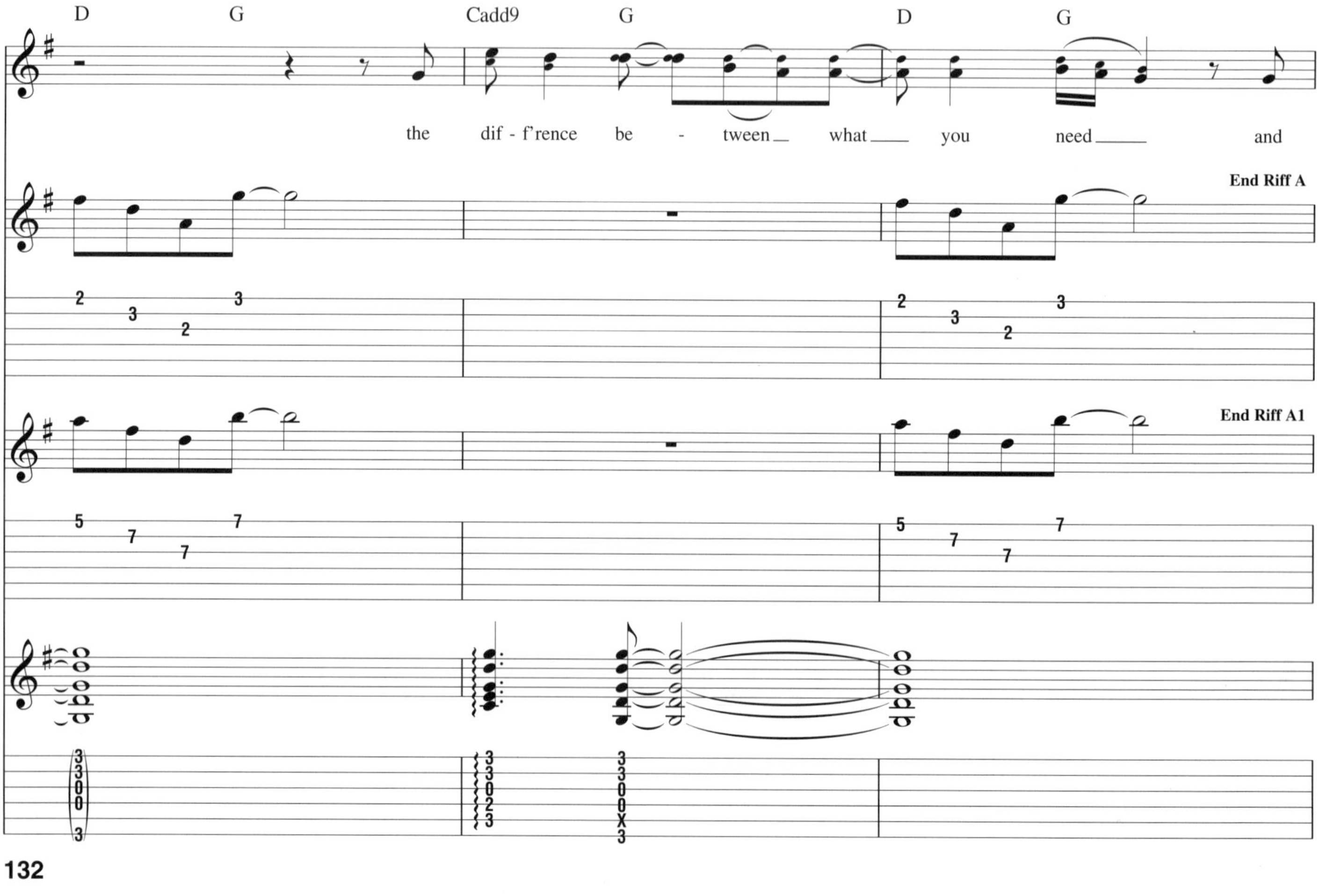

D G Cadd9 G D G

the dif - f'rence be - tween___ what___ you need___ and

End Riff A

End Riff A1

Gtr. 5 tacet
Am
Cadd9
what you want to be,
yeah, what you want to be.
Gtr. 1
Gtr. 6
End Rhy. Fig. 3
Gtr. 6 tacet
G
C
G
C
G
Gtr. 5
Gtr. 1
Verse
Gtr. 2: w/ Rhy. Fig. 1 (2 times)
D
G
C
G
2. Night swim - ming in her dia - mond dress, mak - ing

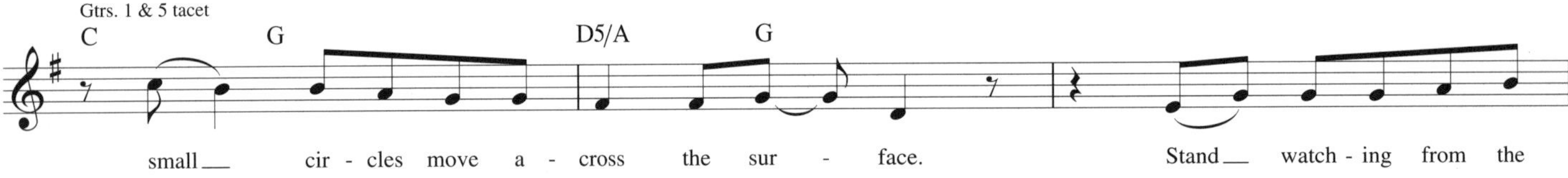

Bridge

Chorus

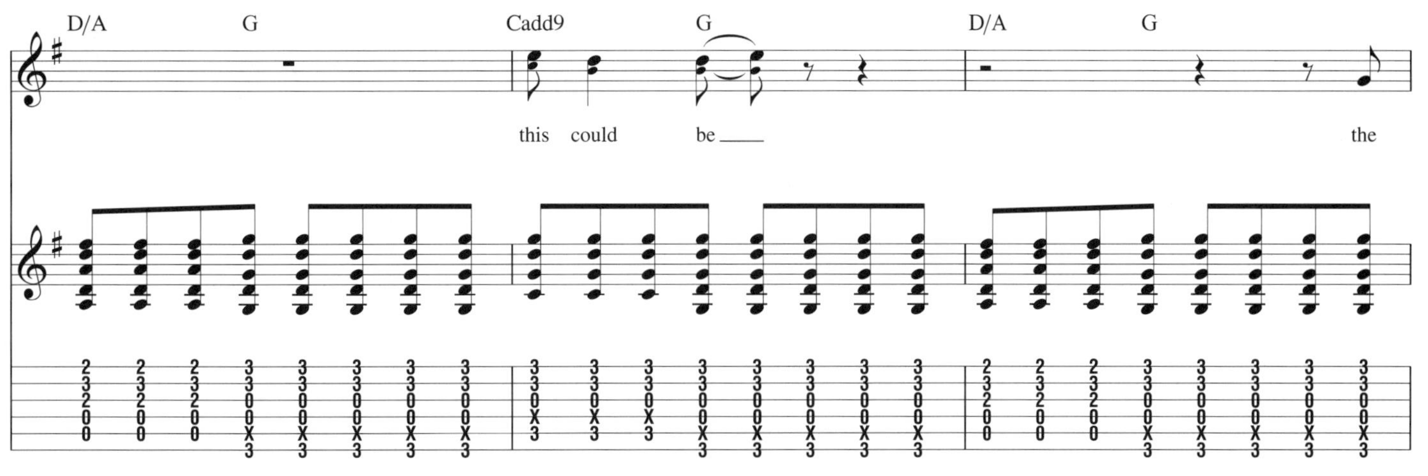
D/A
G
Cadd9
G
D/A
G
this could be
the

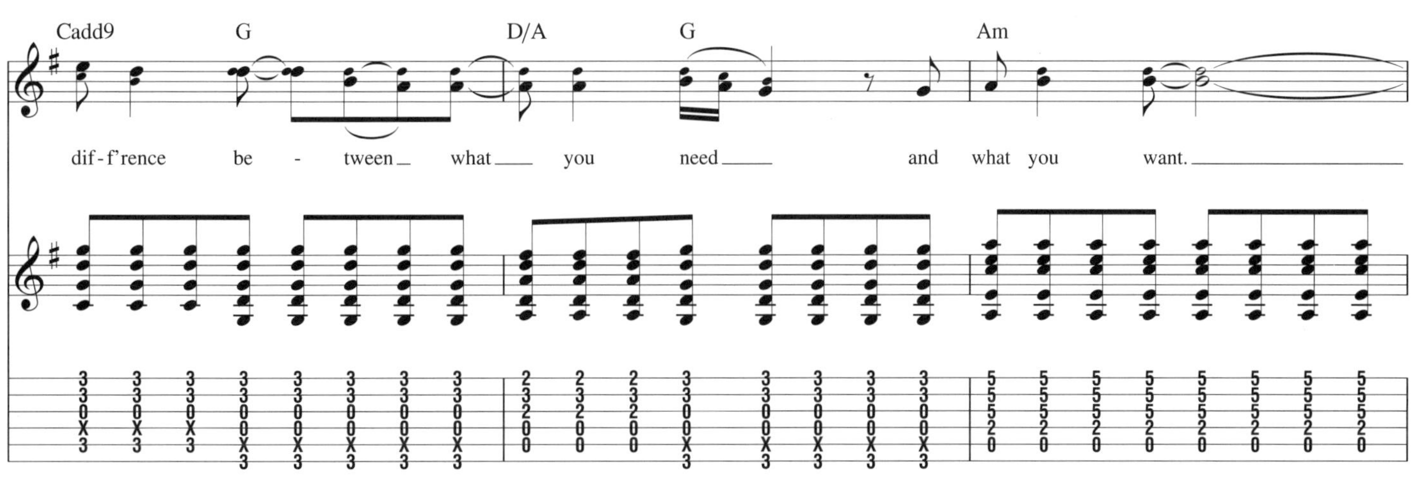
Cadd9
G
D/A
G
Am
dif - f'rence be - tween what you need and what you want.

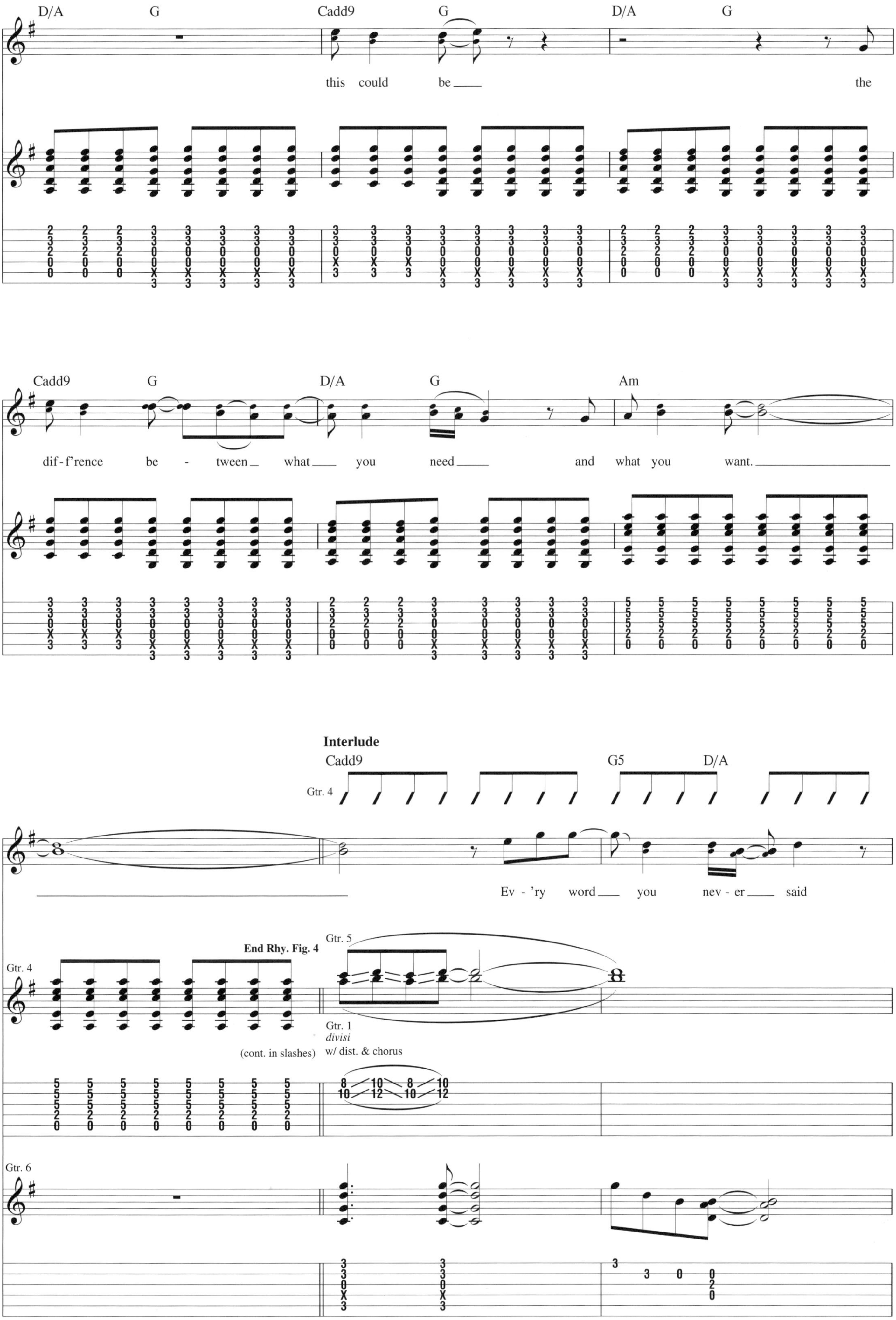

Interlude

Cadd9 G5 D/A

Gtr. 4

Ev - 'ry word you nev - er said

Gtr. 4

End Rhy. Fig. 4

(cont. in slashes)

Gtr. 5

Gtr. 1
divisi
w/ dist. & chorus

Gtr. 6

Cadd9 G5 D/A Cadd9

echoes down your empty hallway. And ev-'ry-thing
(Oh.)

G5 D/A

Gtr. 5 tacet

Am

that was your world just came down.

Gtr. 1

Verse
Gtr. 1 tacet
Cadd9
Gtr. 6 tacet
Gtr. 2: w/ Rhy. Fig. 1 (1 3/4 times)
G
3. Day break - ing on the
Gtr. 6
Gtr. 4 tacet
C G C G D5/A G
bou - le - vard feel the sun warm - ing up your sec - ond - hand heart.
C G C G
Light swim - ming right a - cross your face and you think may - be some - day yeah.
Chorus
Gtrs. 1 & 5: w/ Riffs A & A1
Gtr. 2 tacet
Gtr. 4: w/ Rhy. Fig. 4
Gtr. 6: w/ Rhy. Fig. 3 (1st 6 meas.)
D/A Cadd9 G D/A G
Gtr. 2
May - be some - day. For all you know yeah,
Gtr. 7 (elec.)
mp
w/ clean tone
Cadd9 G D/A G Cadd9 G
this could be the dif - f'rence be - tween what

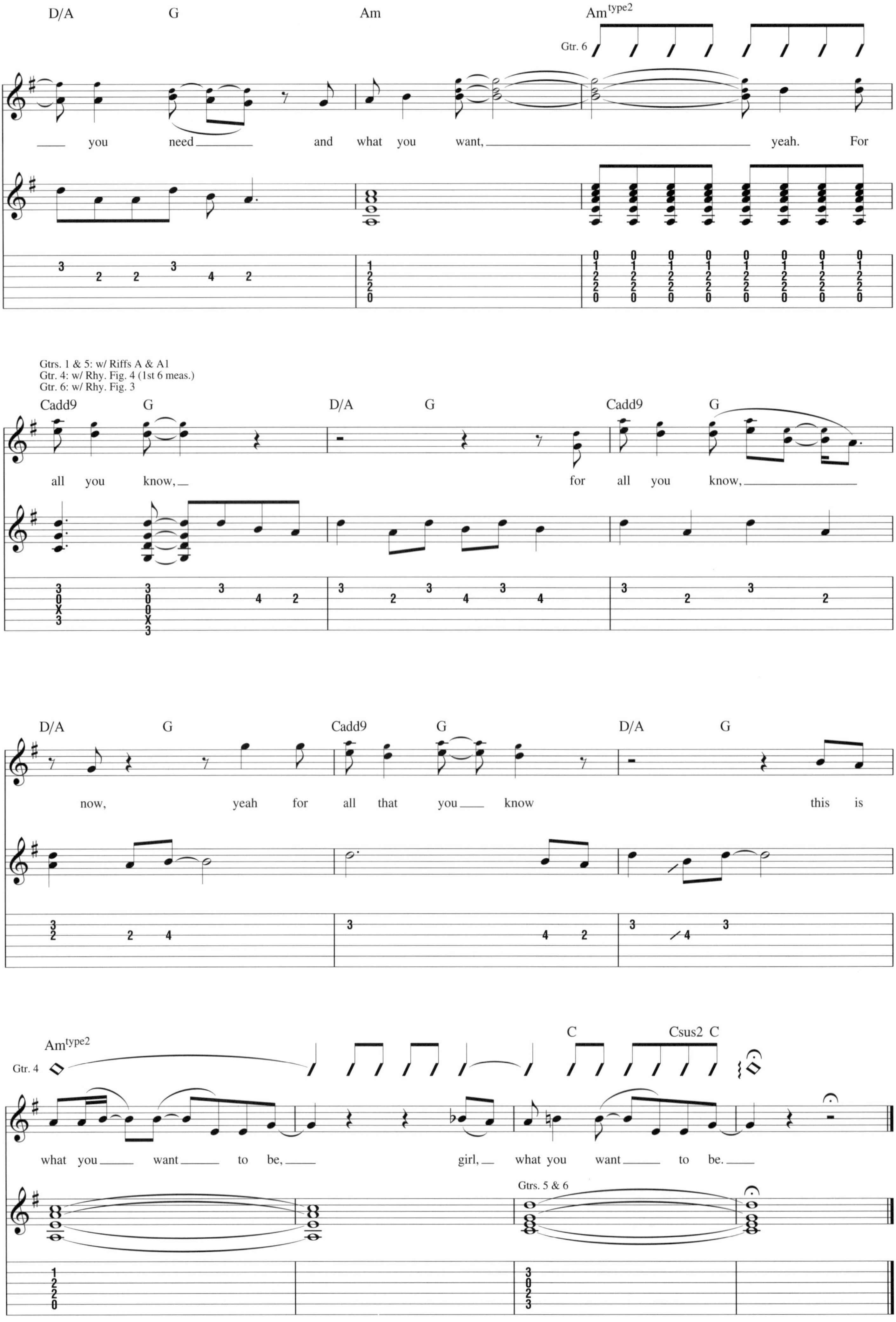

D/A G Am Am type2
Gtr. 6
you need and what you want, yeah. For
Gtrs. 1 & 5: w/ Riffs A & A1
Gtr. 4: w/ Rhy. Fig. 4 (1st 6 meas.)
Gtr. 6: w/ Rhy. Fig. 3
Cadd9 G D/A G Cadd9 G
all you know, for all you know,
D/A G Cadd9 G D/A G
now, yeah for all that you know this is
Am type2 C Csus2 C
Gtr. 4
what you want to be, girl, what you want to be.
Gtrs. 5 & 6

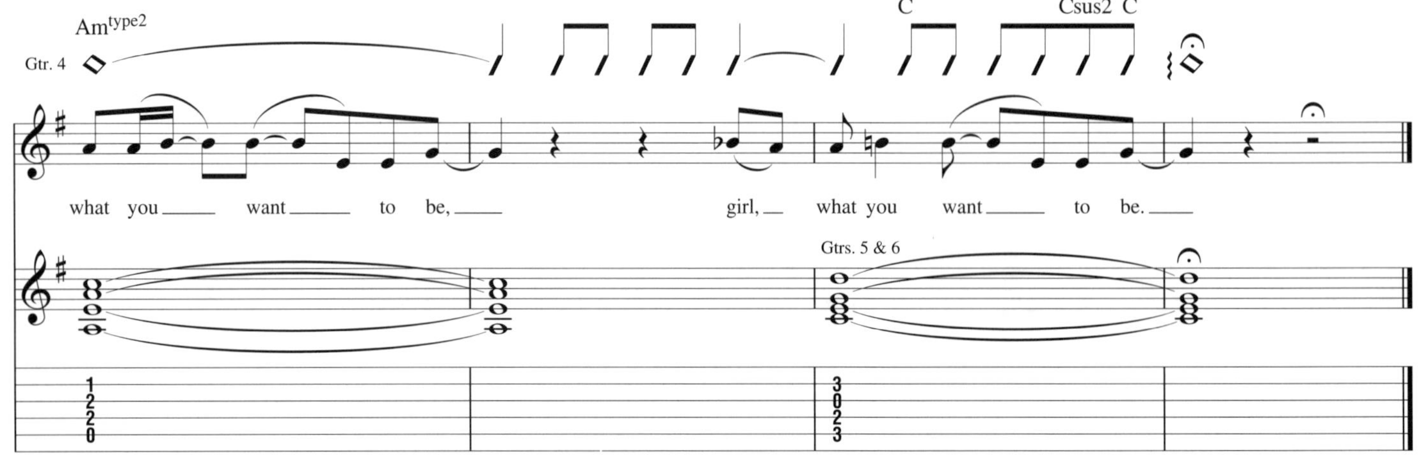

So Sad So Lonely

Words and Music by Rob Thomas

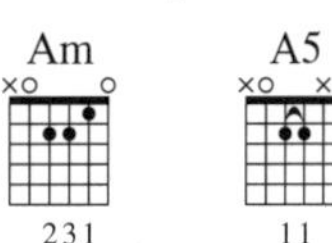

*Chord symbols reflect overall harmony.

**Gtr. 3 to left of slash in tab.

***Gtr. 2 only

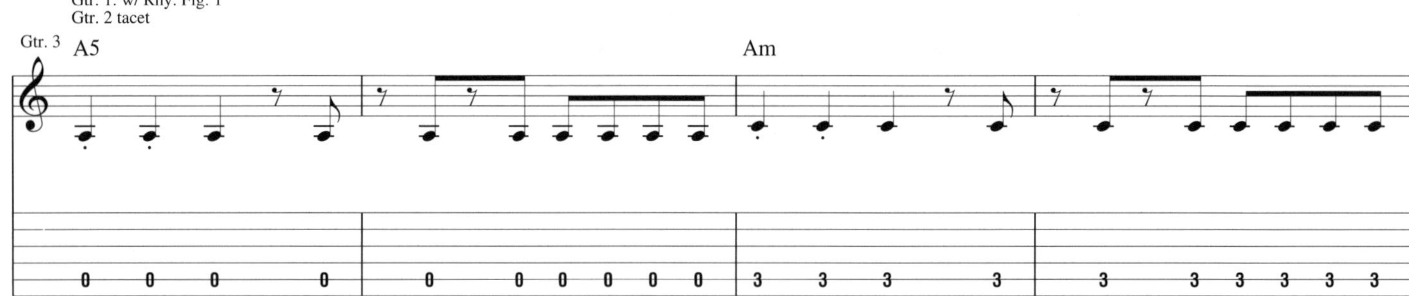
Gtr. 1: w/ Rhy. Fig. 1
Gtr. 2 tacet
Gtr. 3
A5
Am

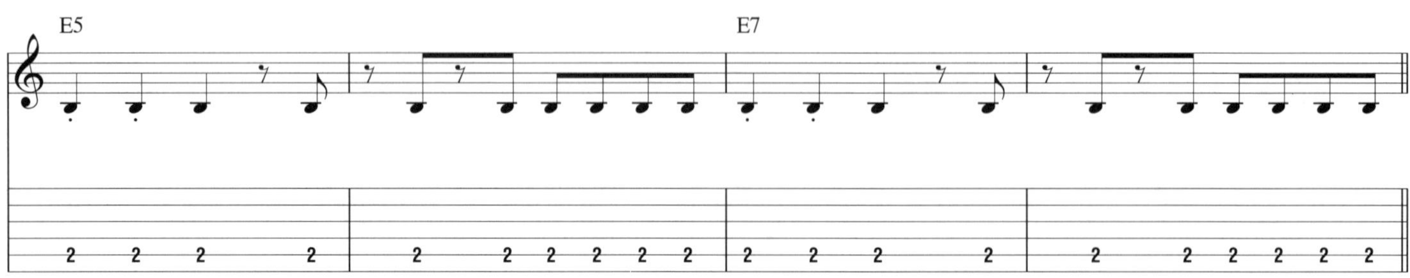
E5
E7

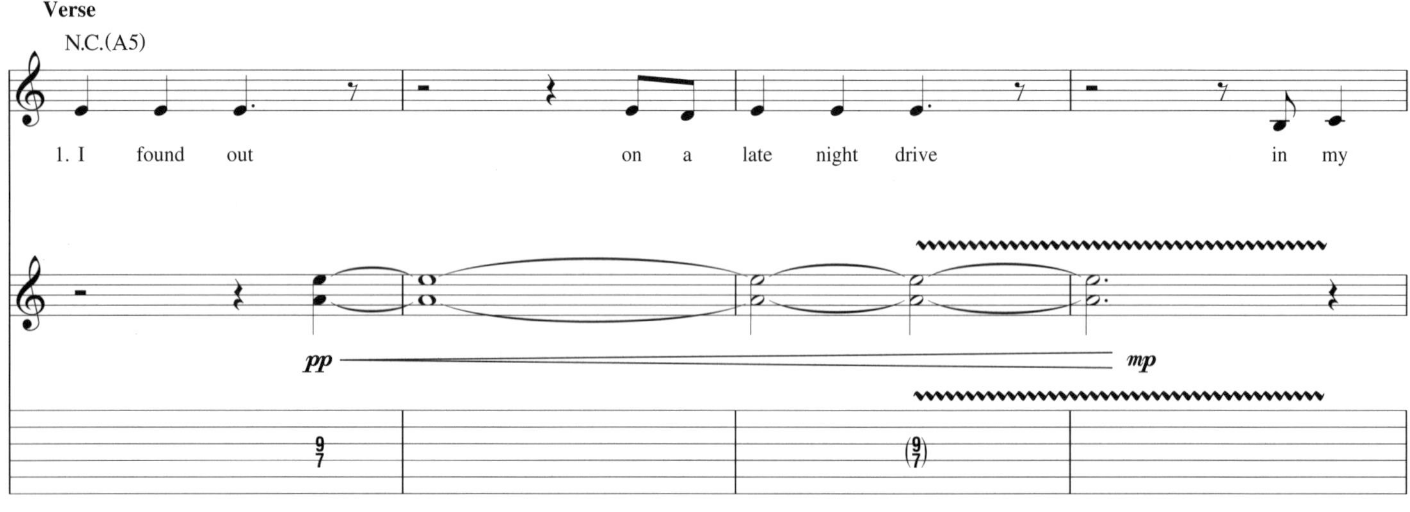
Verse
N.C.(A5)
1. I found out on a late night drive in my
pp
mp

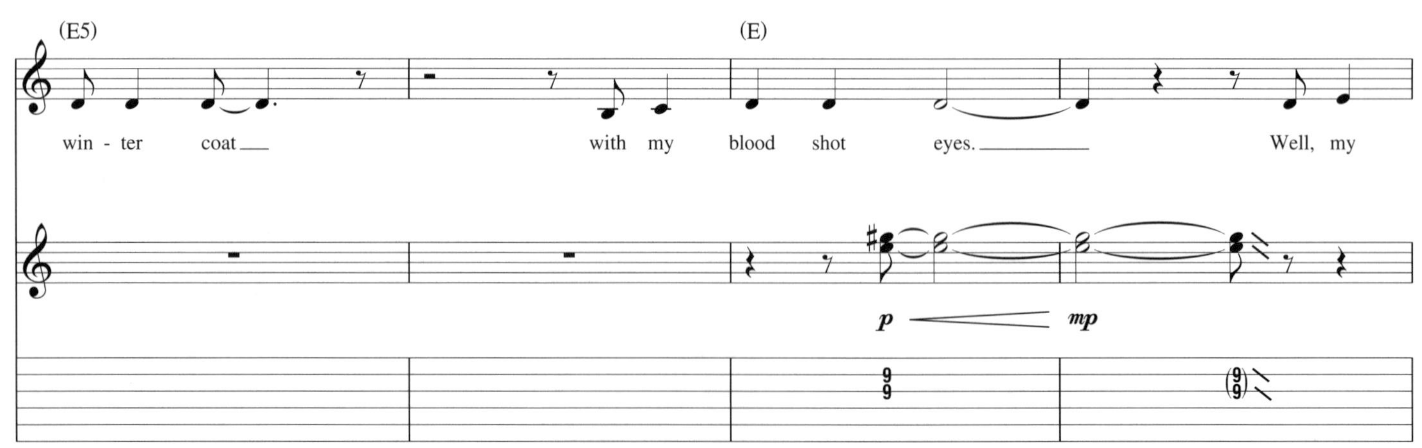
(E5)
(E)
win - ter coat with my blood shot eyes. Well, my
p
mp

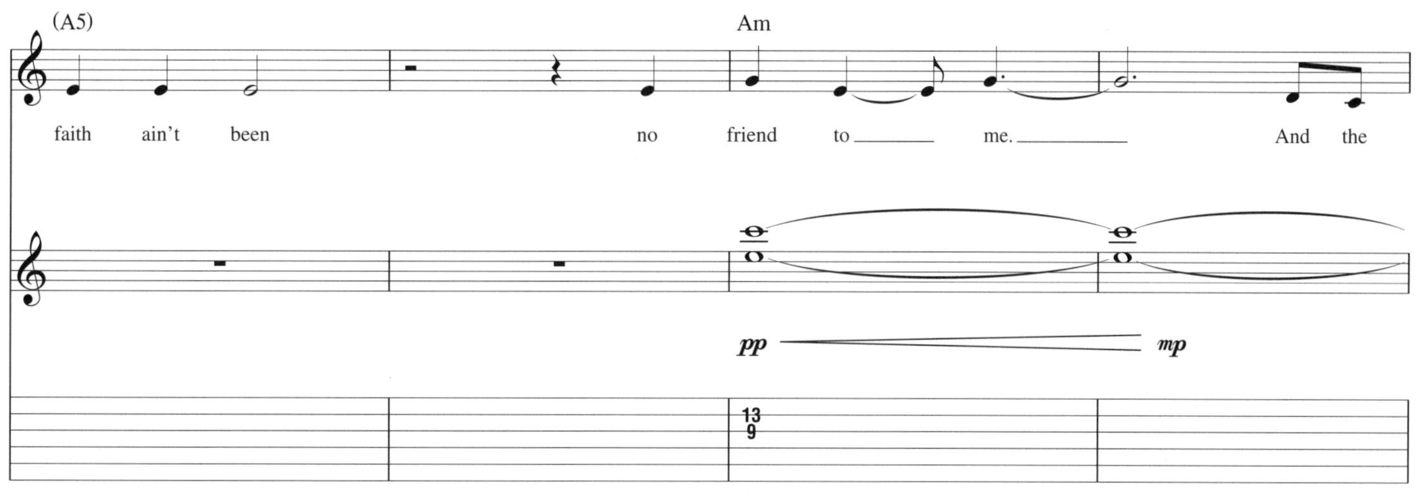
(A5)
Am
faith ain't been no friend to me. And the
pp
mp
13
9

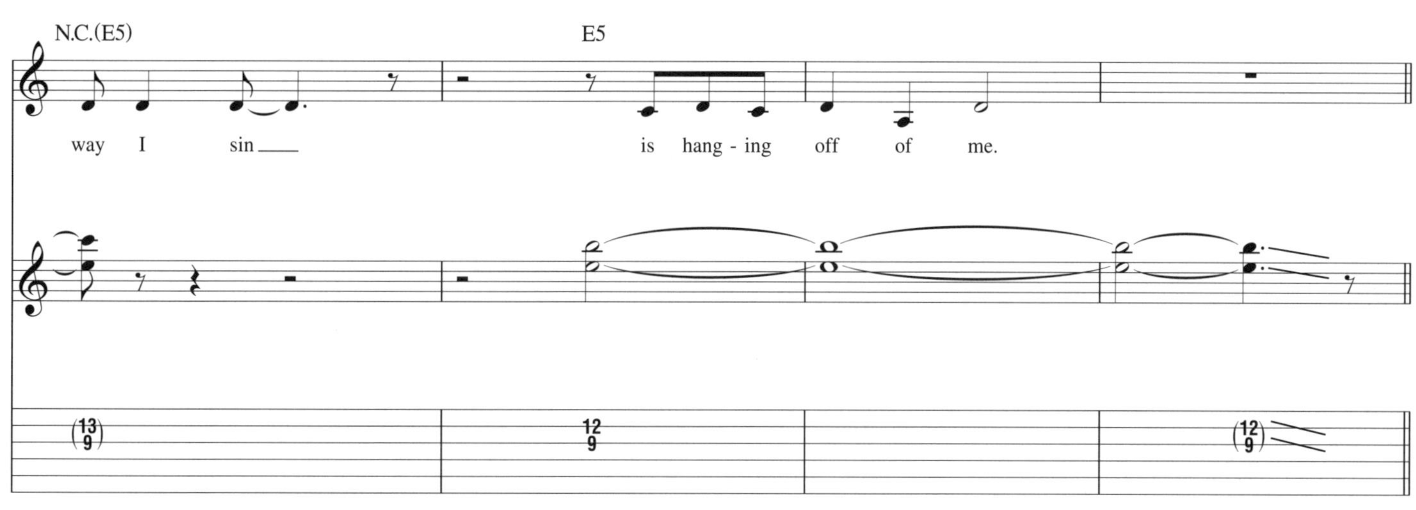
N.C.(E5)
E5
way I sin is hang - ing off of me.
(13)
(9)
12
9
(12)
(9)

Bridge

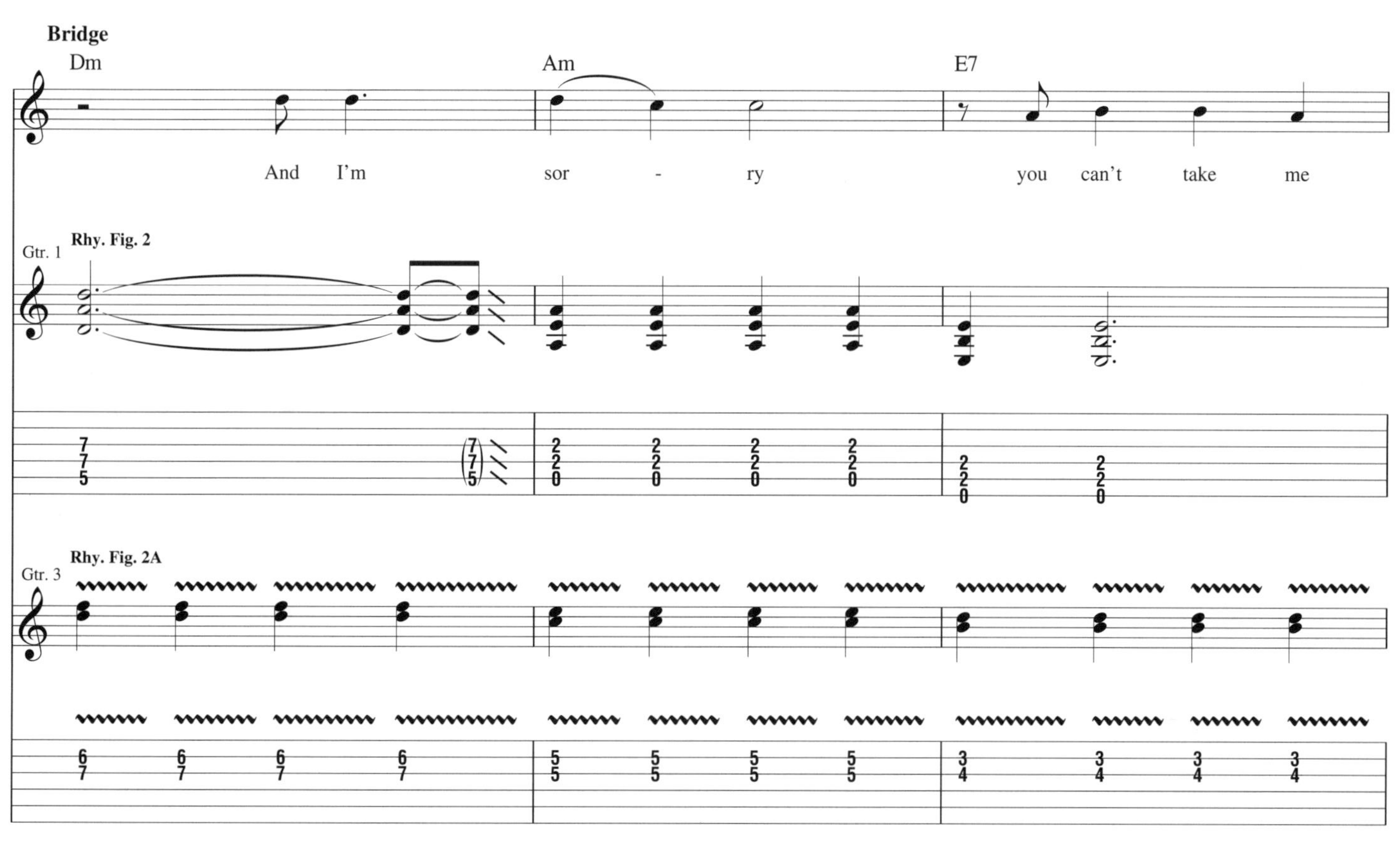
Dm
Am
E7
And I'm sor - ry you can't take me
Gtr. 1
Rhy. Fig. 2
Gtr. 3
Rhy. Fig. 2A

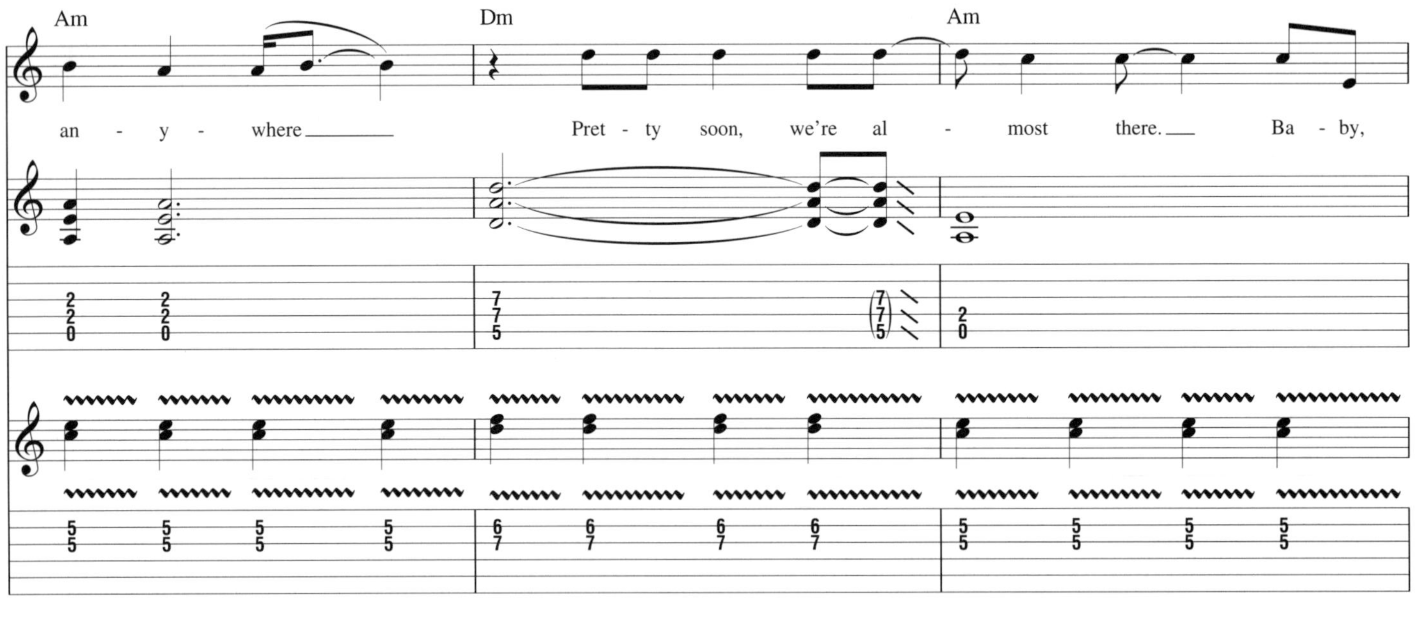
Am
Dm
Am
an - y - where
Pret - ty soon, we're al - most there.
Ba - by,

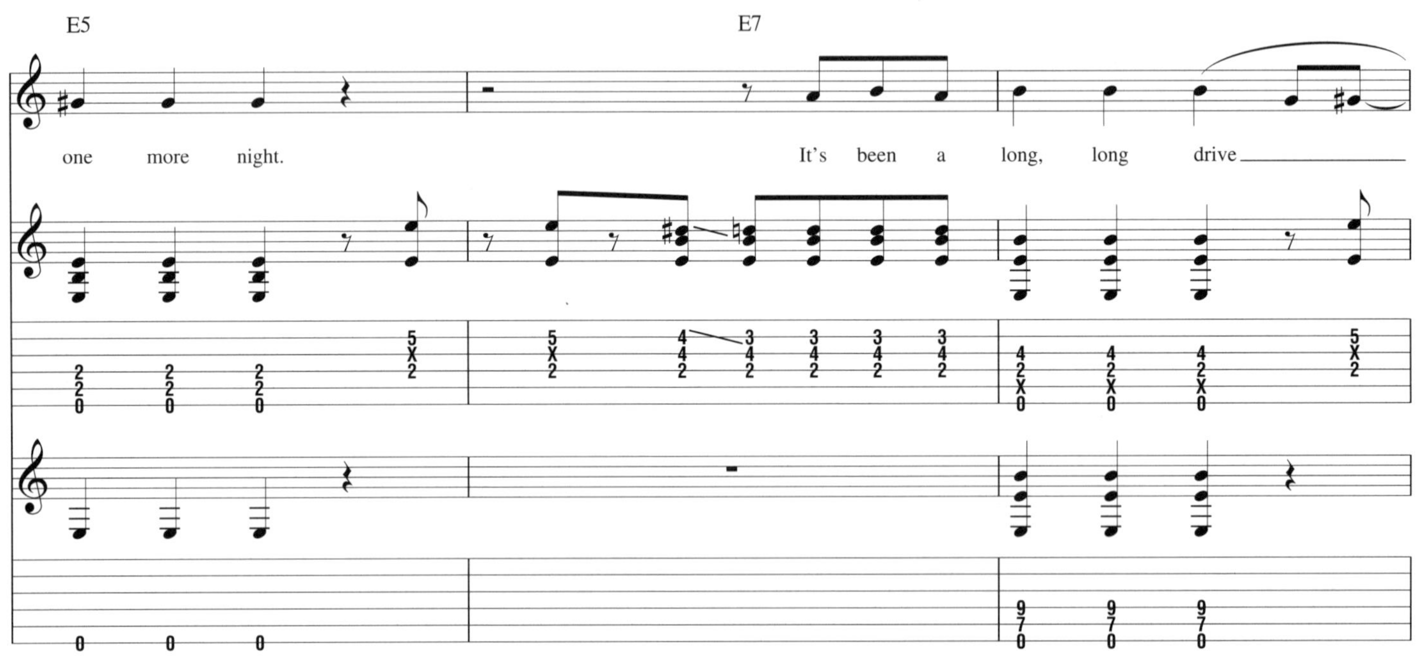
E5
E7
one more night.
It's been a long, long drive

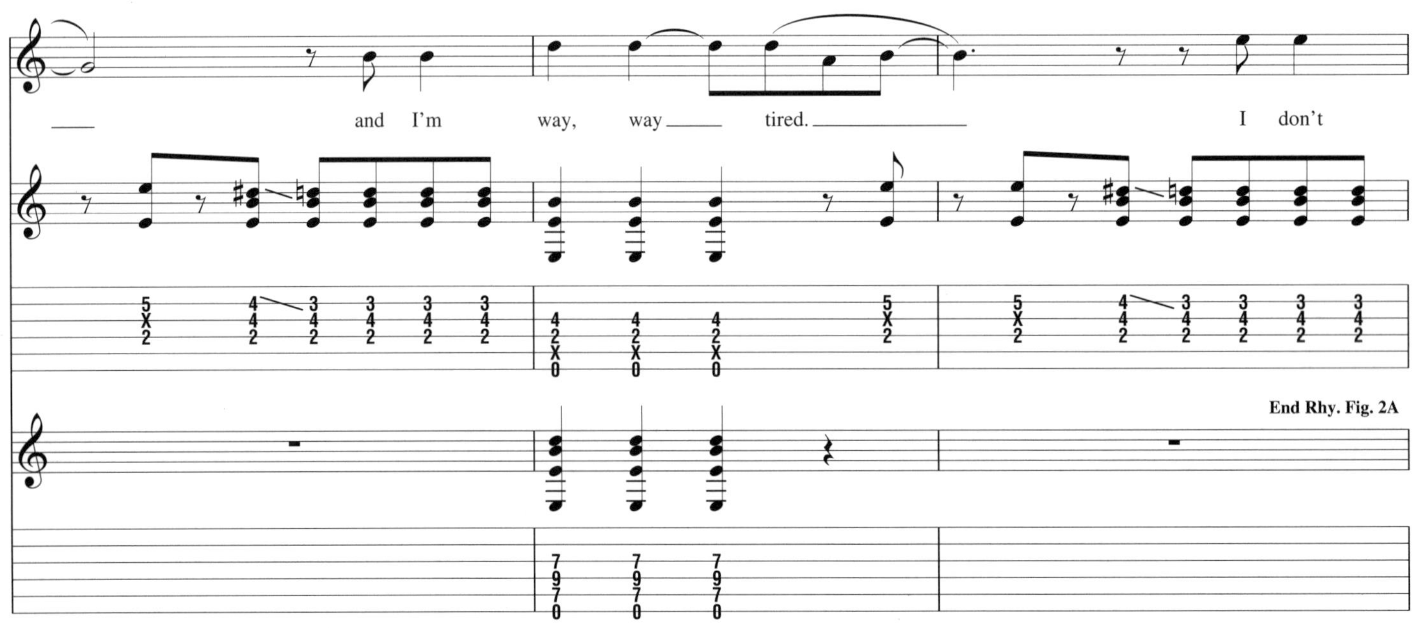
and I'm way, way tired.
I don't
End Rhy. Fig. 2A

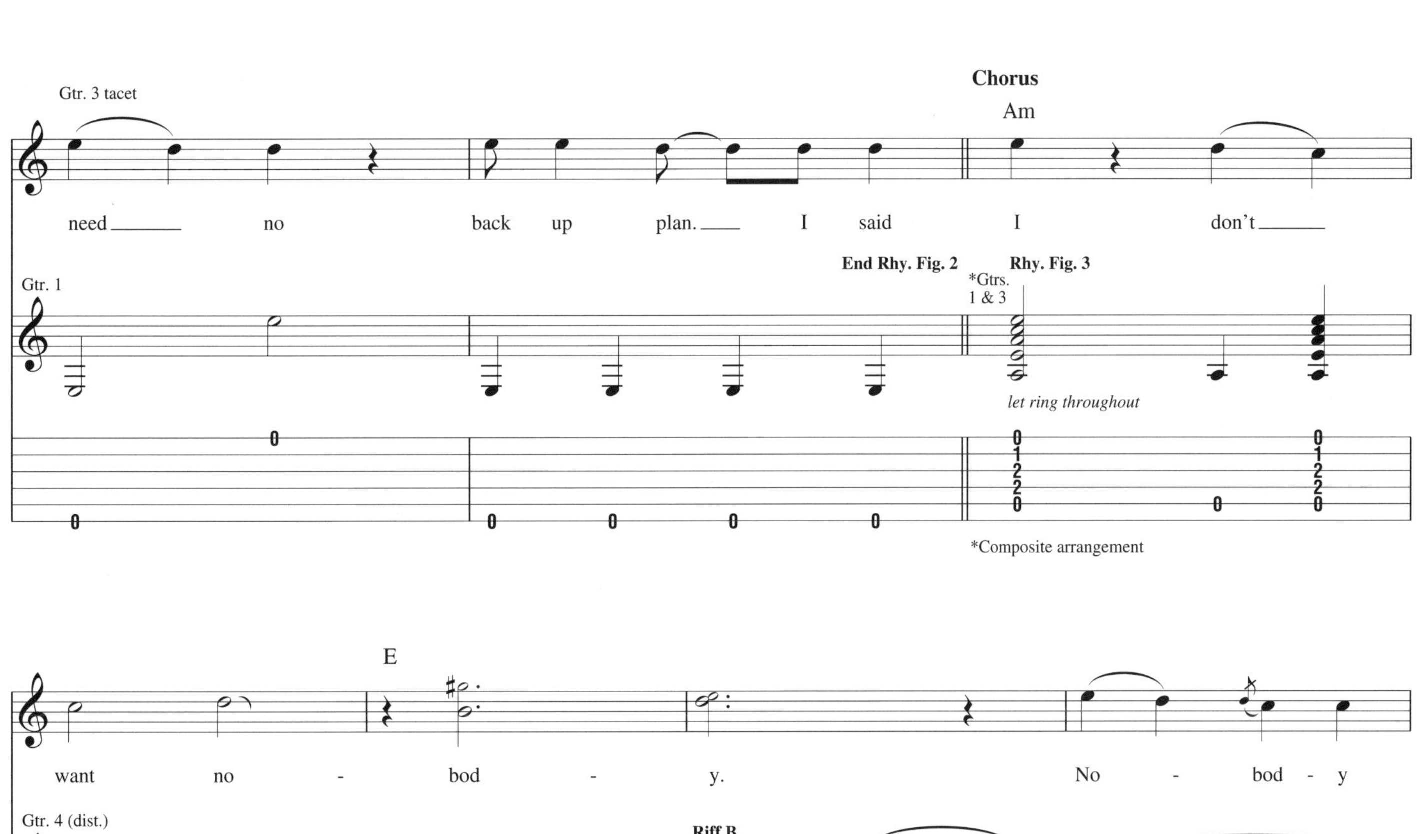
Gtr. 3 tacet
Chorus
Am
need no back up plan. I said I don't
Gtr. 1
End Rhy. Fig. 2
Rhy. Fig. 3
*Gtrs. 1 & 3
let ring throughout
*Composite arrangement

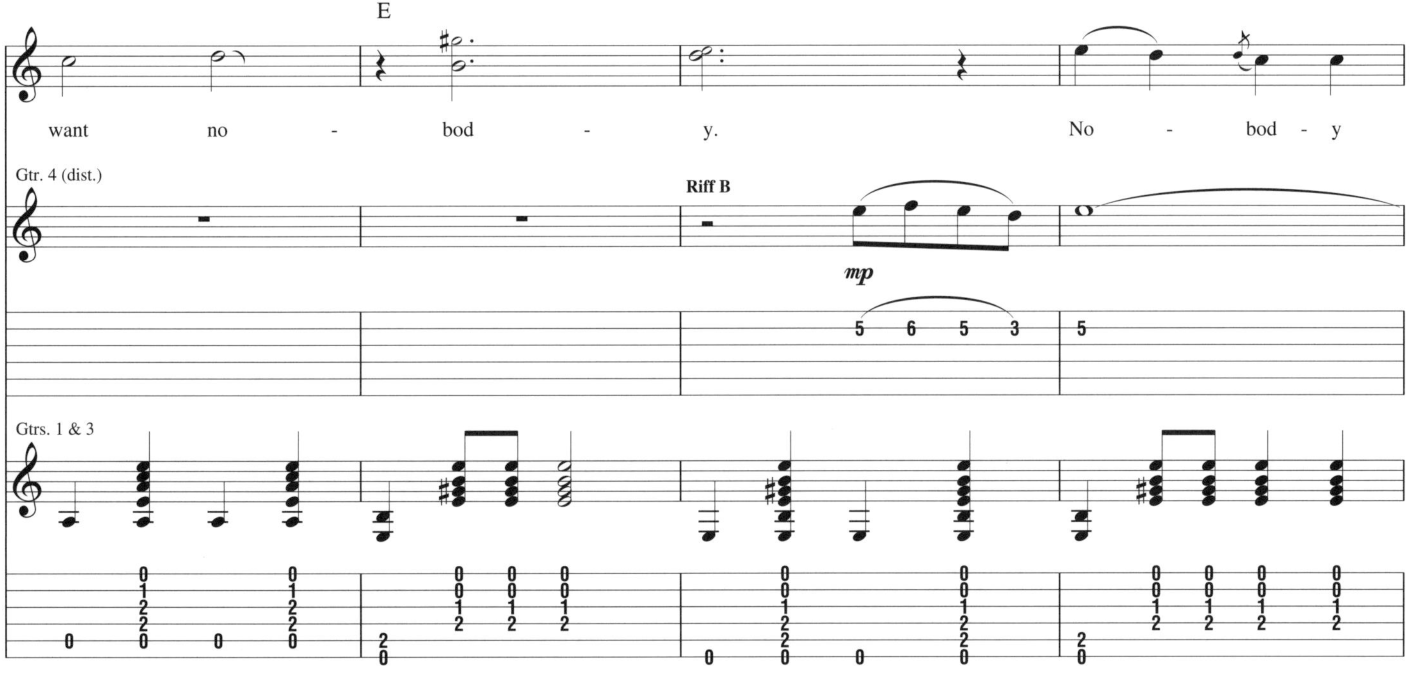
E
want no - bod - y. No - bod - y
Gtr. 4 (dist.)
Riff B
mp
Gtrs. 1 & 3

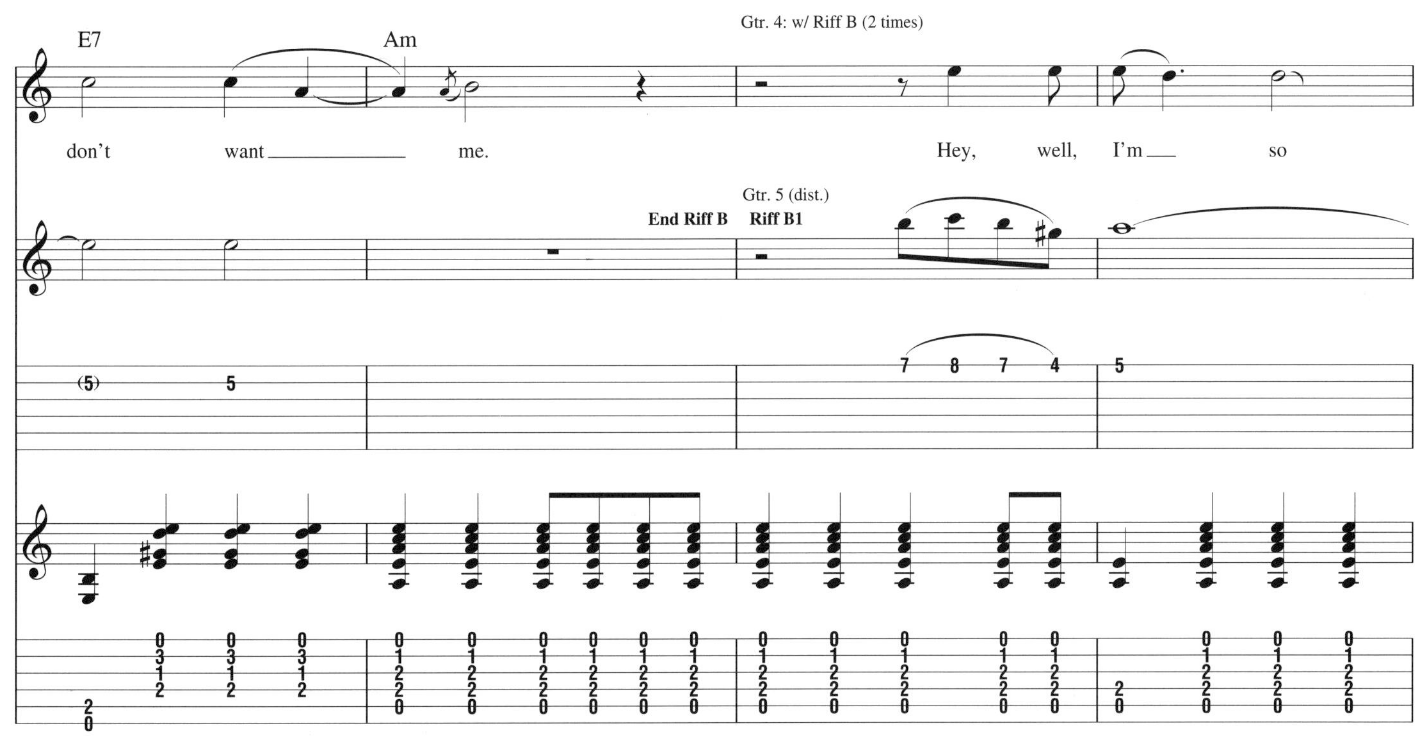
E7
Am
Gtr. 4: w/ Riff B (2 times)
don't want me. Hey, well, I'm so
Gtr. 5 (dist.)
End Riff B
Riff B1

E
sad, so lone - ly. Yeah, well, I'm al - ways

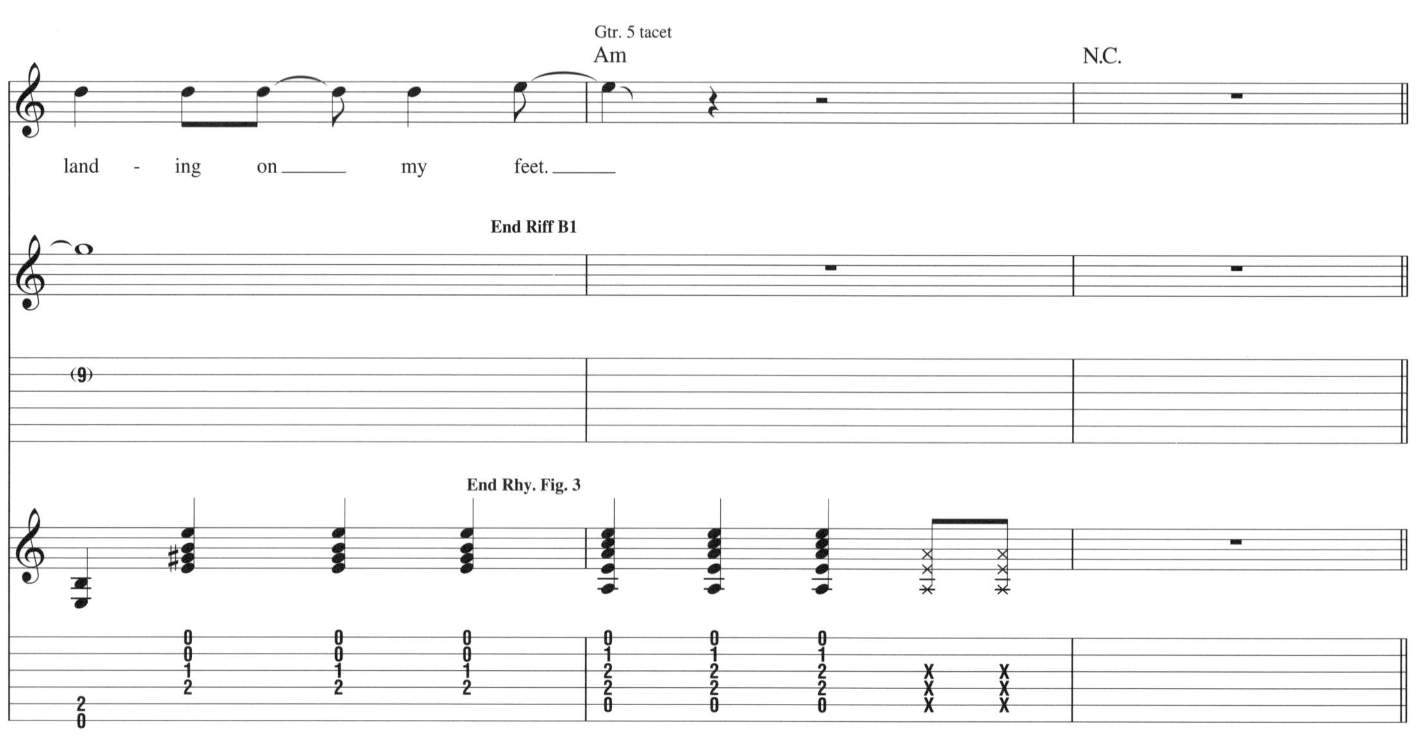
Gtr. 5 tacet
Am
N.C.
land - ing on my feet.
End Riff B1
End Rhy. Fig. 3

Verse
Gtr. 2: w/ Riff A (2 times)
A5
Am
2. One more time with a sad, sad smile and your
Gtr. 1
p
w/ auto-wah

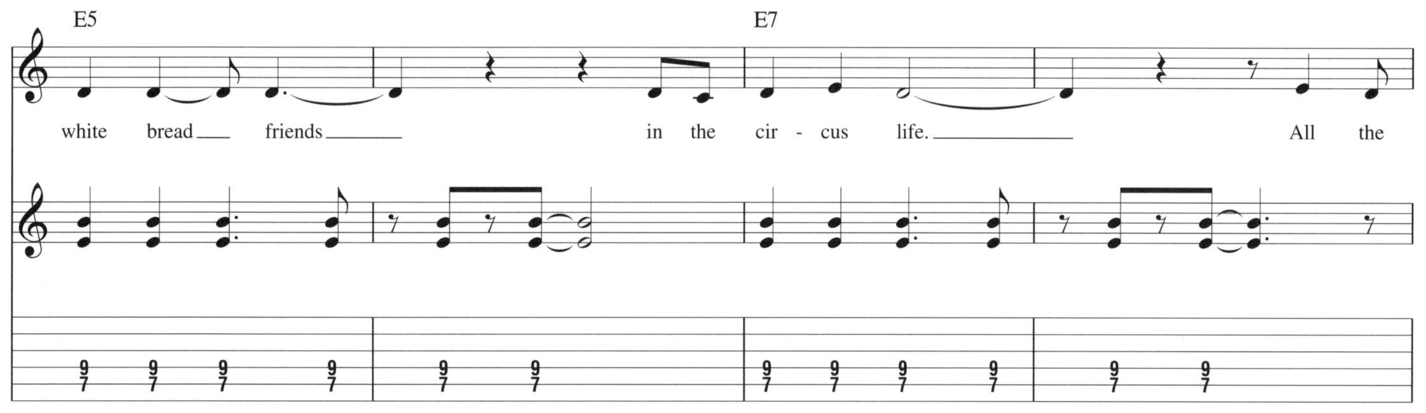
E5
E7
white bread friends in the cir - cus life. All the

Gtr. 1: w/ Rhy. Fig. 1

A5
Am
one way rides and those sweet be - gin - ners pas - sing on the

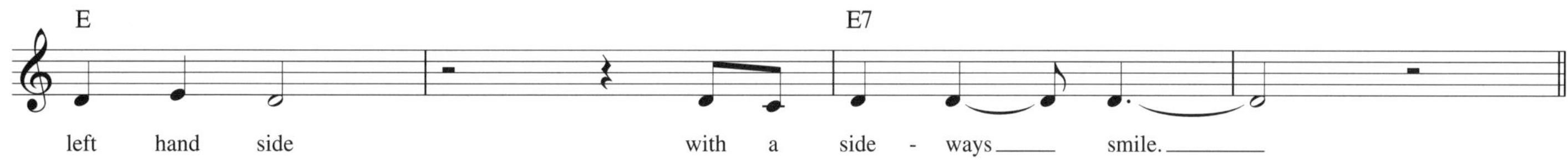
E
E7
left hand side with a side - ways smile.

Bridge

Gtrs. 1 & 3: w/ Rhy. Figs. 2 & 2A

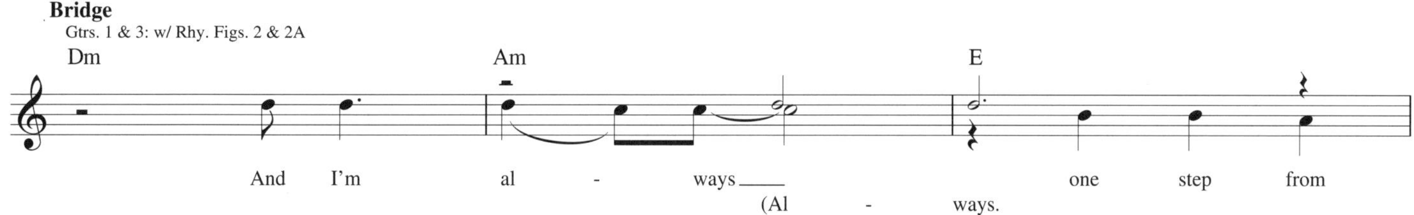
Dm
Am
E
And I'm al - ways one step from
(Al - ways.

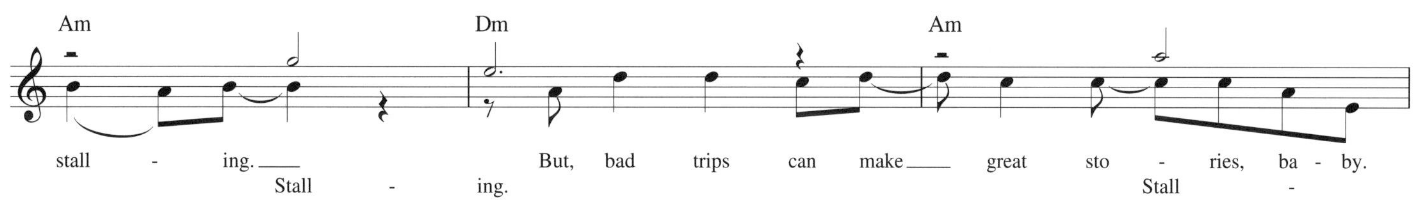
Am
Dm
Am
stall - ing. But, bad trips can make great sto - ries, ba - by.
Stall - ing. Stall -

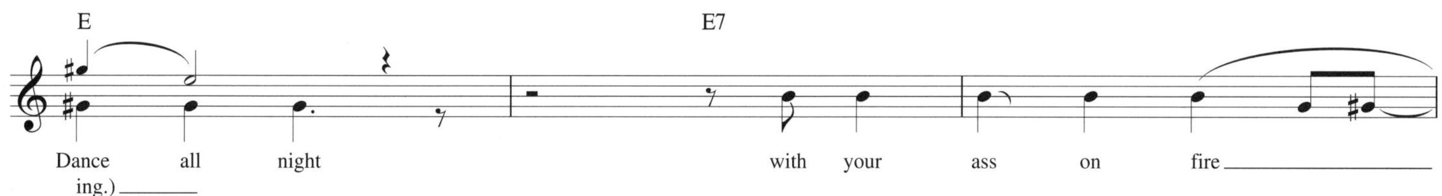
E
E7
Dance all night with your ass on fire
ing.)

and your hands up high and

Chorus

Gtrs. 1 & 3: w/ Rhy. Fig. 3
Am
feel me one more time. I said I don't want no -
Gtr. 5
1/2
Gtr. 4
1/2

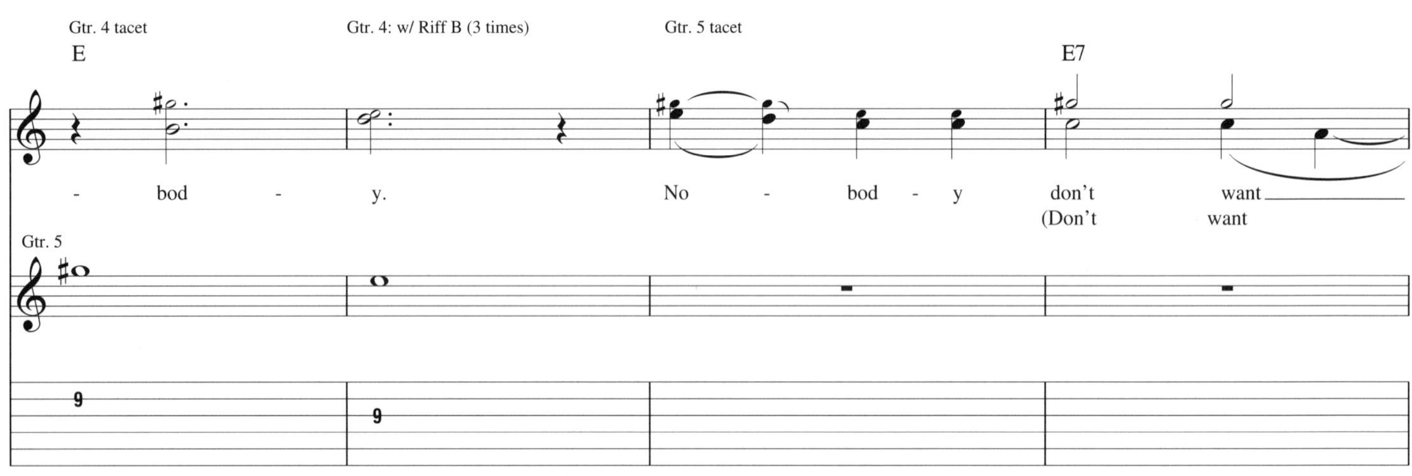
Gtr. 4 tacet
Gtr. 4: w/ Riff B (3 times)
Gtr. 5 tacet
E
E7
- bod - y. No - bod - y don't want
(Don't want
Gtr. 5

Gtr. 5: w/ Riff B1
Am
me. Hey, well, I'm so
me.)

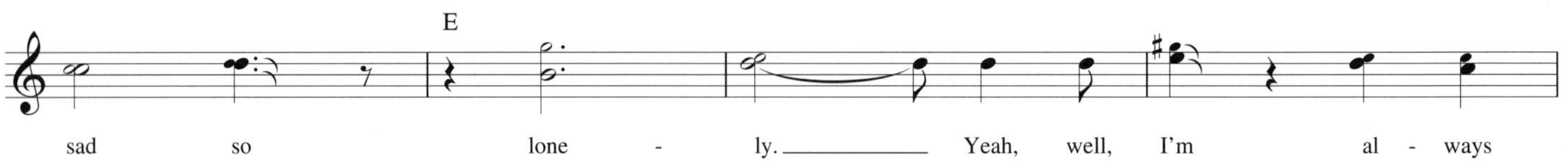
E
sad so lone - ly. Yeah, well, I'm al - ways

Am
Rhy. Fill 1
End Rhy. Fill 1
Gtrs. 1 & 3
land - ing on my feet, yeah. Hey.
Gtr. 6 (dist.)

Guitar Solo

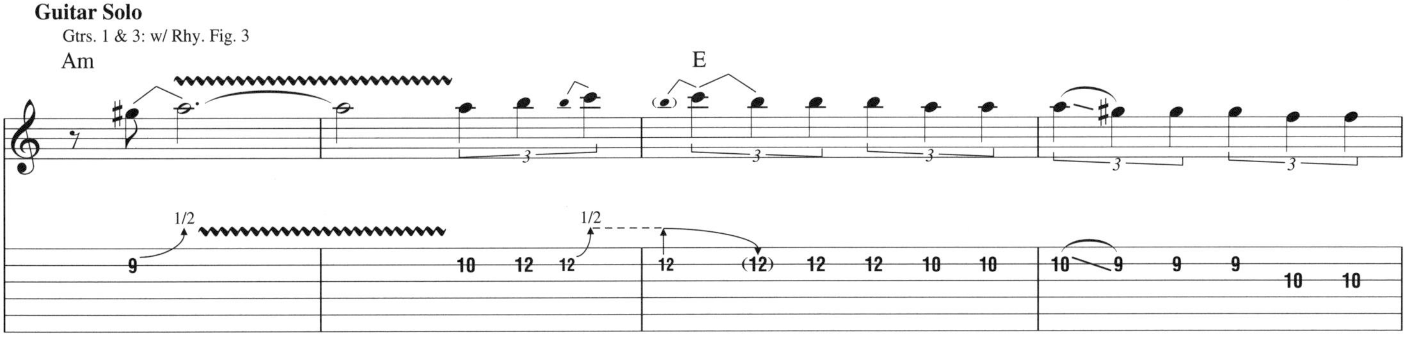
Gtrs. 1 & 3: w/ Rhy. Fig. 3
Am
E

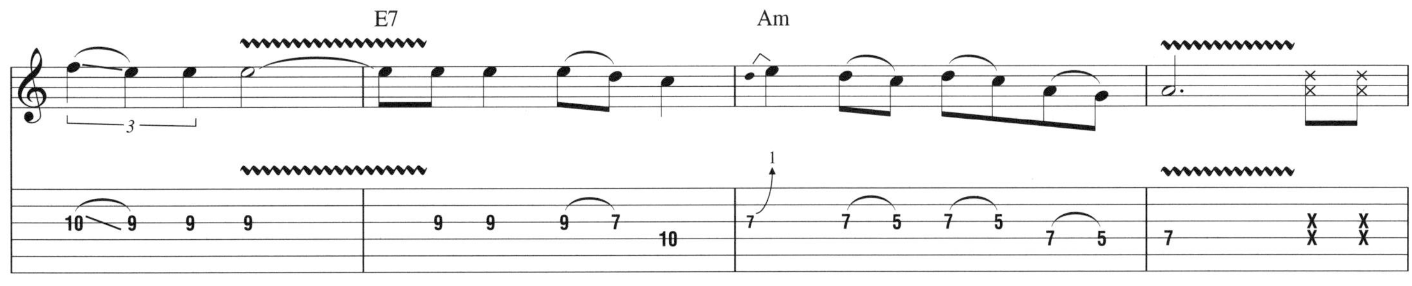
E7
Am

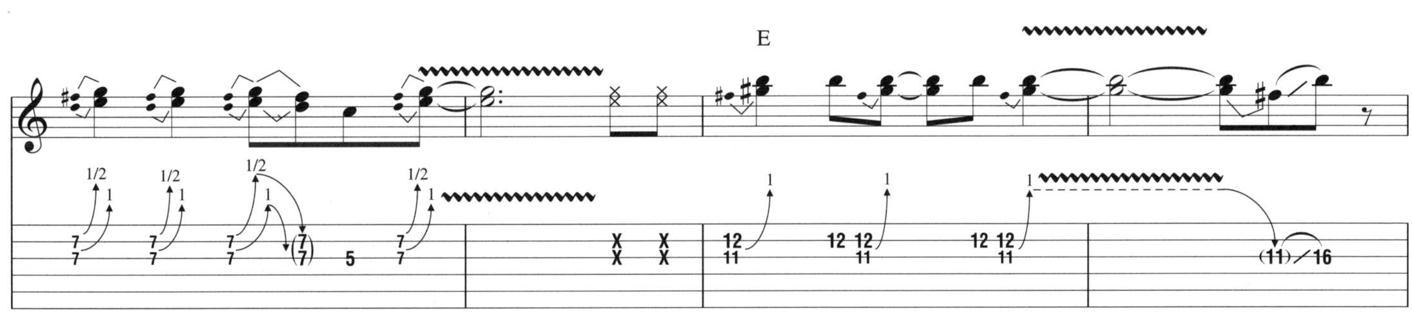
E

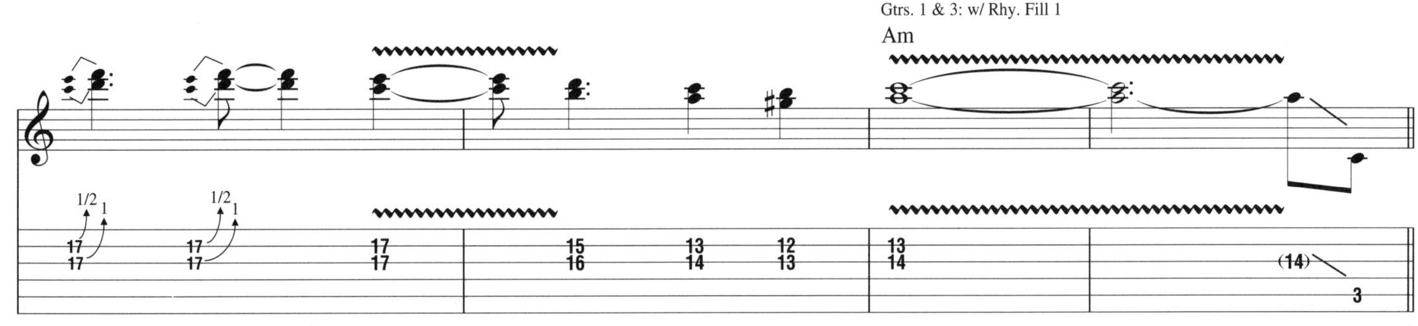
Gtrs. 1 & 3: w/ Rhy. Fill 1
Am

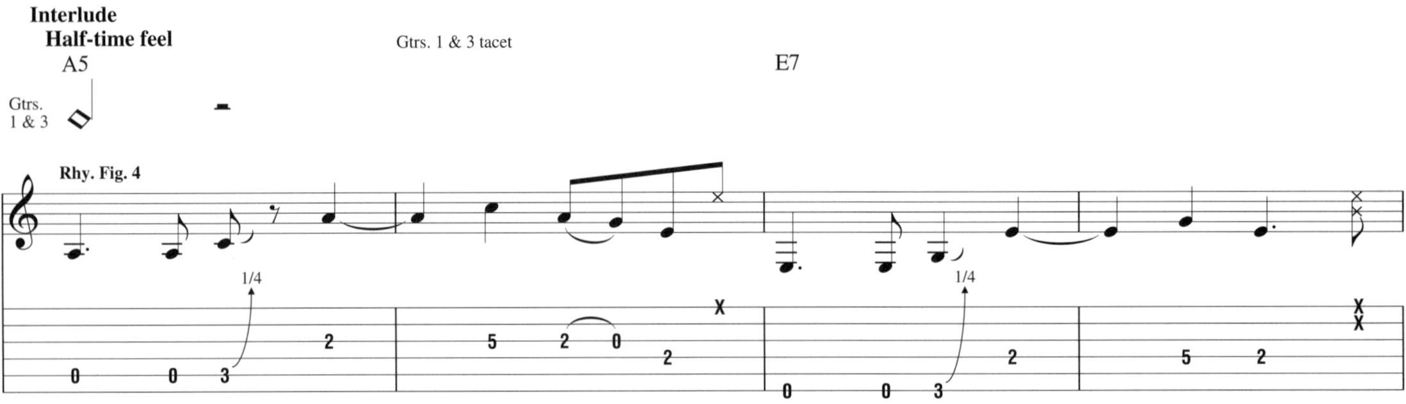
Interlude
Half-time feel
A5
Gtrs. 1 & 3 tacet
E7
Gtrs. 1 & 3
Rhy. Fig. 4
1/4
1/4

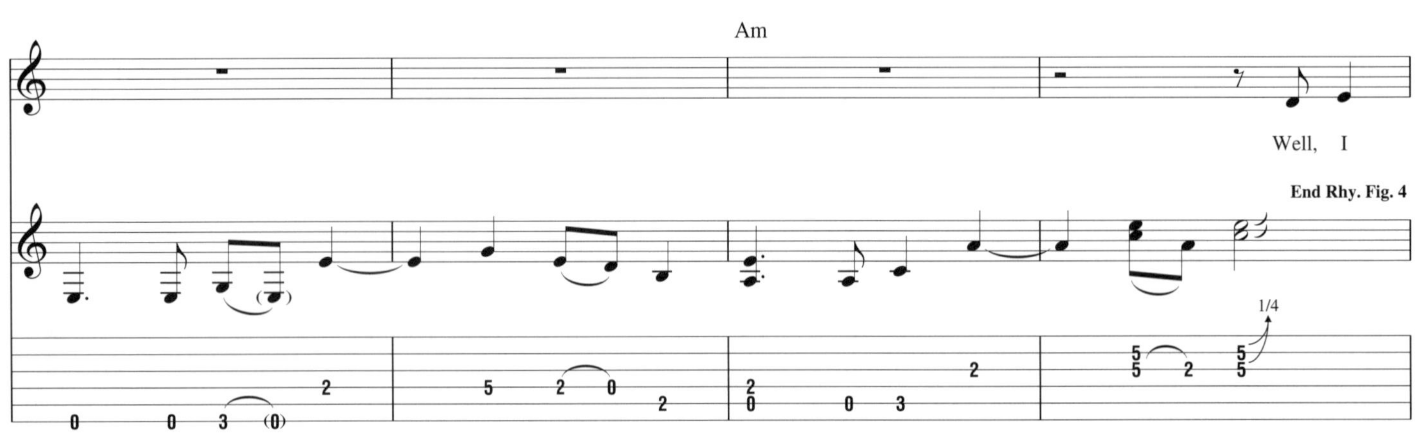
Am
Well, I
End Rhy. Fig. 4
1/4

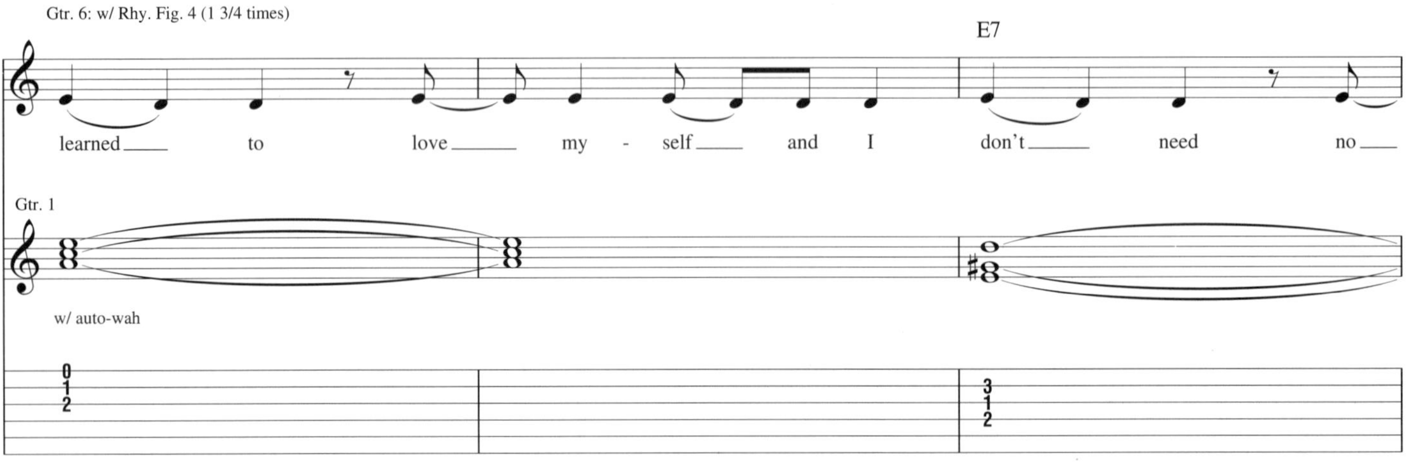
Gtr. 6: w/ Rhy. Fig. 4 (1 3/4 times)
E7
learned to love my - self and I don't need no
Gtr. 1
w/ auto-wah

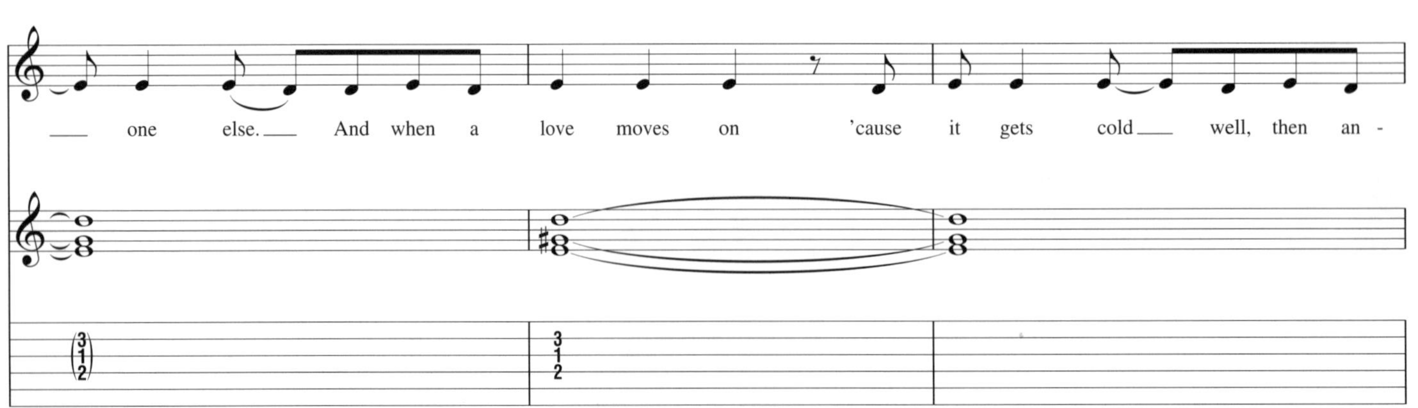
one else. And when a love moves on 'cause it gets cold well, then an -

Am
oth - er moves in and it can fill the hole. Well, I'm one more hope -
E7
- ful ly - ing on the bed - room floor. No sense try - ing. When the
Gtr. 1 tacet
End half-time feel
whole thing drops you lose your nerve. I hope you get what you de - serve. I said
Gtr. 6
Chorus
Gtrs. 1 & 3: w/ Rhy. Fig. 3
Gtr. 4: w/ Riff B (3 times)
Am
E
I don't want no - bod - y.
E7
Am
Gtr. 5: w/ Riff B1
No - bod - y don't want me. Hey, well,
(Don't want me.)
E
I'm so sad so lone - ly. Yeah, well

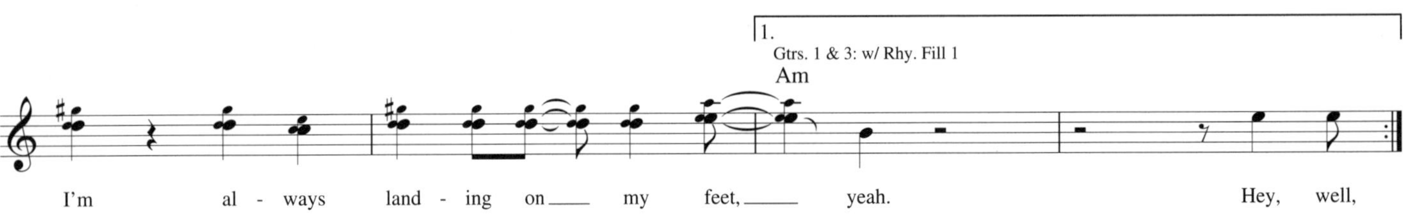

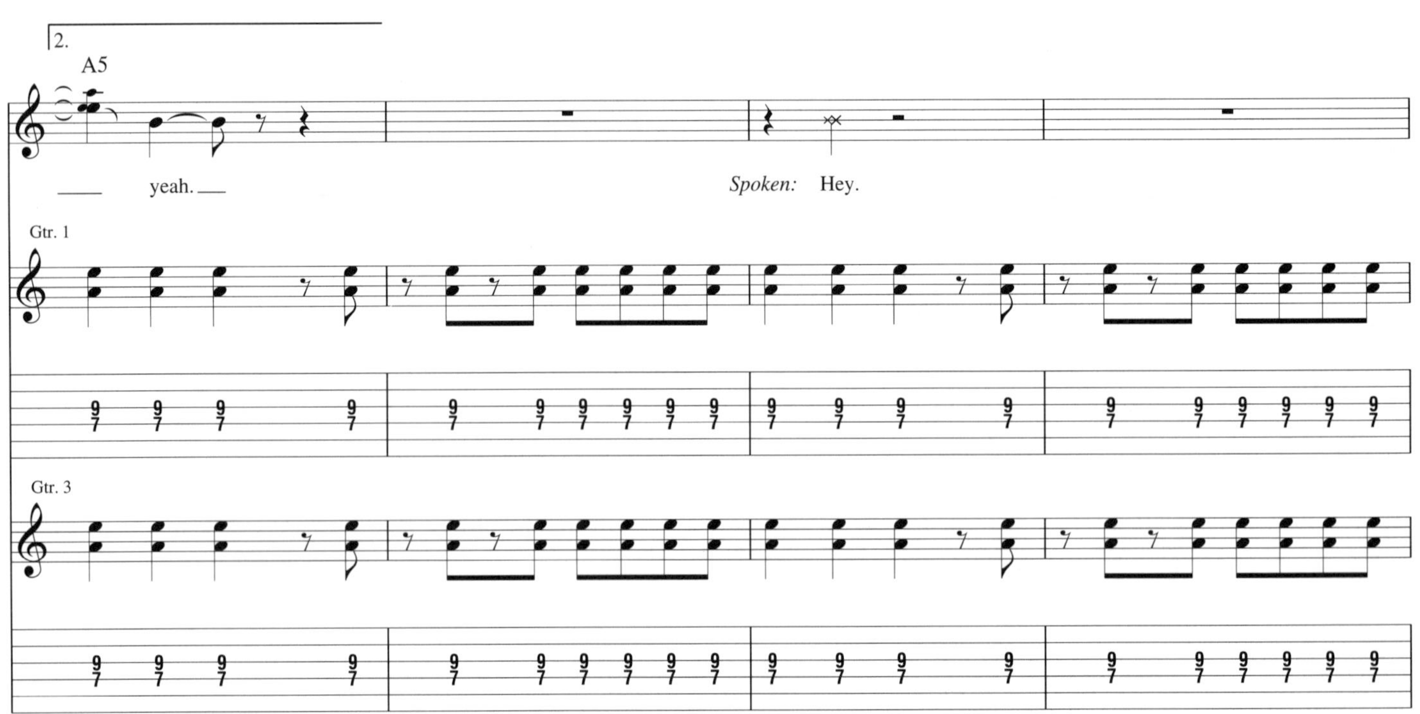

Fade out

It's lame, man. That's lame.
I say we do it man. We'll do it right now.
That's lame. Come on.
Dude, that's lame, lame, lame.
We'll see you tomorrow.

NATURAL HARMONIC: Strike the note while the fret-hand lightly touches the string directly over the fret indicated.

PINCH HARMONIC: The note is fretted normally and a harmonic is produced by adding the edge of the thumb or the tip of the index finger of the pick hand to the normal pick attack.

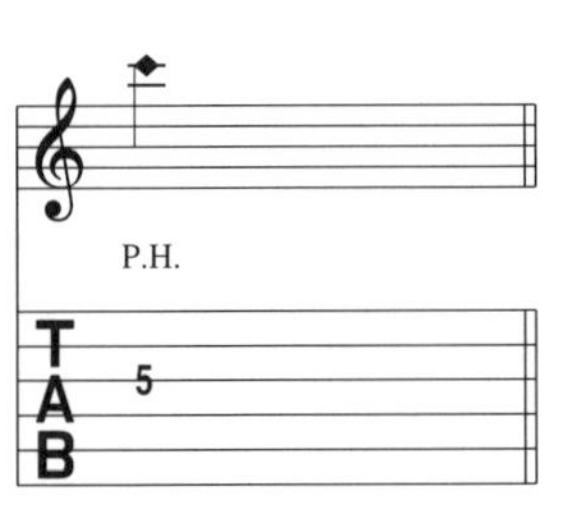
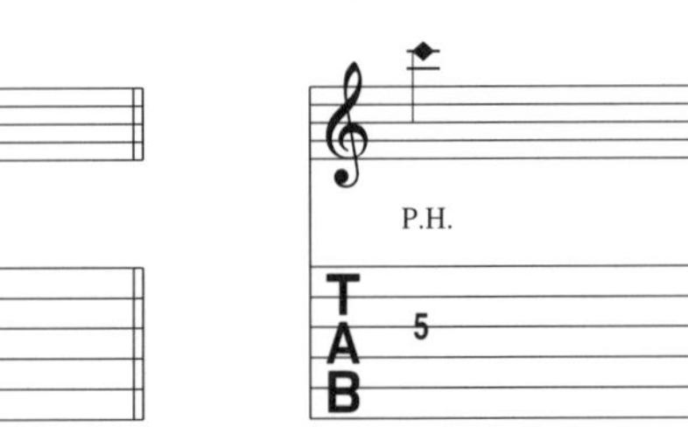

HARP HARMONIC: The note is fretted normally and a harmonic is produced by gently resting the pick hand's index finger directly above the indicated fret (in parentheses) while the pick hand's thumb or pick assists by plucking the appropriate string.

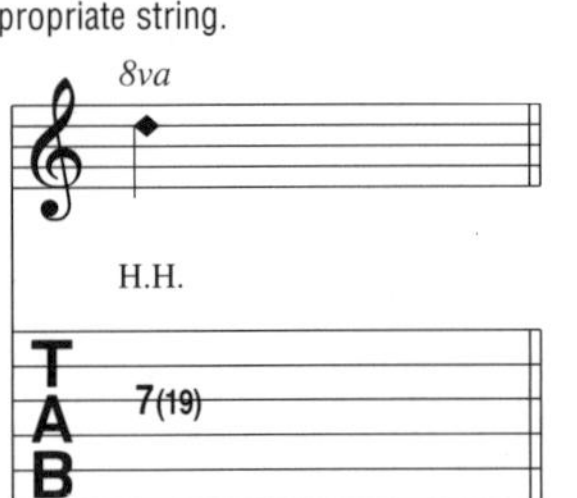

PICK SCRAPE: The edge of the pick is rubbed down (or up) the string, producing a scratchy sound.

MUFFLED STRINGS: A percussive sound is produced by laying the fret hand across the string(s) without depressing, and striking them with the pick hand.

PALM MUTING: The note is partially muted by the pick hand lightly touching the string(s) just before the bridge.

RAKE: Drag the pick across the strings indicated with a single motion.

TREMOLO PICKING: The note is picked as rapidly and continuously as possible.

ARPEGGIATE: Play the notes of the chord indicated by quickly rolling them from bottom to top.

VIBRATO BAR DIVE AND RETURN: The pitch of the note or chord is dropped a specified number of steps (in rhythm) then returned to the original pitch.

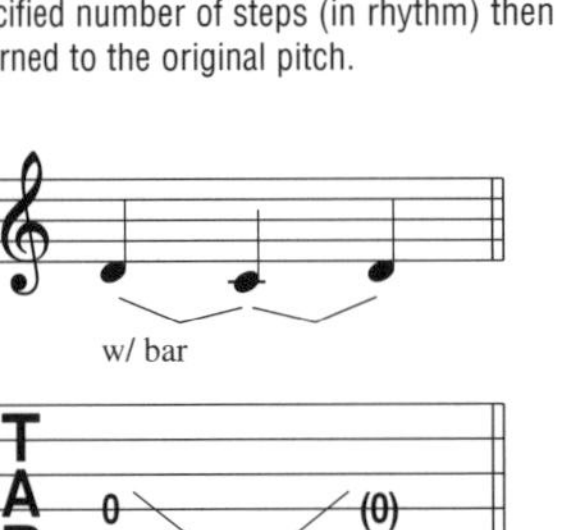
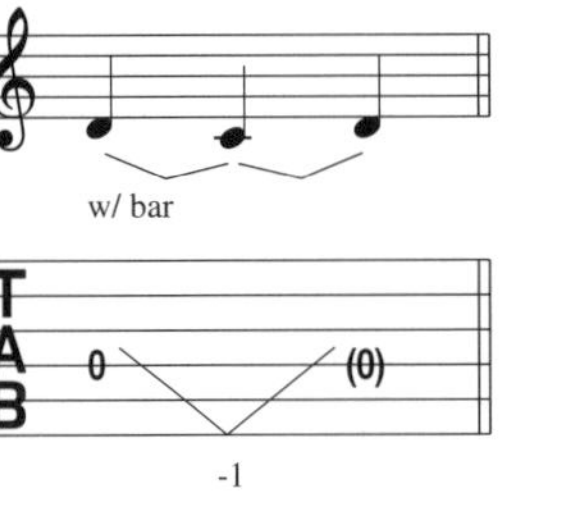
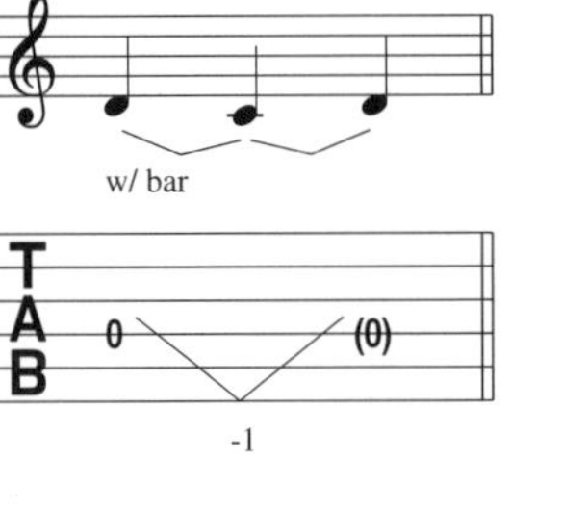

VIBRATO BAR SCOOP: Depress the bar just before striking the note, then quickly release the bar.

VIBRATO BAR DIP: Strike the note and then immediately drop a specified number of steps, then release back to the original pitch.

Additional Musical Definitions

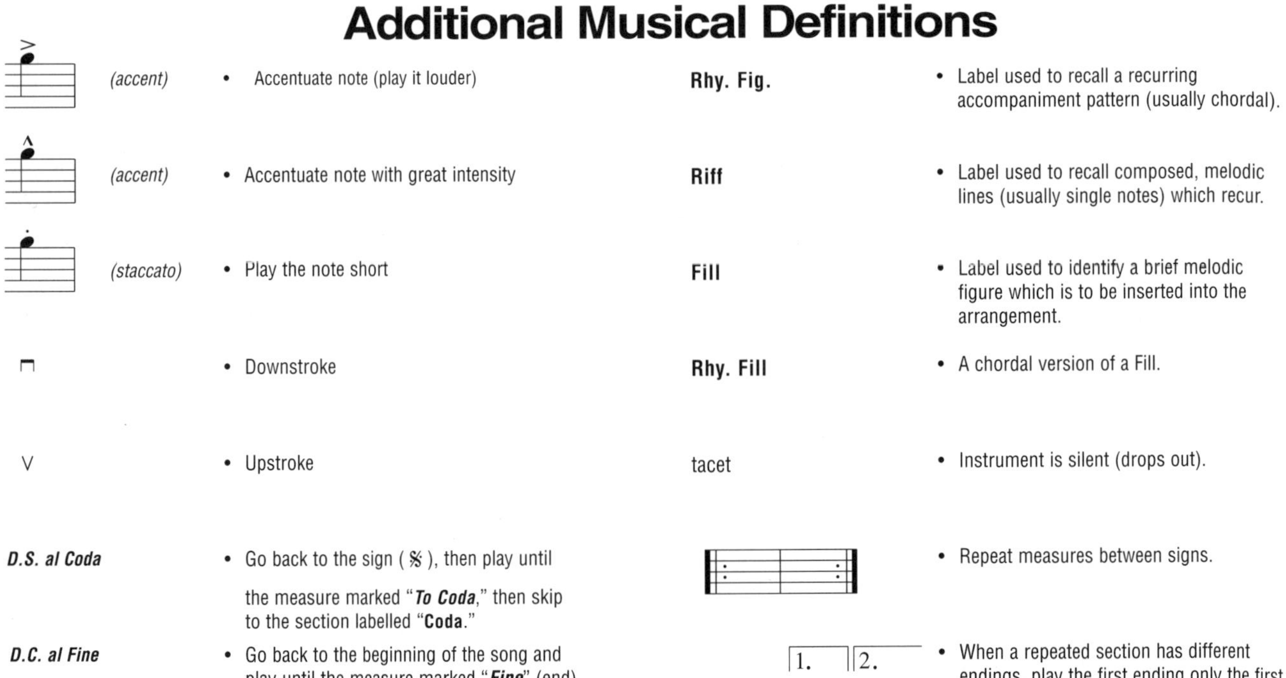

	(accent)	• Accentuate note (play it louder)	**Rhy. Fig.**	• Label used to recall a recurring accompaniment pattern (usually chordal).
	(accent)	• Accentuate note with great intensity	**Riff**	• Label used to recall composed, melodic lines (usually single notes) which recur.
	(staccato)	• Play the note short	**Fill**	• Label used to identify a brief melodic figure which is to be inserted into the arrangement.
⊓		• Downstroke	**Rhy. Fill**	• A chordal version of a Fill.
V		• Upstroke	tacet	• Instrument is silent (drops out).
D.S. al Coda		• Go back to the sign (𝄋), then play until the measure marked "***To Coda***," then skip to the section labelled "**Coda**."		• Repeat measures between signs.
D.C. al Fine		• Go back to the beginning of the song and play until the measure marked "***Fine***" (end).	1. 2.	• When a repeated section has different endings, play the first ending only the first time and the second ending only the second time.

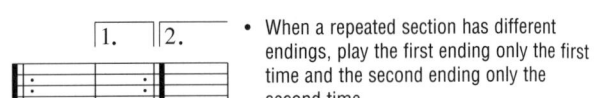

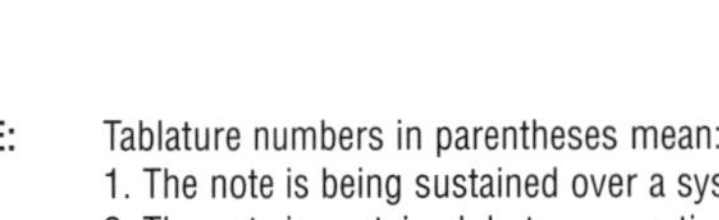

NOTE: Tablature numbers in parentheses mean:
1. The note is being sustained over a system (note in standard notation is tied), or
2. The note is sustained, but a new articulation (such as a hammer-on, pull-off, slide or vibrato begins), or
3. The note is a barely audible "ghost" note (note in standard notation is also in parentheses).

Guitar Notation Legend

Guitar Music can be notated three different ways: on a *musical staff*, in *tablature*, and in *rhythm slashes*.

RHYTHM SLASHES are written above the staff. Strum chords in the rhythm indicated. Use the chord diagrams found at the top of the first page of the transcription for the appropriate chord voicings. Round noteheads indicate single notes.

THE MUSICAL STAFF shows pitches and rhythms and is divided by bar lines into measures. Pitches are named after the first seven letters of the alphabet.

TABLATURE graphically represents the guitar fingerboard. Each horizontal line represents a a string, and each number represents a fret.

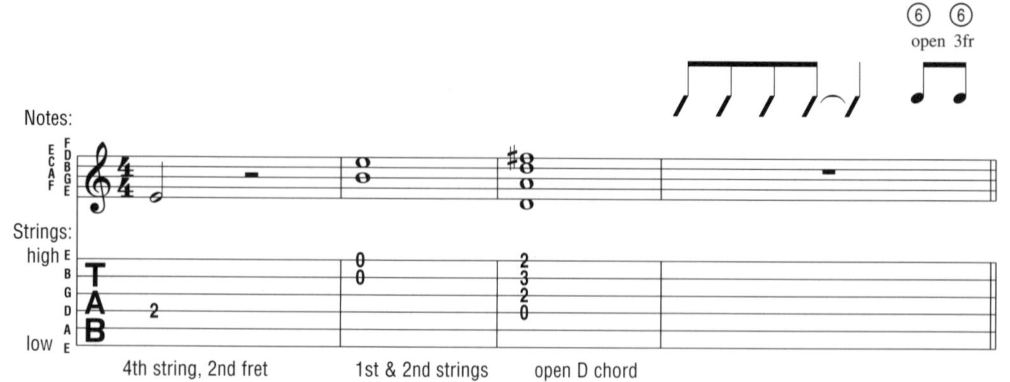

Definitions for Special Guitar Notation

HALF-STEP BEND: Strike the note and bend up 1/2 step.

WHOLE-STEP BEND: Strike the note and bend up one step.

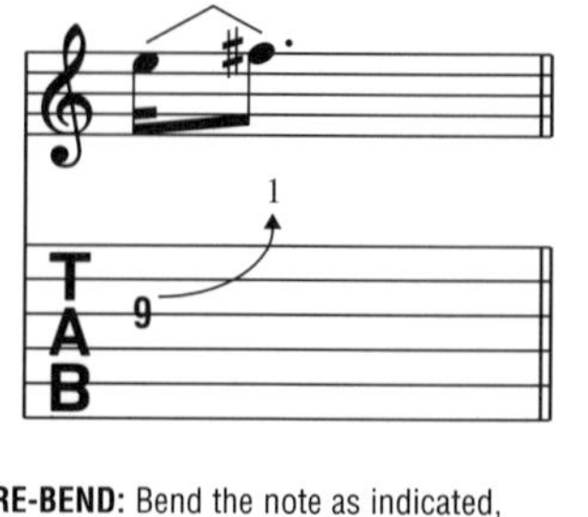

GRACE NOTE BEND: Strike the note and immediately bend up as indicated.

SLIGHT (MICROTONE) BEND: Strike the note and bend up 1/4 step.

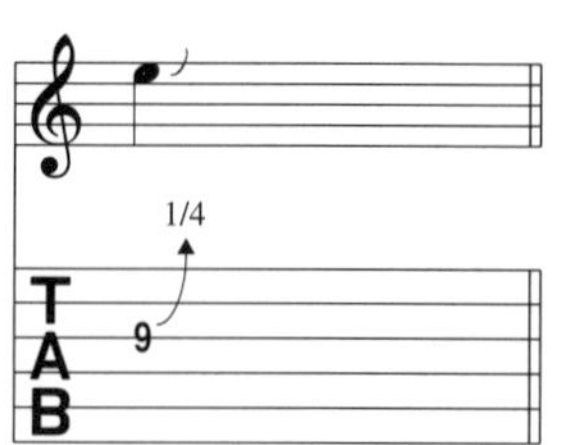

BEND AND RELEASE: Strike the note and bend up as indicated, then release back to the original note. Only the first note is struck.

PRE-BEND: Bend the note as indicated, then strike it.

PRE-BEND AND RELEASE: Bend the note as indicated. Strike it and release the bend back to the original note.

UNISON BEND: Strike the two notes simultaneously and bend the lower note up to the pitch of the higher.

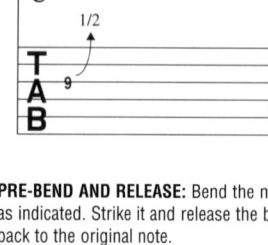

VIBRATO: The string is vibrated by rapidly bending and releasing the note with the fretting hand.

WIDE VIBRATO: The pitch is varied to a greater degree by vibrating with the fretting hand.

HAMMER-ON: Strike the first (lower) note with one finger, then sound the higher note (on the same string) with another finger by fretting it without picking.

PULL-OFF: Place both fingers on the notes to be sounded. Strike the first note and without picking, pull the finger off to sound the second (lower) note.

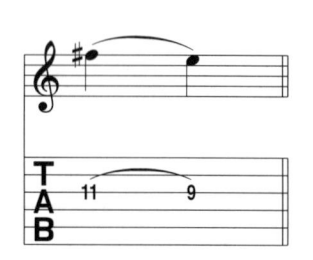

LEGATO SLIDE: Strike the first note and then slide the same fret-hand finger up or down to the second note. The second note is not struck.

SHIFT SLIDE: Same as legato slide, except the second note is struck.

TRILL: Very rapidly alternate between the notes indicated by continuously hammering on and pulling off.

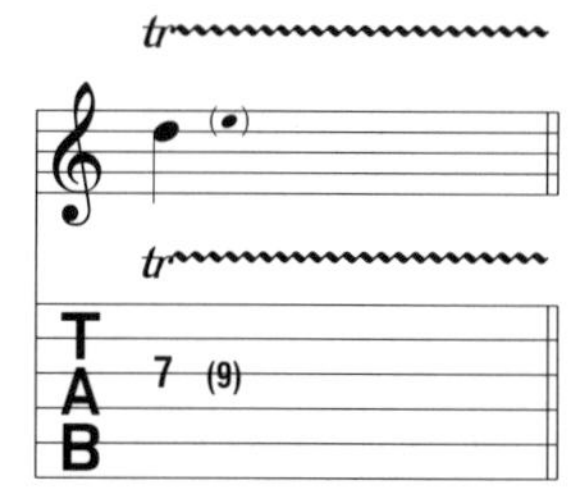
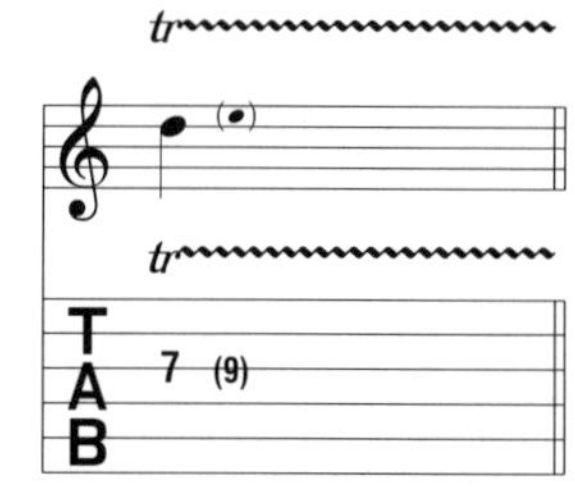

TAPPING: Hammer ("tap") the fret indicated with the pick-hand index or middle finger and pull off to the note fretted by the fret hand.

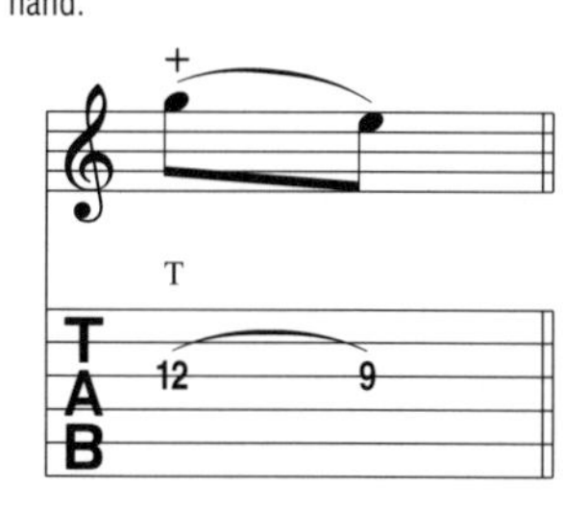

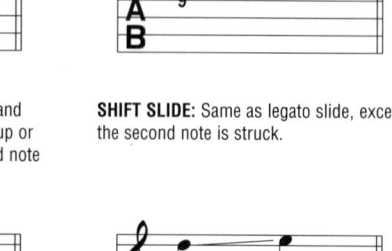